OPTICAL ROTATORY DISPERSION

OPTICAL
ROTATORY
DISPERSION

APPLICATIONS TO ORGANIC CHEMISTRY

CARL DJERASSI

Vice President, Syntex, S.A. (Mexico)
and Professor of Chemistry, Stanford University

McGRAW-HILL BOOK COMPANY, INC.

1960   New York   Toronto   London

OPTICAL ROTATORY DISPERSION

II

PREFACE

Although the phenomenon of optical rotatory dispersion has been known and studied by physical chemists for well over a century, its widespread application to organic chemical research really did not begin until 1953, when one of the first commercially available spectropolarimeters was installed in our laboratory. Our studies differed substantially from those of most of the earlier workers in that emphasis was placed on using rotatory dispersion for structural, stereochemical, and conformational problems in organic chemistry. Our initial results were recorded in a series of thirty-one publications under the title "Optical Rotatory Dispersion Studies" between 1955 and 1959. During the same period, very important advances along different lines have also been made in other laboratories on the optical rotatory dispersion of peptides and proteins and, as a consequence, interest in rotatory dispersion has undergone a major revival.

Nearly fifty laboratories in America, Europe, and Asia are now equipped with spectropolarimeters, and during the past twelve months over one hundred publications have appeared in which rotatory dispersion was used in an organic or biochemical problem. The situation is very reminiscent of that prevailing fifteen years ago in the field of infrared spectroscopy, and a great deal of active research can now be expected. Obviously, in this state of flux and rapid progress, a definitive treatise on optical rotatory dispersion would very soon be outdated. Since a very complete book, covering rotatory dispersion work until 1934, has been published by one of the pioneers (T. M. Lowry, "Optical Rotatory Power," Longmans, Green & Co., Ltd., London, 1935), and as relatively little work was carried out in this area between that time and the early 1950's, it was felt that a book published now should perform a very particular service.   Specifically, it should be addressed to the organic and perhaps to the biological chemist—whose interests until very recently have been largely ignored by physical and theoretical chemists working and writing on rotatory dispersion—and it should cover the most recent studies bearing on organic chemistry.   No assumptions are made concerning prior knowledge on the part of the reader about rotatory dispersion and it is hoped that the treatment is sufficiently general to be of interest to a wide chemical audience and to stimulate use as well as to prevent abuse of this tool in organic chemistry.

This book does not list all the references that have appeared since 1955 but gives selected examples, many of them hitherto unpublished, to illustrate the power and scope of the tool as well as to indicate the directions that research by organic chemists in optical rotatory dispersion will take.   Since our group has probably had more practical experience with modern spectropolarimetry than any other, a fairly detailed discussion of this subject is included in this book.   A review article by the author [C. Djerassi, *Record Chem. Progr.* **20**, 101 (1959)] contains a bibliography covering the period 1955 to April, 1959.

Just as in infrared spectroscopy, many of the subtle correlations between molecular structure and rotatory dispersion features were first noted in the steroid series, and a large number of illustrations are cited from this field.   Although a knowledge of steroid chemistry is not required to follow these examples, it may be helpful to refer to Appendix B, which contains a brief description of the numbering and stereochemical conventions employed with steroids and related triterpenoids. Rotatory dispersion has been found to be particularly useful in the solution of conformational problems, and it is expected that the reader is familiar with the basic tenets of conformational analysis, which derived much of its initial impetus from D. H. R. Barton's generalizations among steroids.

A book with such a specific purpose should be written by an author who has had intimate and personal experience with the subject matter. Consequently, I have asked other investigators to write some of the sections or chapters on subjects where I have personally made little or no contribution.   This applies to Dr. Albert Moscowitz (University of Minnesota), the author of Chapter 12, who with the late Professor William Moffitt carried out important theoretical work in this area at Harvard University; to Dr. Elkan R. Blout (Polaroid Corporation and Children's Cancer Research Foundation, Harvard Medical School), who wrote Chapter 17, dealing with polypeptides and proteins; and to Dr. John A. Schellman (University of Oregon), who contributed Section

15-4 on amino acids as well as much unpublished information on that subject.   Two of my former postdoctorate research fellows, Dr. Anthony N. James and Dr. Berndt Sjöberg, have supervised as well as carried out personally so many rotatory dispersion measurements that they seemed to be the ideal choices for preparing most of the sections in Chapter 3 dealing with instrumentation.   I am greatly indebted to these colleagues and friends for acceding so generously and rapidly to my requests for writing these sections and to Dr. A. Savitzky and collaborators of The Perkin-Elmer Corporation for a description (Section 3-6A) of a new spectropolarimeter attachment.

Were it not for the diligent work of my many students who collaborated with me experimentally on so many facets of optical rotatory dispersion, there would have been no *raison d'être* for this book.   In fact, it is largely written to acknowledge this important debt, and their names are listed in the bibliography of Appendix A.   The investigations covered by our publications listed in this Appendix were supported by the National Science Foundation, the Damon Runyon Memorial Fund for Cancer Research, and especially the National Cancer Institute of the U.S. Public Health Service.

The short time interval between completion of the book and its appearance in printed form is due to the cooperation of the publisher as well as to my extremely rapid and competent secretaries, Srta. María del Rosario Arrieta Curiel and Sra. Mary Urquidi de Franco, who not only made no mistakes but also corrected many of mine.   The entire manuscript has been read by a gentle but experienced critic—Dr. W. Klyne of the University of London's Postgraduate Medical School—and I am grateful to him for his comments and some unpublished experimental results.   Finally, I should like to thank my wife Norma, who was not only willing to forego the pleasure of my company for the better part of two months, but who was even prepared to change the ribbons of my typewriter during that time.

Carl Djerassi

Mexico City
June, 1959

CONTENTS

1 | INTRODUCTION TO OPTICAL ROTATORY DISPERSION

1-1. Historical Introduction

The phenomenon of optical rotatory dispersion—the change of optical rotation with wavelength—was discovered by Biot in 1817.[1] For the next 50 years most measurements of optical rotation were performed at several wavelengths, and to that extent represented rotatory dispersion measurements. The discovery of the bunsen burner constituted a serious blow to the development of rotatory dispersion studies, because it provided the organic chemist (who, more than any other chemist, accumulates optical rotation data incidental to his work) with a very convenient and nearly monochromatic source of light—the sodium flame. Since that time (ca. 1866) virtually all optical rotations have been measured at the sodium D line (essentially at 589 mµ). The chief message of this book can actually be construed as a complaint against this unfortunate temporary victory of monochromatic polarimetry over rotatory dispersion. It is indeed remarkable how much information the organic chemist derived from this single measurement [2] at a wavelength (589 mµ) which, for most colorless compounds, represents an extremely insensitive region of the spectrum. This is largely due to the fact that in most instances the sign and even the magnitude of the rotation at the sodium D line are already controlled by these same parameters of the corresponding rotatory dispersion curve.

For reasons that will become apparent in Chap. 2, we are employing

---

[1] J. B. Biot, *Mem. acad. sci. Toulouse,* **2,** 41 (1817).

[2] For review see W. Klyne in E. A. Braude and F. C. Nachod (eds.), "Determination of Organic Structures by Physical Methods," chap. 3, Academic Press, Inc., New York, 1955.

a system of nomenclature differing to some extent from that [3] employed by physical chemists.   It is largely this latter group, with a few striking exceptions (e.g., Tschugaeff,[4] Rupe,[5] Levene,[6] and Freudenberg [7b]), which has carried out until very recently most of the basic research on optical rotatory dispersion.   Consequently, research was limited largely to physicochemical rather than organic chemical aspects.   Excellent reviews (see also the Bibliography, Appendix A) have already been published by two of the pioneers, T. M. Lowry (Cambridge University)[3] and W. Kuhn (University of Basel),[7a] so this material will not be discussed to any extent herein.

1-2.   Cotton Effect and Circular Dichroism

This subject will be discussed in more detail in Chap. 12, but a very simple description will be given at this point since it is required for purposes of nomenclature (Chap. 2) and for a proper understanding of the types of organic compounds that can, at the present stage of instrumental development, be used to best advantage.

A beam of plane polarized light may be considered to be made up of a left and a right circularly polarized component.   No rotation will be observed if these two components are transmitted with equal velocity through a medium.   On the other hand, if the refractive indices of the medium for left and right circularly polarized light of given wavelength are different,[8] the two components will be transmitted through the medium with unequal velocities.   Consequently, upon recombination of the right and left circularly polarized components after passage through the medium, there will be a phase difference, and the plane of polarization of the emergent light will have been rotated.   In summary, optical rotation will be observed when a medium transmits the two circularly polarized components with unequal velocity.

---

[3] T. M. Lowry, "Optical Rotatory Power," Longmans, Green & Co., Ltd., London, 1935.

[4] L. Tschugaeff and W. Pastanogoff, Z. physik. Chem. (Leipzig), **85**, 553 (1913), and preceding papers.

[5] A complete bibliography of H. Rupe's work can be found in the obituary article by H. Dahn and T. Reichstein, Helv. Chim. Acta, **35**, 1 (1952).

[6] For review see P. A. Levene and A. Rothen in H. Gilman (ed.), "Organic Chemistry," vol. 2, chap. 21, John Wiley & Sons, Inc., New York, 1938.

[7] (a) W. Kuhn, Ann. Rev. Phys. Chem., **9**, 417 (1958); (b) K. Freudenberg and W. Kuhn, Ber., **64**, 703 (1931).

[8] This difference in refractive indices needs to be only very small to produce a reasonably large rotation. Thus, in a substance with $[\alpha]_D = 100°$, it is only of the order of 10^{-6}.

If in addition to unequal velocity, there occurs unequal absorption of left and right circularly polarized light, the emergent light also will be elliptically polarized; this unequal absorption is referred to as "circular dichroism." The combined phenomenon of unequal absorption (circular dichroism) and unequal velocity of transmission of left and right circularly polarized light is known as the "Cotton effect," [9] so named after its discoverer.[10]

Experimentally, circular dichroism in the ultraviolet is measured only with difficulty,[3,11] and the Cotton effect of a substance with a chromophore absorbing in the ultraviolet is obtained most conveniently by measuring the rotatory dispersion (i.e., optical rotation at different wavelengths) in the spectral region of maximal absorption. An ideal

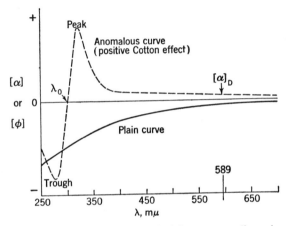

Fig. 1-1. Examples of anomalous and plain rotatory dispersion curves.

case, that of a positively rotating compound which exhibits an absorption maximum near 300 mμ (e.g., a ketone) is illustrated in Fig. 1-1. It will be noted that as measurements are conducted toward shorter wavelength, starting in the visible, the optical rotation increases as one approaches the absorption maximum. If rotation measurements can be carried out through this region of absorption, it will be seen that the rotation reaches a peak, rapidly drops until it reaches a corresponding trough, and then gradually increases again as one recedes further from the region of maximal absorption. In the ideal case, one in which the observed rotation is due to a single electronic transition and there are

[9] S. Mitchell, "The Cotton Effect," G. Bell & Sons, Ltd., London, 1933.
[10] A. Cotton, *Compt. rend.,* **120,** 989 (1895); *Ann. chim. et phys.,* **8,** 347 (1896).
[11] W. Kuhn and E. Braun, *Z. physik. Chem. (Leipzig),* **(B)8,** 445 (1930).

no contributions to the rotatory dispersion from other bands, the mean of the wavelengths (λ_0 in Fig. 1-1) at which the peak and trough occur coincides almost exactly with the point of zero rotation and is also approximately identical with the wavelength of maximal ultraviolet absorption. The latter is conventionally referred to as an "optically active absorption band," since all absorption bands of a given chromophore do not necessarily exhibit circular dichroism (differential absorption of right and left circularly polarized light). For instance, if the hypothetical compound, whose positive rotatory dispersion Cotton effect curve is reproduced in Fig. 1-1, had shown ultraviolet absorption maxima at 300 and 400 mµ, one could have stated with confidence that only the absorption band corresponding to the former wavelength is "optically active." Otherwise another peak and trough, or at least some irregularity, would have been noticeable between 420 and 380 mµ. Conversely, if the rotatory dispersion curve exhibits a "multiple Cotton effect curve" (for definition see Chap. 2), then it can be anticipated that careful examination of the ultraviolet absorption spectrum will show several absorption bands corresponding to these "Cotton effects." A striking illustration of this uncovering of fine structure in the ultraviolet absorption spectrum of an unsaturated ketone is shown in Fig. 5-8.

Most of the work performed in our laboratory, in fact most of the results that are of particular interest to the organic chemist, is concerned with anomalous dispersion curves such as the one shown in Fig. 1-1, since these can vary greatly in shape and magnitude (see Chap. 4), thus offering much more scope for correlations with structural or stereochemical features. Dispersion curves can also be normal (we prefer the term "plain," as noted in Chap. 2) over the currently measurable spectral range, but this simply means that the region of the optically active absorption band has not been reached yet and that this occurs somewhere in the far ultraviolet. Indeed the positive Cotton effect curve of Fig. 1-1 is normal (or plain) over the range 700 to approximately 450 mµ and only then becomes anomalous.

From these considerations it becomes obvious that to measure Cotton effect curves within the presently accessible range (700 to 250 mµ) of current instruments, one should deal with substances that show maximal absorption somewhere in that region, preferably above 290 mµ. Furthermore, in order to locate experimentally the position of the peak and trough, it is necessary to take rotation measurements through this region of maximal absorption (λ_0 in Fig. 1-1). This is often possible only with a chromophore whose extinction coefficient is quite low,[12] preferably

[12] Exceptions are provided by substances with large extinction coefficients which show such high rotation in that spectral region that very dilute solutions can be

below ε = 100. As will be shown subsequently, the carbonyl chromophore is nearly ideal in satisfying all these requirements, and the proper choice of an absorbing system can at times afford very useful derivatives for rotatory dispersion work of "nonchromophoric" substances (see Chap. 15). A necessary corollary of this statement is that derivatives with such chromophores will not only show Cotton effect curves (if the absorption band is optically active), but *ipso facto* the actual rotation values will be considerably larger than those of the parent compound.

1-3.   The Drude Equation

The relationship between optical rotatory power and wavelength outside the region of an optically active absorption band is expressed by an equation due to Drude [13] and experimentally validated by many investigators, notably Lowry.[3]   The first term, $[\phi] = K/(\lambda^2 - \lambda_0^2)$, defines the contribution to the total molecular rotation $[\phi]$ at any particular wavelength λ of a single optically active chromophore which possesses an absorption maximum at λ_0, K being a constant.   If such a one-term Drude equation were applicable to the positive Cotton effect curve of Fig. 1-1, then by using experimental values of the rotation *outside* the region of anomalous dispersion, in this case from 700 to approximately 450 mμ, solution of this equation for λ_0 should yield a value near 300 mμ.   In this particular instance, the applicability of the Drude equation can actually be tested experimentally in two ways: by measuring the ultraviolet absorption as well as the rotatory dispersion *throughout* the region of anomalous dispersion.   Most of the time this equation has been employed with compounds for which λ_0 cannot be determined experimentally (e.g., the plain dispersion curve of Fig. 1-1, where λ_0 lies somewhere below 200 mμ—typical of an optically active alcohol); then a Biot-Lowry plot is used.   If a straight line is obtained over a fairly wide spectral range by plotting $1/[\phi]$ against λ^2, the equation is probably valid and applicable to the compound under consideration.   Heller,[14] in a recent reexamination of the Drude equation, has suggested that a plot of $1/[\phi]\lambda^2$ versus $1/\lambda^2$ would be even more significant.

---

employed. Pertinent examples are hexahelicene [M. S. Newman and D. Lednicer, *J. Am. Chem. Soc.*, **78**, 4765 (1956)], whose rotatory dispersion was measured (unpublished observation by Lin Tsai, Ohio State University) in a region where ε was greater than 30,000, and stercobilin hydrochloride. With the latter, dispersion studies [C. H. Gray, P. M. Jones, W. Klyne, and D. C. Nicholson, *Nature*, **184**, 41 (1959)] were conducted through a portion of the spectrum with ε approaching 80,000.

[13] P. Drude, "Lehrbuch der Optik," 2d ed., S. Hirzel Verlag, Leipzig, 1906.

[14] W. Heller, *J. Phys. Chem.*, **62**, 1569 (1958).

In more complicated cases, a two-term equation of the type $[\phi]$ $= K_1/(\lambda^2 - \lambda_0^2) + K_2/(\lambda^2 - \lambda_1^2)$ has to be used, where the first term expresses the rotatory contribution of a chromophore with an absorption maximum at λ_0 and the second term refers to the contribution of a second optically active absorption band at λ_1, farther in the ultraviolet. A solution of such a two-term equation is extremely cumbersome, and since λ_1, which is smaller than λ_0, will be even smaller than λ, it is usually convenient to ignore λ_1^2 so that an abbreviated equation with only three constants needs to be considered: $[\phi] = K_1/(\lambda^2 - \lambda_0^2) + K_2/\lambda^2$. This can be solved readily by electronic computers; detailed examples have already been published.[15]

Further refinements, especially graphic ones, in evaluating Drude equations have recently been recorded by Heller,[14] who states that "the Drude equation in its simple form has been, is and will continue to be of major usefulness." I personally take exception to this statement. It seems worthwhile to examine in some detail the cause for this disagreement, since it appears to me to offer an example of the fundamental reason—namely, ignoring the realities of life in the organic chemical laboratory—why many of the research results and conclusions by physical chemists on rotatory dispersion have had so small an impact on organic chemistry.

It is my opinion that in so far as the vast body of rotatory dispersion measurements on the part of organic chemists is concerned (and with the present readily available spectropolarimeters this means over 95 per cent of all experimental determinations), the Drude equation will not or cannot be used widely. As will become apparent from even a cursory perusal of the remainder of this book, the future of rotatory dispersion, in organic chemistry as well as in theoretical chemistry,[16] lies principally in the area of anomalous Cotton effect curves. By definition (see Chap. 2), a Cotton effect curve is one in which the Cotton effect can be measured experimentally. Consequently, it is possible to determine λ_0 experimentally by means of the rotatory dispersion curve (see Fig. 1-1) and to confirm the position of λ_0 by obtaining, often in the same instrument (see Chap. 3), the ultraviolet absorption spectrum of the substance. Calculation of the Drude equation of such a substance then frequently

[15] E. W. Foltz, Ph.D. thesis, Wayne State University, Detroit, 1955. See also A. E. Lippman, E. W. Foltz, and C. Djerassi, *J. Am. Chem. Soc.*, **77**, 4364 (1955).

[16] The importance of actually defining the Cotton effect by rotatory dispersion measurements through the region of maximal absorption has been emphasized by several physical chemists, such as Lowry[3] and especially Kuhn [e.g., W. Kuhn and H. Biller, *Z. physik. Chem. (Leipzig)*, **(B)29**, 1, 256 (1935)].

becomes a superfluous and time-consuming operation of little use [17] in the areas of structural organic chemistry, stereochemistry, or determination of absolute configuration. For more intimate quantitative considerations, calculations of "reduced rotational strength" are indicated (see Chap. 12), and, from a theoretical standpoint, the ideal would be to determine experimentally the circular dichroism.

This leaves a Drude equation largely for compounds (e.g., alcohols, hydrocarbons, etc.) that show plain dispersion curves (Fig. 1-1) over the presently accessible spectral range of a spectropolarimeter. In these cases, λ_0 cannot yet be measured experimentally by examining the rotatory dispersion in that region, although far-ultraviolet spectrophotometry will probably soon be available as a routine tool in many organic laboratories. Here again the Drude equation will usually inform the organic chemist that, for instance, a given optically active alcohol should possess an absorption maximum somewhere around 170 mμ. This is a piece of information that most chemists have learned to accept long ago, without it being necessary to belabor the point too frequently by calculating Drude equations for the thousands of rotatory dispersion curves that will be measured in the next few years.

Although the above comments represent largely a personal opinion, the most serious objection is a purely practical one. Most of the rotatory dispersion measurements accumulated laboriously prior to 1940 were quite precise in the 700 to 450 mμ region and the data [3] lent themselves readily to incorporation in Drude equations. The modern spectropolarimetric measurements (see Chap. 3)—largely because they are designed to reveal Cotton effects in the ultraviolet simply and rapidly, and hence are conducted in very dilute solution—are usually quite inaccurate in the region of the spectrum that is useful for Drude equations, since the rotations are usually quite low in the near ultraviolet or visible. Therefore, the vast majority of experimental measurements of rotatory dispersion curves now being performed in the field of organic chemistry are practically useless for this specific purpose.[18] Actually the problem is only serious in certain limited areas of organic and biological chem-

[17] This is currently not true in the protein field; see, for example, J. A. Schellman and C. G. Schellman, *Arch. Biochem. Biophys.*, **65**, 58 (1956), and B. Jirgensons, *ibid.*, **78**, 235 (1958).

[18] W. Heller (private communication) informed us that even the dispersion data accumulated by E. W. Foltz (Ph.D. thesis, Wayne State University, Detroit, 1955) under considerably more careful conditions than are employed routinely with a Rudolph spectropolarimeter were not satisfactory for testing Drude equations by the new graphical methods [14] and that he was reduced to using the data accumulated by T. M. Lowry between 1914 and 1925.

istry [especially peptides and proteins (see Chap. 17)] and may be overcome in the future by improved instrumental accuracy or, more likely, along the lines outlined in Chap. 15 for amino acids.

1-4. Introduction to Recent Rotatory Dispersion Studies

As in infrared spectroscopy [19] and nuclear magnetic resonance work,[20] interest by organic chemists and rapid utilization for the solution of problems in this field were stimulated largely by advances in instrumentation. Prior to 1950, rotatory dispersion measurements in the ultraviolet region were extremely laborious and very few laboratories were equipped to perform such work. In 1952 there was constructed a prototype model of the Rudolph photoelectric spectropolarimeter (see Chap. 3) and the second, commercially manufactured, unit was received in our laboratory in 1953. Although this instrument did not record automatically, it was so much more effective than the earlier spectropolarimeters and so easy to operate [21] that in a period of five years our group alone measured over 2000 rotatory dispersion curves, a far larger number than had been obtained during the preceding 140 years.[22] By securing rapidly a great variety of rotatory dispersion curves, it was possible to undertake an empirical correlation between structural and stereochemical features on the one hand and shape and sign of Cotton effect curve on the other, an achievement that would not have been possible with the limited number of ultraviolet dispersion curves available prior to 1953,[3,6] even though this problem had been recognized by some organic chemists (such as Tschugaeff [4]) almost 50 years ago.

Of nearly equal importance was the fact that our initial studies [15,23] were performed on steroid ketones. Here again a parallel will be observed with the rapid progress that infrared spectroscopy underwent in organic chemistry by investigations on steroids.[19] Structurally steroids may appear to be very complex molecules, but stereochemically they, as

---

[19] R. N. Jones, *Trans. Roy. Soc. Can.*, **(III)52**, 9 (1958).

[20] J. D. Roberts, "Nuclear Magnetic Resonance," McGraw-Hill Book Company, Inc., New York, 1959.

[21] Once initial instrumental difficulties were overcome, most of the measurements at Wayne State University have been conducted by wives of graduate students, who had no chemical or technical background.

[22] An indication of the output of rotatory dispersion curves, which can be expected, is given by the observation that in the period 1955 to 1959 over 50 organic and biochemical laboratories in 10 countries have obtained photoelectric spectropolarimeters.

[23] C. Djerassi, E. W. Foltz, and A. E. Lippman, *J. Am. Chem. Soc.*, **77**, 4354 (1955); E. W. Foltz, A. E. Lippman, and C. Djerassi, *ibid.*, **77**, 4359 (1955).

well as their close relatives, the triterpenes, are characterized by marvelous simplicity.   There exists probably no other group of organic compounds for which so much information has been accumulated [24] on stereochemical and conformational features, for which the absolute configuration has been established, and for which an enormous variety of closely related substances are available, often differing only in some minor stereochemical detail.   Most importantly for our purposes, they are all optically active and usually of frozen conformation, in contrast to the flexible conformations of monocyclic cyclohexanes.   As will be shown in Chaps. 7, 9, and 13, the structurally simple cyclohexanones present considerable difficulties because of this conformational mobility.   These problems could be attacked readily only after much information had been accumulated with steroids.

The attractive feature of the steroids is that they are all based on the skeleton I and that in the saturated members there is present a contiguous chain of seven asymmetric centers (see circles in I).   If a suitable chromophore is selected, it will be noted that regardless of where this is placed in the steroid molecule, it can at most be separated by only one carbon atom from the asymmetric chain.   Furthermore, in each location the chromophore would find itself in a different asymmetric environment, and this might reflect itself in differently shaped, anomalous rotatory dispersion curves.   Finally, if the chromophore also involves changing one of the tetrahedral ring carbon atoms to a trigonal one, the resulting distortion of the valency angles, slight as it may be, should also affect the geometry and hence possibly the rotatory dispersion curve of the substance.

I

The ideal properties of such a chromophore have already been outlined in Sec. 1-2, and the carbonyl group seems to satisfy them all.   In addition, it happens to be one of the most commonly occurring chromophores in organic chemistry as well as in the steroid field, and, if one considers that hydroxyl groups, other than tertiary, can also be converted with ease into a carbonyl function, it becomes obvious why we selected steroid ketones as the test case.

---

[24] See L. F. Fieser and M. Fieser, "Steroids," Reinhold Publishing Corporation, New York, 1959.

The initial results [23] proved to be so promising that our studies were extended to other compounds and especially to developing rotatory dispersion as a tool for the solution of organic chemical problems for which other physicochemical methods are inadequate or at least need support.

Fortunately, the historical course of events also followed a rather logical sequence, and the presentation in this book can, therefore, proceed to a large extent in the manner in which the actual research was performed. Most of the work during the past five years has centered on the carbonyl chromophore, and this facet is bound to retain an important place in the future, just as it did in ultraviolet and infrared spectroscopy. Chapters 4 through 9 will deal, therefore, with rotatory dispersion measurements of various optically active ketones and aldehydes, and attention will be called to the uses to which this information can be put in solving structural, conformational, stereochemical, and analytical problems. One of the most important contributions of rotatory dispersion studies has been the addition of a very powerful tool to the relatively few now available for the determination of absolute configurations; this is discussed in some detail in Chap. 10. Most of the remainder of the book is concerned with certain rules, which frequently permit a prediction of the Cotton effect for any given conformation of a cyclic ketone and with chromophores other than carbonyl groups. The latter area will surely see very rapid development during the next few years, and it will greatly increase the scope of rotatory dispersion applications to organic chemical problems.

An outline of recent work on rotatory dispersion of peptides and proteins [25] will also be given, since this area—although it uses a somewhat different approach from that discussed above—represents another very important modern application of rotatory dispersion in organic and biological chemistry.

[25] For recent reviews see C. G. Schellman and J. A. Schellman, *Compt. rend. trav. lab. Carlsberg, Sér. chim.,* **30,** 463 (1958); K. Imahori, *Kagaku no Ryôiki,* **13,** 92 (1959).

2 | NOMENCLATURE

2-1. Introduction

The nomenclature employed by earlier physical chemists [1] in describing rotatory dispersion curves was based to a considerable extent on a mathematical criterion: A *simple* curve is one that obeys a one-term Drude equation (see Sec. 1-3), whereas a *complex* one requires a many-term Drude equation. Other terms that have been employed are *normal,* referring to a dispersion curve lacking irregularities (inflections, maxima, minima, crossing of zero rotation axis) and thus including simple curves, and *anomalous.* An anomalous dispersion curve exhibits one or more of the above-mentioned irregularities and thus includes complex curves, although the two terms are not synonymous.

As was pointed out in Secs. 1-3 and 1-4, the vast majority of rotatory dispersion measurements are presently performed by organic chemists, who are usually not calculating Drude equations but rather are concerned with a very rapid evaluation of an anomalous (Cotton effect) curve in terms of sign, shape, and amplitude. Indeed, this is very similar to the "fingerprinting" of organic compounds by means of infrared spectrometry. The immediate practical problem that arises is how to record such data in the literature. Just as the flood of spectroscopic measurements by organic chemists, once convenient instruments were available, made it necessary for journals to limit strictly the reproduction of spectra, so a similar problem is already being created in the area of optical rotatory dispersion. For this reason, there has been proposed [2] a modified system of nomenclature, which satisfies the needs of organic

[1] See T. M. Lowry, *Trans. Faraday Soc.,* **26,** 266 (1930).
[2] C. Djerassi and W. Klyne, *Proc. Chem. Soc.,* **1957,** 55.

11

chemists and yet does not conflict with earlier physical chemical definitions. Furthermore, these proposals were submitted, prior to publication, to a group of interested chemists and editors of chemical journals, and they have found rather general acceptance. Our nomenclature proposals[2] do not only include terms to describe a given rotatory dispersion curve but also a uniform procedure for reporting experimental data in organic chemical publications. The following sections represent slightly modified excerpts of the original article [2,3] and cover the three principal types of rotatory dispersion (abbreviated RD) curves encountered at the present time. It must be emphasized that each curve, typical examples of which are given in Figs. 2-1, 2-2, 2-3, and 2-4, can exist in two mirror-image (antipodal or enantiomeric) forms.

2-2. Plain Curves

This type of curve exhibits no maximum (peak) or minimum (trough) and is typical of compounds that have no optically active absorption band within the spectral range under experimental observation. The name *plain* curve is suggested for them regardless of whether they can be expressed by a one-term Drude equation, whether they cross the zero rotation axis and therefore change sign at some stage (see curve B in Fig. 2-1), or whether they possess a very broad peak (or trough) not related to a Cotton effect (see Fig. 12-14). At the present time, their chief utility lies in the fact that rotations in the ultraviolet region are (for colorless compounds) invariably greater than for the conventional sodium D line. Comparisons of compounds with small $[\alpha]_D$ are therefore better carried out at a lower wavelength, which can be selected from the dispersion curve. Comparisons of plain dispersion curves, rather than of $[\alpha]_D$, are particularly meaningful for cases in which the curve changes sign in the visible region. Pertinent examples of this phenomenon are given in Chap. 16.

Plain dispersion curves may be called *positive* or *negative* depending upon whether they rise or fall toward *shorter wavelengths*. They may be described adequately in the experimental section of an article without a figure in the following manner.

Specific rotation $[\alpha]_D$ or molecular rotation $[\phi]$ should be noted at the following wavelengths: (1) the longest wavelength measured, usually 700 mμ; (2) 589 mμ, the sodium D line, used in nearly all earlier determinations of optical rotation; and (3) the shortest wavelength measured. It is usually desirable to include other points at 20 to 50 mμ

[3] Appreciation is expressed to the Publication Committee of The Chemical Society (London) for permission to quote from our article (Ref. 2).

intervals, especially at lower wavelengths, in order to describe more accurately the steepness of the curve, since this may often be a characteristic feature of a plain dispersion curve.[4] Solvent, concentration, and temperature should also be stated if this has not already been done in a general description (see Sec. 2-5).

Example 1: $3\alpha,12\alpha$-dihydroxycholanic acid;[4] RD in methanol $(c,$ 0.10), $24°$; $[\alpha]_{700} + 35°$, $[\alpha]_{589} + 50°$, $[\alpha]_{400} + 119°$, $[\alpha]_{350} + 159°$, $[\alpha]_{320} + 212°$, $[\alpha]_{300} + 258°$, $[\alpha]_{280} + 304°$, $[\alpha]_{260} + 387°$, $[\alpha]_{250} + 474°$.

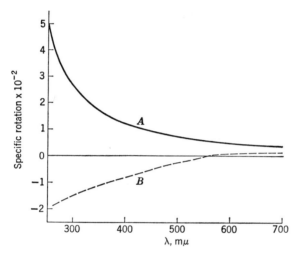

Fig. 2-1. Examples of plain positive (A) and plain negative (B) dispersion curves.

The above example of curve A in Fig. 2-1 represents a *positive plain dispersion curve*. Curve B of Fig. 2-1 is a *negative plain curve* even though it starts on the positive rotation side in the visible. In an experimental section, it would be described in the manner illustrated in Example 1 except that it would also be desirable to record the wavelength where the curve crosses the zero rotation axis.

2-3. Single Cotton Effect Curves

As outlined in this book, for organic chemical purposes the most important and interesting dispersion curves are *anomalous* ones, which are usually of two types (see Figs. 2-2 and 2-4). Figure 2-2 contains

[4] For pertinent examples see C. Djerassi and W. Closson, *J. Am. Chem. Soc.*, **78,** 3761 (1956); C. Djerassi, J. Osiecki, and W. Closson, *ibid.*, **81,** 4587 (1959).

examples of curves, showing a single Cotton effect (see Sec. 1-2), each with one geometrical "maximum" and one geometrical "minimum." Since the mean of the "maximum" and "minimum" of the dispersion curve (in terms of wavelengths) usually corresponds approximately to the ultraviolet absorption maximum of the particular chromophore (see Sec. 1-2), it is extremely important that the "maximum" of a rotatory dispersion curve not be confused with the "maximum" of the corresponding ultraviolet absorption spectrum. We have proposed, therefore, the terms *peak* and *trough,* since these are not misleading and equiv-

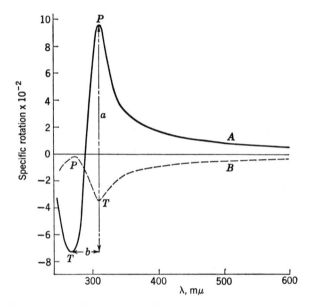

Fig. 2-2. Examples of single Cotton effect curves: *A,* positive Cotton effect; *B,* negative Cotton effect; *P,* peak; *T,* trough; *a,* amplitude; *b,* breadth. (*Modified from C. Djerassi and W. Klyne, Proc. Chem. Soc., 1957, 55.*)

alents can be found readily in other languages (e.g., German, *Gipfel* and *Tal*).

A *positive Cotton effect curve* (e.g., curve *A* in Fig. 2-2) is one in which the peak occurs at the longer wavelength, while a *negative* curve (curve *B* in Fig. 2-2) is defined by the fact that the trough is found at the longer wavelength. The actual sign of rotation is of no consequence; in curve *B* of Fig. 2-2 the peak has in fact a negative rotation value.

The vertical distance (*a* in Fig. 2-2) between peak and trough is called the *amplitude* and the horizontal distance (*b* in Fig. 2-2) the *breadth* of the Cotton effect curve. At times, a name that will cover both *peaks* and *troughs* is required and *"extremum"* has been suggested.[5]   It is often necessary [6] to designate the peak *or* trough—whichever occurs on the higher wavelength side of the Cotton effect curve—and the term [5] *"first extremum"* appears to satisfy this need.

A description of a single Cotton effect curve in the experimental portion of an article should include the rotations at the highest wavelength (e.g., 700 mμ), at 589 mμ, and at the shortest wavelength measured.   Most important, rotation values at each marked change of direction, such as peaks, troughs, and shoulders (or inflections), should be

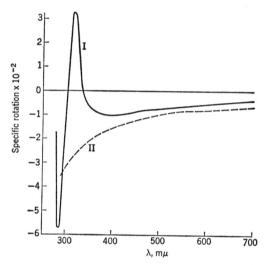

Fig. 2-3.   Positive Cotton effect curve of tigogenone (I) superimposed on plain negative "background" curve of deoxytigogenin (II).

listed *in order of decreasing wavelength,* which will then make it unnecessary to define each point by the words "peak" and "trough."   It should be noted that these selected rotation data do not indicate the wavelength intervals between readings (see Sec. 2-5).

Example 2 (curve *A* in Fig. 2-2): cholestan-3-one; [7] RD in methanol (*c,* 0.10), 29–31°; $[\alpha]_{700} + 37°$, $[\alpha]_{589} + 55°$, $[\alpha]_{307} + 959°$, $[\alpha]_{267} - 740°$, $[\alpha]_{245} - 362°$.

The Cotton effect, caused by the particular chromophore, invariably is superimposed on a plain curve, which represents the rotatory con-

[5] Private communication from the late W. Moffitt, Harvard University.

[6] C. Djerassi, O. Halpern, V. Halpern, O. Schindler, and C. Tamm, *Helv. Chim. Acta,* **41,** 269, table 4 (1958).

[7] C. Djerassi, W. Closson, and A. E. Lippman, *J. Am. Chem. Soc.,* **78,** 3163 (1956).

tribution of the parent system *without* the particular chromophore; this is referred to as the *background* curve. Often, although by no means always, the signs of the Cotton effect curve and of the background curve coincide. At times, however, this is not the case. A pertinent example from the literature [8] is shown in Fig. 2-3; here the Cotton effect curve of 5α-spirostan-3-one (tigogenone) (I) is positive, while the background curve of the ketone-free parent substance, 5α-spirostan (deoxytigogenin) (II), is characterized by a negative plain dispersion curve.

2-4. Multiple Cotton Effect Curves

The third type of dispersion curve is more complicated in the region of ultraviolet absorption in that it possesses two or more peaks with a corresponding number of troughs and therefore is called a *multiple Cotton effect curve*. Such features are usually observed with α,β-unsaturated ketones,[9] and in these cases it is also often necessary to distinguish between broad peaks and troughs, as well as between shoulders and inflections.

A broad peak (or trough) usually does not indicate entrance into the optically active absorption band (in contrast to the usual peak or trough). Thus in Fig. 2-4 the broad peak at 420 to 405 mμ is not related to the peak of such an absorption band but represents the partial, positive rotation in the 700 to 500 mμ region now falling under the influence of a stronger negative partial rotation owing to entry into the optically active absorption band around 363 mμ, the first extremum of which is the trough at 366 mμ.

Example 3 (Fig. 2-4): testosterone;[9] RD in dioxane (c, 0.10), 25–26°; $[\alpha]_{700} + 62°$, $[\alpha]_{589} + 103°$, $[\alpha]_{420-405} + 180°$ (broad peak), $[\alpha]_{366} - 177°$, $[\alpha]_{360} - 95°$, $[\alpha]_{352} - 282°$, $[\alpha]_{340-337} + 390°$ (shoulder, $[\alpha]_{325} + 1339°$ (inflection), $[\alpha]_{275} + 2935°$.

2-5. General Statements concerning Recording of Experimental Data

In any article dealing with rotatory dispersion curves it is desirable to indicate the interval between wavelengths at which readings were

[8] C. Djerassi and R. Ehrlich, *J. Am. Chem. Soc.*, **78**, 440 (1956).

[9] C. Djerassi, R. Riniker, and B. Riniker, *J. Am. Chem. Soc.*, **78**, 6377 (1956).

taken [10] and the range of the probable errors,[9] since neither one of these points would be apparent from the manner in which experimental data are recorded (see Examples 1 to 3).   Other factors, such as temperature, solvent, and concentration, which may be common to rotatory dispersion measurements of several compounds in one investigation, can most conveniently be described in an introductory paragraph to the experimental section rather than repeated each time.

Rotatory power is usually reported as specific rotation ([α]) or as molecular rotation ([φ] = [α] × mol. wt/100).   In most of our papers we have used specific rotations for pedagogical reasons, to emphasize

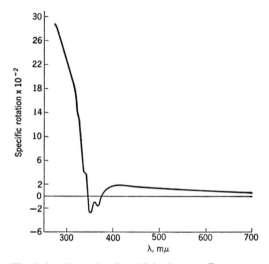

Fig. 2-4.   Example of multiple Cotton effect curve.

to organic chemists one of the major advantages of dispersion measurements in the ultraviolet—the greatly magnified rotation values as compared with rotations obtained at the sodium D line.   In work limited to steroids or triterpenes, it is not important whether specific or molecular rotations are used since the molecular weights of most members of these classes resemble each other sufficiently to be within the range of error of the experimental rotation measurements.   On the other hand, when comparisons are made [11] between rotatory dispersion curves of substances of widely divergent molecular weights (e.g., steroids versus bicyclic ketones), molecular rotations should be employed.

[10] See, for example, C. Djerassi, E. W. Foltz, and A. E. Lippman, *J. Am. Chem. Soc.*, **77**, 4354 (1955).
[11] W. Klyne and C. Djerassi, *Angew. Chem.*, **69**, 683 (1957).

3 | INSTRUMENTATION [1]

3-1. Introduction

The single most important factor responsible for the renewed interest in rotatory dispersion has been the recent advances in ultraviolet spectropolarimetry, which in turn have been made possible by many modern electronic developments, including the advent of photomultiplier tubes.

Many instruments have been constructed in the past [2] that permitted the determination, mostly by photographic methods, of rotation in the ultraviolet region of the spectrum. The measurements were laborious, usually requiring several days for one substance, and the instruments had to be specially constructed. It is not surprising, therefore, that with very few exceptions organic chemists did not have the opportunity or the inclination to employ rotatory dispersion as a routine tool for their research problems. The situation was changed suddenly by the development of a rather simple photoelectric spectropolarimeter,[3] which permitted fairly rapid measurements of rotatory dispersion over an appreciable ultraviolet spectral range. Most important to the organic chemist, the instrument was simple to operate, commercially available (O. C. Rudolph and Sons, Caldwell, New Jersey), and easily maintained. It had

[1] Sections 3-1, 3-2, and 3-3 were contributed by Anthony N. James and Berndt Sjöberg of the author's laboratory.

[2] For reviews see (a) R. Descamps, *Trans. Faraday Soc.*, **26**, 357 (1930); (b) W. Heller in A. Weissberger (ed.), "Physical Methods of Organic Chemistry," 2d ed., vol. 1, part 2, chap. 13, Interscience Publishers, Inc., New York, 1949; (c) M. K. Hargreaves, *J. Chem. Soc.*, **1953**, 2953.

[3] E. Brand, E. Washburn, B. F. Erlanger, E. Ellenbogen, J. Daniel, F. Lippmann, and M. Scheu, *J. Am. Chem. Soc.*, **76**, 5037 (1954); H. Rudolph, *J. Opt. Soc. Am.*, **45**, 50 (1955).

several drawbacks, as was to be expected from a "first" instrument, but nevertheless it undoubtedly represented the prince who awoke the sleeping beauty of rotatory dispersion. All the dispersion curves reproduced in this book were obtained with a Rudolph photoelectric spectropolarimeter. Its operation, scope, and limitations are discussed in detail below.

3-2. The Rudolph Photoelectric Spectropolarimeter

A. Description of the Instrument. An over-all view of the Rudolph photoelectric spectropolarimeter (Model 200AS/80Q/650) and its attachments (with the exception of the power-supply unit for the light

Fig. 3-1. Rudolph spectropolarimeter (Model 200AS/80Q/650).

sources) can best be gained from the photograph in Fig. 3-1. The chief components are illustrated schematically in Fig. 3-2, and a list of attachments is given in Table 3-1.

The quartz optical system (Fig. 3-3) consists of a Beckman DU quartz monochromator, supplying light of a desired wavelength to the polarimeter, placed at an included angle of approximately 30° to it. This arrangement is solely to save space. The light is passed by reflection from the light source A (Fig. 3-3) via a focussing lens B and a mirror C through the manually operated slit D into the monochromator, which contains a quartz dispersion prism F. The emergent monochromatic light passes through a collimating lens G and is reflected by an adjustable aluminized mirror H to the quartz Rochon polarizer prism

Table 3-1

Item	Manufacturer
Zirconium concentrated arc lamp (C) Type K100	Sylvania
Xenon compact arc lamp (B):	
Type 510Cl	Hanovia
375-watt xenon lamp Type XC	Siemens (Germany)
Power-supply unit (A) for xenon lamp	O. C. Rudolph
Power-supply unit (A) for zirconium lamp	George W. Gates Co.
Voltage stabilizer (2000 watts; input: 95–130 volts; output: 115 volts)	Raytheon
Electronic multiplier photometer (H) Model 520-M	Photovolt Corp.
Monochromator (E):	
Model DU	Beckman Instruments, Inc.
Model SP 500	Unicam (England)

I. This polarizing prism is mounted at the center of a ball bearing so that it may be rotated with a minimum of effort. Adjustable stops are provided for fixing its angular movement between precise limits, and a "symmetrical angle scale" indicates the range of this movement. Rotation of the polarizer is effected by a lever that engages in a fork integral with the polarizer (visible in Fig. 3-1).

The oscillating motion of the lever, which is transmitted to the polarizer, is effected by a unit that may be termed the "polarizer drive." The most recent and successful design of this unit [4] is illustrated in Fig. 3-4 and consists of two parts: a motor *A,* whose direction of rotation can be reversed, and a simple cam *B* and roller *C,* driven by a second 15-rpm synchronous motor *D.*

This arrangement operates a microswitch relay system, reversing the first motor *A* about every 2 seconds. The shaft *E* of the first motor is stepped and the smaller radius is threaded part of its length. The bottom part *G* of the lever *F* is a running fit on the smaller radius of the shaft *E* and a friction disk with a locking washer *H* screws onto the shaft *E* in such a way that the lever *F* is held lightly between the friction disk and the buttress of the shaft. As the shaft *E* rotates in one direction, the lever *F* is carried to a stop position on the "symmetrical angle scale," and at this point the lever is held stationary by the revolving "clutch plates." Reversal of the motor *A* repeats the procedure in the opposite direction.

Returning again to Fig. 3-3, the polarized light from the Rochon prism *I* passes through the polarimeter tube *K* and enters, via an aper-

[4] H. Rudolph, *Proc. Instr. Soc. Am.,* Paper 56-3-1, September, 1956.

ture *L* fitted with a safety target, the quartz Rochon analyzer *M*. Finally, the light impinges on the photomultiplier tube *P* and the latter's current output is measured on the electronic multiplier photometer *Q*.

B. Operation of the Instrument (see Fig. 3-2).   After the photometer unit *H* has been switched on and allowed to stabilize, the mono-

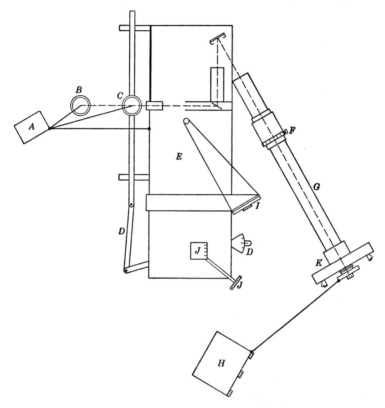

Fig. 3-2. Main components of Rudolph spectropolarimeter: *A*, power-supply units for light sources; *B*, xenon lamp; *C*, zirconium lamp; *D*, traveling bar and device for fixing lamps in position; *E*, monochromator; *F*, symmetrical angle adjuster with polarizer drive immediately below; *G*, polarimeter; *H*, photometer; *I*, slit-width adjuster; *J*, wavelength adjuster and scale; *K*, analyzer; dashed line represents the path of light.

chromator *E* is set (*J*) at 546 mμ and the position of the zirconium lamp *C* is adjusted on the traveling bar *D* to obtain a maximum response on the photometer *H* at an appropriate slit opening *I*.   (An approximate adjustment can be made first by observing the green light on the mirror *H* in Fig. 3-3.)   It should be emphasized that this procedure can be used only for routine purposes and that very careful realignment of the light source *B* or *C*, monochromator *E*, and polarimeter *G* is necessary when lamps are renewed or when the instrument has been disturbed in any way.

The photometer (*H*) zero setting is adjusted and the polarimeter tube is placed always in the same predetermined position in the polarimeter

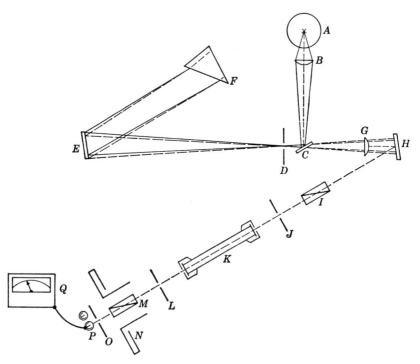

Fig. 3-3. Diagram of optical system of Rudolph spectropolarimeter: *A*, light source; *B*, focusing lens; *C*, mirror; *D*, slit; *E*, mirror; *F*, quartz dispersion prism; *G*, collimating lens; *H*, mirror; *I*, quartz Rochon polarizer prism; *J*, aperture; *K*, polarimeter tube; *L*, aperture; *M*, quartz Rochon analyzer prism; *N*, analyzer scale; *O*, aperture; *P*, photomultiplier tubes; *Q*, photometer.

trough [in our laboratory always very close to the polarizer prism (see Fig. 3-1)]. After setting the wavelength (*J*) of the monochromator *E* at 700 mμ, an arbitrarily chosen wavelength, and the symmetrical angle (*F*) at 5°, the monochromator slit *I* is opened to give a photometer (*H*) response of 30 to 40 per cent of full galvanometer scale deflection at maximum sensitivity. Switching on the polarizer drive (*F*) completes the preliminaries for using the instrument. A symmetrical angle setting of 2° is more desirable in the longer wavelength range but changes in the symmetrical angle should be avoided as far as possible; a 2° angle setting hardly ever suffices for work in the ultraviolet and this is the reason a 5° setting is recommended for routine work.

To make a reading, the analyzer K is rotated manually so that each successive stroke of the polarizer drive causes the deflected photometer needle to return to the same position on the scale.   Angular rotation is read from the polarimeter in the normal manner.   Full details of these

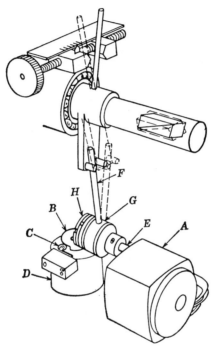

Fig. 3-4. Polarizer drive of Rudolph spectropolarimeter: A, motor; B, cam; C, roller; D, synchronous motor; E, shaft; F, lever; G, lever mount; H, locking washer.

steps are given in the operating manual supplied with the Rudolph spectropolarimeter.

This operation must be repeated for each selected wavelength down to about 320 mμ, where the energy emission from the zirconium lamp C is insufficient to produce an adequate photometer response with maximum slit opening.   At this point, the xenon source is substituted by moving the traveling bar D, which in turn moves the zirconium lamp C clear of the monochromator entrance.   Since the xenon lamp B is always in a fixed position with respect to the monochromator entrance, this substitution is simple.   As still lower wavelengths are chosen, the xenon-lamp energy will also eventually prove insufficient.   Further readings may then be obtained by opening the symmetrical angle to 10° and/or diluting the sample solution.   These last two steps will enable measurements as low as 250 mμ to be made under ideal circumstances, but they carry with them the greater error inherent in larger symmetrical angle settings.

The above procedure is only a general one and cognizance must be taken of the nature of the sample, especially when deciding on the optimum concentration, provided this is not governed automatically by the supply of material.   For example, α,β-unsaturated ketones often exhibit fine structure in the dispersion curve below 400 mμ (see Fig. 5-8), and sample solutions containing 4 to 10 mg in 2 cc are preferable in order to recognize all the detail.   On the other hand, strong absorption in that region may preclude the use of such concentrated solutions. The rotation of the substance also plays an important role, and with certain very highly rotating compounds as little as 0.05 mg per 2 cc has been employed in our laboratory.

It is absolutely indispensable to run blank determinations for each solvent and to perform these for each light source and for each symmetrical angle setting.   The wavelength intervals chosen for blank and sample solutions are arbitrary, but as very few compounds (except colored ones) show significant rotatory dispersion abnormalities above 450 mμ, it is obvious that usually short intervals are necessary only below this value.   In general, blank readings in our laboratory are conducted at 10-mμ intervals below 325 mμ and much less frequently at longer wavelengths (700, 589, 500, 400, and 325 mμ).

For the sample solutions, readings are invariably taken at 700 mμ, at 589 mμ (the sodium D line), and at intervals to the lowest wavelength feasible under the particular experimental conditions.   These intervals depend upon the nature of the substance and the dispersion curve.   With a plain curve, readings below 589 mμ can be conducted in 50-mμ intervals until 350 to 320 mμ is reached, at which point 10 to 20 mμ intervals are employed.   It must be emphasized that these recommendations apply only for dispersion curves used for the purposes outlined in this book.   When calculations of Drude equations (Sec. 1-3) are contemplated, more frequent readings will usually be taken in the visible region, and concentrations, coupled with a small symmetrical angle, should be selected which permit a high order of accuracy in readings at those wavelengths.

For Cotton effect curves, which at present are of the greatest interest and utility, 5-mμ intervals should be employed below 400 mμ, and in regions of fine structure, peaks, or troughs much closer readings (1 to 2.5 mμ) must be taken.   Rotations are frequently dependent upon concentration (see Sec. 3-3E) and it is, therefore, most desirable to measure the entire rotatory dispersion curve at one concentration; if this is not feasible, the spectral range for each concentration should be indicated. Since the main emphasis lies on determinations in the ultraviolet, usually requiring concentrations no higher than 1 to 3 mg per cc, the rotations in the visible region will be subject to a much larger error because there the absolute rotation values are much lower, unless a higher concentration is employed for the spectral range 589 ± 100 mμ.

A complete rotatory dispersion curve, including the blank, will probably take an experienced operator about 1½ hours.   However, it should be noted that most individuals are unable to sustain this effort beyond 4 hours, as the eye strain produced by the continuously moving galvanometer needle of the photometer is considerable.

C. Critical Survey of Spectropolarimeter Components. *i. Light Sources.*   The zirconium lamp commonly employed in the spectral range 700 to 320 mμ usually performs with great consistency, giving stable emission for long periods of time, often for several hundred hours.

The xenon high-pressure arc lamp, however, is less stable and of much shorter effective life.   For this reason and because it is also more expensive, it is used only outside the range of the zirconium lamp (i.e., below 320 mμ) even though it yields high energy emission as a continuum in the visible as well as in the ultraviolet region.   The stable life of the xenon lamps is unpredictable and varies from 2 to over 100 hours. Table 3-2 lists the limits of ultraviolet penetration for the most commonly used solvents with a xenon lamp.

Table 3-2

Spectral Range of Xenon Lamp for Various Solvents *

Solvent	Symmetrical angle setting		
	2°	5°	10°
	Wavelength, mμ		
Water	285	263	252
Methanol	282	260	250
(Iso)octane	281	261	250
Dioxane	287	272	265

* For a 5-cm polarimeter tube of 1.9 cc capacity.

A xenon-mercury compact arc lamp is also commercially available, and it produces more energy in certain parts of the visible and ultraviolet regions than the xenon lamp. Although it has been possible to conduct measurements on some compounds as low as 242 mμ with xenon-mercury arc lamps, the stability of those presently available is so unpredictable that their practical use for rotatory dispersion measurements is debatable.

A stable light source is one of the most critical variables in photoelectric polarimetry, especially with automatically recording instruments (Sec. 3-6B), and there remains considerable room for improvement. A stabilized line current is of some help, and it is advisable to employ an entirely separate circuit in conjunction with a very efficient voltage stabilizer.

ii. Monochromator. The only necessary maintenance of this component lies in the occasional checking of wavelength calibration. This is simply done by mounting a mercury lamp in the available position on the traveling bar and matching several of the well-defined spectral lines (365.0, 435.8, 546.1, and 690.7 mμ).

iii. Polarizer Prism and Phototubes. A well-adjusted instrument will result in solvent blank readings that are more or less constant throughout the spectral range for a given light source and symmetrical angle. "Curving" of the blank toward shorter wavelengths over a period of time indicates movement of the quartz Rochon polarizer prism in its metal housing or, alternatively, a change in position of the phototube. Both these components are positioned very critically, but this type of maladjustment occurs infrequently.

The Rudolph spectropolarimeter is equipped with two phototubes marked IP21 and IP28. For the purposes described in this book, the IP28 phototube performs entirely satisfactorily over the useful spectral range, and the IP21 tube, inherently limited to the visible, is not necessary.

iv. Polarimeter Tubes. For routine work, microtubes are required. These must be of center-filling design, because the end plates (fused silica) must be permanently fastened to avoid stress-produced birefringence. In most of our earlier studies, we employed 10-cm tubes of 3.5 to 4.0 mm bore and a capacity of less than 2.0 cc. Subsequently, it was found that 5-cm tubes of 1.9 cc capacity but with a 7.0-mm bore are far superior (see Sec. 3-3C) and these are now used exclusively in our laboratory. The larger bore permits much easier filling with aqueous solutions and in general is also more convenient as far as cleaning the polarimeter tubes is concerned.

3-3.   Variables and Errors in Rotatory Dispersion Measurements

The conclusions drawn below are derived from experience gained during several years with the Rudolph spectropolarimeter, but many of them will also apply to other instruments.   No general statements can be made about accuracy, because this depends on so many variables inherent in the substance itself.   The errors in carefully controlled [5] as well as routine [6] dispersion measurements of a variety of steroids have already been recorded, but a number of general variables have been examined by us with $(+)$-3-methylcyclohexanone, a substance whose rotatory power in the visible (less than $10°$) and ultraviolet (ca. $900°$) regions can be considered as fairly representative.

A. Weighing and Dilution.   Most of the rotatory dispersion measurements conducted by organic chemists, especially in the natural-products field, will be limited to 0.1 to 2 mg of material.   The weighing of such a sample necessitates a microbalance and, unless due care is exercised, the errors in weighing and in the subsequent dilution of the solution (2.0 cc) may be very appreciable.

B. Temperature.   Temperature variations over the range 16 to $47°$ do not appreciably affect the rotatory dispersion of $(+)$-3-methylcyclo-hexanone.   Indeed most of the errors inherent in the present photo-electric rotatory dispersion measurements are of such an order of magnitude that ordinary variations of room temperature are without significance, and the use of jacketed tubes or other temperature control is not necessary, although it is desirable to record the temperature fluctuations during a given series of measurements.   These statements do not, of course, apply to kinetic measurements, for which careful temperature control is important, nor to other measurements for which more than average accuracy (± 5 to 10 per cent) is required.   The effect of temperature in accurate measurements has been demonstrated numerous times,[7] but these studies have been concerned largely with rotations obtained in the visible range of the spectrum.

[5] C. Djerassi, E. W. Foltz, and A. E. Lippman, *J. Am. Chem. Soc.*, **77**, 4354 (1955); E. W. Foltz, A. E. Lippman, and C. Djerassi, *ibid.*, **77**, 4359 (1955); A. E. Lippman, E. W. Foltz, and C. Djerassi, *ibid.*, **77**, 4363 (1955); E. W. Foltz, Ph.D. thesis, Wayne State University, Detroit, 1955.

[6] C. Djerassi, R. Riniker, and B. Riniker, *J. Am. Chem. Soc.*, **78**, 6377, footnote 34 (1956).

[7] See, for example, (*a*) L. Tschugaeff and W. Pastanogoff, *Z. physik. Chem.* (*Leipzig*), **85**, 553 (1913); (*b*) T. M. Lowry, "Optical Rotatory Power," chap. 28, Longmans, Green & Co., Ltd., London, 1935; (*c*) J. A. Schellman, *Compt. rend. trav. lab. Carlsberg, Sér. chim.*, **30**, 395 (1958); (*d*) M. K. Hargreaves, *J. Chem. Soc.*, **1954**, 1781.

C. Refractive Index Gradients. A beneficial aspect of polarimeter tubes of short length and larger diameter (Sec. 3-2C*iv*) is especially noticeable where a foreign reagent must be added to the tube *in situ* or where the tube is subjected to sudden temperature changes. Both tend to set up refractive index gradients, which in many cases will temporarily cause complete loss of sensitivity of the photometer. This effect is even observed in some instances when a solution in the tube is changed. These refractive index gradients, causing refraction of the light to the sides of the polarimeter tube, account for the "blanking-out" phenomenon noted in the spectropolarimetric examination [8] of ketal formation (Chap. 11) during the addition of hydrochloric acid as well as in the thermal and urea denaturation of proteins.[9] In the latter case, 1-cm cuvettes or gold-plated brass tubes have eliminated this problem.

D. Slit-width Variations. In Sec. 3-2B it was mentioned that for routine measurements the photometer needle should be maintained between 30 and 40 per cent of full scale deflection. The reason for this recommendation is that below 30 per cent the accuracy is too low, while above 40 per cent the needle fluctuations are so rapid as to become quickly tiring for the operator. To stay in the 30 to 40 per cent range as wavelength changes are made it is necessary to vary the monochromator slit width; this in turn affects the spectral purity of the light used, especially at larger slit openings. For $(+)$-3-methylcyclohexanone (c, 0.12 in methanol), it was found that over a spectral range in which the rotation is changing rapidly (vicinity of peak or trough), changes in slit width corresponding to 30 and 40 per cent of full scale deflection caused a deviation of $0.015°$ in the angular rotation with a symmetrical angle of $5°$ and $0.030°$ with an angle of $10°$. A corollary of this is observed in substituting light sources, the more powerful xenon lamp requiring much smaller slit openings. The effect is also noticed when the amount of light from the xenon lamp varies because of the movement of the arc.

E. Concentration. It is well known [7b] that changes in concentration of some optically active substances can affect the rotation appreciably. This effect is often already noticeable at the sodium D line and may be enhanced in rotatory dispersion measurements. For example, with $(+)$-3-methylcyclohexanone the specific rotations in methanol at the peak (307.5 mμ) were found to be $910°$, $840°$, and $720°$, corresponding to concentrations of 0.132, 0.103, and 0.029 g per 100 cc. It is

[8] C. Djerassi, L. A. Mitscher, and B. J. Mitscher, *J. Am. Chem. Soc.*, **81**, 947 (1959).

[9] Private communication from J. G. Foss, University of Oregon.

recognized that these results also include the slit-width factor (Sec. 3-3D), but this is of minor importance in this example.

F. Conclusion. From the foregoing discussion, it can be seen that as far as possible comparative rotatory dispersion measurements should be conducted at the same concentration and if possible at the same slit width. This statement applies even more to solvents, which are discussed separately in Sec. 3-4. Furthermore, not too much reliance, especially of a quantitative nature, should be placed upon readings obtained at the limits of lower wavelength, because at this stage one is usually operating at the highest symmetrical angle (10° or higher), with its concomitant loss in sensitivity, and at the greatest dilution, which may introduce a further source of error.

3-4. Selection of Solvents

It has been generally recognized [7b] in monochromatic polarimetry that variations in solvents may reflect upon the rotation. This can be particularly noticeable in rotatory dispersion work,[10] where even inversion of the sign of the Cotton effect has been noted [11] upon altering the polarity of the medium. The polarity of the solvent may also involve association phenomena, which will make the rotatory dispersion more sensitive to changes in concentration and temperature.

These factors must be counterbalanced with certain practical considerations which apply particularly to rotatory dispersion applications in organic chemistry and which limit considerably the choice of solvent. The main consideration is that as few different solvents as possible be used so that comparisons of rotatory dispersion curves are easily made without having to repeat the measurements. This, in turn, requires solvents that can dissolve the majority of organic substances within the necessary concentration range.

Within these limitations at least two solvents of varying polarity must be chosen; we have selected methanol and dioxane. As the aim of nearly all rotatory dispersion measurements is to go as far into the ultraviolet as possible, spectral purity is important and the solvents should be purified as rigorously as is common for other spectral measurements.

A. Methanol. Methanol is an excellent example of a polar solvent with good transparency through the currently available spectral range.

[10] See, for example, W. Kuhn, K. Freudenberg, and R. Seidler, *Z. physik. Chem. (Leipzig),* **(B)13,** 379 (1931); M. K. Hargreaves and P. J. Richardson, *J. Chem. Soc.,* **1957,** 2260.

[11] C. Djerassi and L. E. Geller, *Tetrahedron,* **3,** 319 (1958).

Because so much of the present rotatory dispersion work concerns the carbonyl chromophore, the special applicability of methanol to ketones and aldehydes must be emphasized. It is the only solvent that lends itself readily to measurement of ketal or acetal formation and, as indicated in Chap. 11, this can offer a great deal of useful information. In rotatory dispersion measurements of α-haloketones, it is often indispensable to conduct studies in both a polar and a nonpolar medium (see Sec. 9-3C), and methanol will serve very satisfactorily as the former.

Current work with α,β-unsaturated ketones (see Secs. 4-3 and 5-3) is largely confined, because of instrumental difficulties, to the long-wavelength, low-intensity absorption band above 300 mμ. Since this is particularly well resolved in a nonpolar solvent and is shifted to a longer wavelength in such a medium, methanol is quite unsuited for such purposes. However, the high-intensity band in the 220 to 260 mμ region shows exactly the opposite behavior—a bathochromic shift occurring in a polar solvent. As spectropolarimeters that can handle strongly absorbing substances become available, rotatory dispersion studies of this absorption band of α,β-unsaturated ketones will be best conducted in methanol or another solvent of high polarity.

B. Dioxane. The ideal nonpolar solvent would be a hydrocarbon such as octane, but its solvent power is insufficient in many important areas of natural-product chemistry, especially for the polycyclic terpenes. Consequently, we have chosen dioxane, and, as illustrated in Figs. 4-13 and 5-8, the difference between octane and dioxane is not so great as to be of material significance. Dioxane is particularly important in rotatory dispersion measurements of α,β-unsaturated ketones, since most of the fine structure of multiple Cotton effect curves is revealed in a nonpolar solvent.

Dioxane is equally satisfactory in rotatory dispersion work with saturated ketones, except that it should be recalled that the change in going from methanol to dioxane is accompanied [6] by a bathochromic shift of approximately 8 mμ. At times, resolution of the rotatory dispersion extremum of a saturated ketone can be seen in dioxane; a shoulder or even a second extremum may appear in the nonpolar solvent, whereas only one extremum is noted in methanol. Several examples of this resolution have been recorded among triterpenoid ketones.[12]

C. Other Solvents. One of the main drawbacks of dioxane is its reduced transparency (see Table 3-2); where this factor becomes important, a hydrocarbon solvent such as octane should be substituted. This should also be used where a larger range of polarities is indicated [11]

[12] C. Djerassi, J. Osiecki, and W. Closson, *J. Am. Chem. Soc.*, **81**, 4587 (1959).

or where special attention is paid to resolution of fine structure (Fig. 5-8). Other solvents that have been employed from time to time are hexane, other hydrocarbons, water, various alcohols, chloroform, etc. The latter has not been used extensively by us because of its relatively high vapor pressure, formation of impurities such as phosgene, and especially because of leakage problems encountered in polarimeter tubes with cemented end plates.

Recently,[13] diethyleneglycol dimethyl ether has been suggested as a substitute for dioxane. The dimethyl ether is an even better solvent than dioxane for many organic substances; it is sufficiently nonpolar to give at least as good resolution of fine structure with α,β-unsaturated ketones as dioxane and, most importantly, it is considerably more transparent in the lower ultraviolet spectral region. The only disadvantage of diethyleneglycol dimethyl ether may be encountered in cases in which the sample has to be recovered subsequent to rotatory dispersion measurements.

3-5.   Recording Spectropolarimeters

The first recording polarimeters [14] have been concerned largely with monochromatic saccharimetry. The recent activity in the rotatory dispersion field has greatly stimulated interest in designing recording spectropolarimeters for rotatory dispersion work in the ultraviolet. At least four different prototype models have been constructed (Glaxo, Ltd.,[15] Ciba, Ltd.,[15] H. Rudolph,[15] and Günthard et al.[16]), and the Rudolph instrument is now in commercial production.[15] Nothing has been published yet about the performance of these instruments, but there is little doubt that several satisfactory models will be available in the near future.

The polarimeters discussed so far rotate the plane of polarization to reestablish an original null condition either by movement of the analyzer or by employing the Faraday effect.[14b] An alternative is to take advantage of the energy change that normally accompanies the rotation of the plane of polarization when the light beam passes through a system of polarizer-sample-analyzer. Since there are currently in use many double-beam recording ultraviolet spectrophotometers, it would

---

[13] W. A. Struck, E. C. Olson, and R. L. Houtman, Abstracts of the American Chemical Society Meeting, Boston, April, 1959, p. 23–O.

[14] See (a) G. B. Levy, P. Schwed, and D. Fergus, Rev. Sci. Instr., 21, 693 (1950); (b) J. W. Gates, Chem. & Ind. (London), 1958, 190.

[15] Private communication.

[16] T. Bürer, M. Kohler, and H. H. Günthard, Helv. Chim. Acta, 41, 2216 (1958).

be desirable to convert these by means of an accessory [17] into recording spectropolarimeters. This would have the advantage of allowing the rapid recording of rotatory dispersion curves without interfering with the use of the instrument for recording ultraviolet spectra. Indeed, the intimate relationship of rotatory dispersion phenomena with ultraviolet absorption makes it almost mandatory to measure both properties, and this is best done under the same conditions and even on the same graph (see Fig. 3-10).

A prototype model of such an attachment has recently been developed by The Perkin-Elmer Corporation.[18] As some preliminary experience with it has been gained in our laboratory, a more detailed description follows.

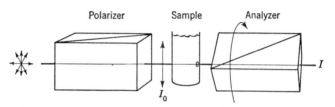

Fig. 3-5. Energy relations of simple polarizer-analyzer combination. Rotation of analyzer reduces the energy as the cosine² of the angle between polarizer axis and analyzer axis [Eq. (3)].

3-6. The Perkin-Elmer Recording Spectropolarimeter Attachment

A. Description of the Instrument.[19] Let us consider the rotation of one polarizing prism (or a sheet of polaroid) in front of another, from a position that allows passage of a maximum of light to the position of extinction (Fig. 3-5). One unit is the polarizer, the second unit is the analyzer, and the observed intensity of the light varies as the cosine² of the angle of rotation between the polarizer and the analyzer. The exact statement is given in Eq. (1):

$$I = I_0 K \cos^2 \theta \tag{1}$$

---

[17] The Keston unit, manufactured by the Standard Polarimeter Co., New York, represents an attachment to the Beckman DU spectrophotometer but is not a recording instrument. Furthermore, measurements below 400 mμ are not feasible with the Keston unit, so that it cannot be employed for ultraviolet spectropolarimetry.

[18] Paper presented by A. Savitzky, W. Slavin, and R. E. Salinger, Pittsburgh Conference on Analytical Chemistry and Applied Spectroscopy, March 3, 1959.

[19] Section 3-6A was very kindly prepared by A. Savitzky, R. H. Noble, Walter Slavin, and Tom Porro of The Perkin-Elmer Corporation, Norwalk, Conn.

where the factor K takes care of the various losses incurred by reflection in the polarizer and analyzer. I_0 is the intensity of the original light beam, and I is the intensity of the light after passage through the analyzer.

If there is now inserted between the polarizer and analyzer a material that rotates the plane of polarization, the equation becomes

$$I = I_0 K \cos^2 (\theta \pm \alpha) \tag{2}$$

Since the sample may also absorb at the particular wavelength, a Beer's law term must be included. The complete relationship is

$$I = I_0 e^{-kcl} K \cos^2 (\theta \pm \alpha) \tag{3}$$

The usual double-beam spectrophotometer is a device for obtaining the ratio R of the energy I_s contained in a sample beam to the energy

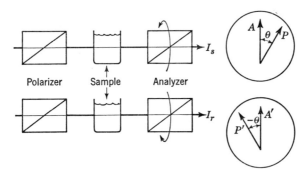

Polarizer   Sample   Analyzer

Fig. 3-6. Sample-beam and reference-beam energy relations. Spectrophotometer measures ratio of I_s to I_r.

I_r contained in a reference beam. Therefore, if two polarizer-analyzer assemblies are employed, one having an angle $+\theta$ between the polarizer and analyzer and the second having an angle $-\theta$ between the polarizer and analyzer, the situation shown in Fig. 3-6 is realized.

The consequence of placing the two assemblies described in Fig. 3-6 into a spectrophotometer and allowing it to compute the ratio R is shown in Eq. (4).

$$\frac{I_s = I_{0s} K e^{-kcl} \cos^2 (\theta \pm \alpha)}{I_r = I_{0r} K e^{-kcl} \cos^2 (-\theta \pm \alpha)} = R \tag{4}$$

If the beams are initially balanced, the I_0's cancel. If reflection losses are the same, the K's cancel and, if exactly the same solution is placed in the two cell compartments, the absorption terms cancel. One is then left with the simple relationship

$$\frac{I_s = \cos^2 (\theta \pm \alpha)}{I_r = \cos^2 (-\theta \pm \alpha)} = R \tag{5}$$

which rearranges to

$$\tan \alpha = \frac{1 - \sqrt{R}}{1 + \sqrt{R}} \cot \theta \tag{6}$$

The function R is what the double-beam spectrophotometer normally records as per cent T, and this, then, is the basis for the simplicity of

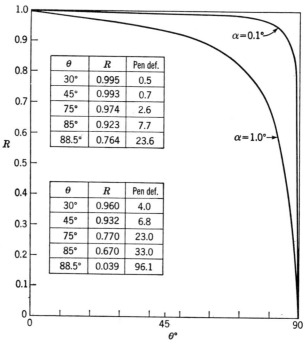

θ	R	Pen def.
30°	0.995	0.5
45°	0.993	0.7
75°	0.974	2.6
85°	0.923	7.7
88.5°	0.764	23.6

θ	R	Pen def.
30°	0.960	4.0
45°	0.932	6.8
75°	0.770	23.0
85°	0.670	33.0
88.5°	0.039	96.1

Fig. 3-7. Ratio (pen deflection) as a function of the parameter θ for two sample rotations.

the device in converting a recording double-beam spectrophotometer into a recording polarimeter.

It should be noted here that if one were to design a complete instrument instead of using an existing double-beam spectrophotometer, one would need only a single polarizer and a single sample cell to split the beam to go through two analyzers arranged at $+\theta$ and $-\theta$ to the polarizer. This saves both on the amount of the sample required and on one polarizing prism but requires major modification of an instrument, whereas what is described here can fit directly into the sample compartments of existing instruments.

A qualitative picture of the operation of this device can be obtained by reference to Fig. 3-6. Assuming a sample that rotates the plane of polarization clockwise, the vertical arrow P represents the light incident on the sample. As the sample rotates the plane of polarization, it reduces the angle between P and A, which therefore increases the amount of light falling on the sample beam detector in the spectrophotometer. This increase causes the pen to deflect upscale. Similarly, the same sample in the bottom beam (I_r, still rotating the plane of polarization in a clockwise direction) increases the effective angle between P' and A'.

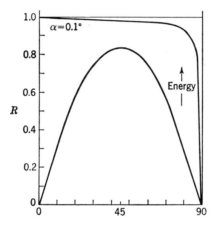

Fig. 3-8. Comparison of the pen deflection for an α of 0.1° and the energy available to produce that pen deflection as a function of the parameter θ.

An increase of angle results in a decrease of light which, in the reference beam of a spectrophotometer, is again translated into an upscale deflection of the pen. Thus, it can be seen that the effect of inserting an optically active substance in both accessory units results in a pen deflection proportional to rotation. No pen deflection results when absorption takes place, since the sample absorbs equally in both beams.

Equation (6) has some interesting properties. For example, the setting of the initial angle θ between polarizer and analyzer is a scale factor, and by the nature of the cotangent function, as θ approaches 90°, one can measure smaller and smaller angles for a given pen deflection R. This is illustrated in Fig. 3-7, where the values of the pen deflection are given for the various values of θ based on an $\alpha = 0.1°$ and $\alpha = 1.0°$.

From Eq. (6) it appears that one should always work at the highest possible θ; but unfortunately this is not the case for several reasons. The most fundamental limitation is that the cosine^2 relationship reduces the energy at just those large angles at which the pen deflection is at a maximum.   One arrives then at the interesting picture shown in Fig. 3-8, which gives the pen deflection for a given angle α and the relative amount of energy available to place across the slide-wire interval represented by that deflection.   As one approaches the area where there is a large deflection for a very small angle α, one also has practically no energy with which to make the measurement.   The maximum signal-to-noise situation exists when $\theta = 45°$, as illustrated here.   Table 3-3 shows the amount of improvement in signal to noise available.

Table 3-3

θ	Relative energy (I), $\cos^2 \theta$	Sensitivity (II) at 10× scale expansion, α/div.	Relative energy per degree α (I/II)
45	0.500	0.014	35
60	0.250	0.008	31
70	0.117	0.005	23
75	0.067	0.004	17
80	0.030	0.003	10

The reason one uses large θ is shown by the column titled "Sensitivity."   If one is limited severely in the amount of sample and the specific rotation is low, a small angle α is all that is available, and one is forced to use large θ in order to see the pen deflection.   However, if α obtained from the sample is greater than the minimum detectable at a large θ, one can get more energy through the system by decreasing θ in order to (1) have a less noisy record, (2) reach a shorter wavelength, or (3) gain resolving power.

It can be seen from the table that while one loses sensitivity in going from 80° to 45°, the gain in energy is so large that there is a net improvement of a factor of three in the energy available to record a given angle α.   This means that one can go to a shorter wavelength while there is sufficient energy to obtain data.

Of course, if energy, or rather signal to noise, is no problem, the magnitude of θ is not limited and should be as large as practicable. However, by its very nature rotatory dispersion work in the ultraviolet is most interesting at wavelengths at which the sample absorbs.   This absorption, the use of polarizers made of natural crystalline materials that are not too transparent, and the limited amount of energy available from the source all combine to produce an energy-limited situation—one in which resolution definitely begins to suffer.

In the practical case one must make a compromise between signal to noise and sufficient pen deflection to be able to read the smallest α to be measured.   Another factor that limits the angle θ is the presence of unpolarized light, which becomes a greater fraction of the total as θ approaches 90°.   Where this is caused merely by the inefficiency of the polarizing prisms, one can use known sucrose solutions for calibration and, as long as the amount of unpolarized light is not too high, this still allows useful work.

There exists a potentially greater problem for materials that exhibit circular dichroism.   In this case there is produced some circularly polarized light which passes unattenuated through the analyzer prism and so acts to reduce the deflections from a given α in the same manner as does unpolarized light.   Although no significant deviations that are demonstrably due to circular dichroism have been observed to date, this may be a problem with some samples and would be most significant, again, at large θ's.

These considerations all argue that one should work with θ's of about 60 to 80° as a practical maximum.   If one were to use a 10× scale expansion, then with a setting of θ = 80° a one-division deflection of the pen would represent a rotation of 0.0025°.

The relationship between α and R for a given θ is relatively complex. There are three ways to get the conversion.   Perhaps the most simple is the use of known sucrose solutions, and this is practically mandatory where unpolarized light is present.   The second is the use of tables of R versus α which have been computed for a number of selected values of θ.   The third is by use of simple graphical computers, utilizing the data of R versus α as a function of θ.

The complete accessory set is shown in Fig. 3-9.   It consists of a polarizing prism at the left, a space for 1-cm square (or round) cells or 5-cm round cells, and an analyzer prism at the right, which can be rotated to the desired θ angle.   Two of these assemblies are necessary, one with the θ's going in the positive direction and the other with them going in the negative direction.   The assembly can be used with a Perkin-Elmer Model 4000A spectrophotometer or with the Cary recording spectrophotometers.   For use with the latter, it is preferable to employ the accessory 0.0 to 0.1 optical density slide-wire.

B. Performance of the Instrument.   The following comments, based on rotatory dispersion measurements conducted by A. N. James and B. Sjöberg with the Perkin-Elmer attachment in conjunction with a

Model 4000A Spectracord, are only of a general nature, since several variables still have to be considered.

Although carefully annealed microcells of 1.25 cc capacity for the attachment are already available, considerably larger amounts of sub-

Fig. 3-9. Complete accessory set for rapid conversion of double-beam spectro-photometer to recording spectropolarimeter.

stance are presently required than with the Rudolph spectropolarimeter. Furthermore, it should be recalled that *two* cells must be filled with sample solution. The sample requirement may be materially reduced with a scale-expansion device and in any event differs greatly from case to case, since factors such as θ, cell length, and especially rotation of the substance play an important role.

The conventional hydrogen-discharge lamp, of much greater stability and longer life than the xenon compact arc lamp, can be used for an appreciable portion of the spectrum and serves very satisfactorily.   For shorter wavelengths the xenon lamp must be employed, although its

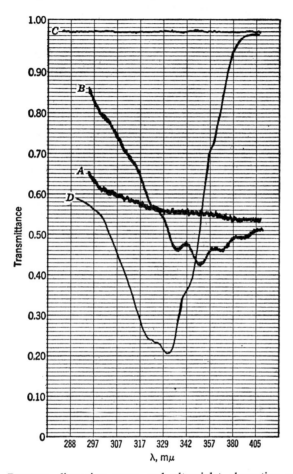

Fig. 3-10.   Rotatory dispersion curve and ultraviolet absorption spectrum of testosterone in dioxane solution (*c*, 1.0) measured with Perkin-Elmer spectro-polarimeter attachment in conjunction with a Spectracord (Model 4000A) and xenon lamp.   For the rotatory dispersion curve a scanning time of 2.5 min with a slit opening of 9 and a θ setting of 75° were employed.   Curve *A*, solvent blank (for RD); curve *B*, RD tracing; curve *C*, solvent blank (for UV spectrum); curve *D*, ultraviolet absorption spectrum.

erratic stability, usually tolerable with the manual Rudolph instrument, is frequently quite unsatisfactory with the Perkin-Elmer attachment. There are two reasons for this.   First, a shift in the arc position of the xenon lamp can be accommodated by the operator of the Rudolph spectropolarimeter, but the recording device cannot so accommodate; this may result in large and erroneous pen deflection. Second, the pulsing characteristic of the xenon lamp results in a higher noise level, which may mask small, but real, pen deflections. For the time being, therefore, the xenon lamp in conjunction with the Perkin-Elmer unit can probably only be used for qualitative work, but at least one real advantage must not be overlooked, namely, greater ultraviolet spectral penetration. For example, with hydratropic acid, measurements in isoöctane solution could only be conducted to 280 mμ with the Rudolph instrument and a xenon lamp, but the same lamp with the Perkin-Elmer attachment clearly demonstrated the existence of a Cotton effect with a peak near 270 mμ.

At the present time, rotatory dispersion measurements with the Perkin-Elmer recording instrument carry with them a larger error when compared with parallel determinations conducted with the manual Rudolph spectropolarimeter. On the other hand, the operations are not fatiguing and, most importantly, a direct comparison of ultraviolet spectral and optical rotatory dispersion curves becomes a simple matter, since the second set of compensators can be used to establish the 100 per cent transmission line for the spectrophotometric measurements. Once this is done for a given spectral range, an ultraviolet spectrum can be conveniently traced on the same paper as the optical rotatory dispersion curve, and this facilitates relating certain dispersion features to different absorption bands. An illustration of this is afforded in Fig. 3-10, which contains the ultraviolet spectrum and the rotatory dispersion curve of testosterone in dioxane as measured with a Perkin-Elmer recording instrument; the correspondence of fine structure is noticeable in both curves.

4 | STEROIDS

4-1. Introduction. Carbonyl-containing Steroids

The carbonyl chromophore, per se, is symmetrical. However, when it is placed into the proper asymmetric environment, asymmetry is induced in the electron distribution of the carbonyl chromophore and Cotton effects may be observed. Granted this premise, which was known for a considerable length of time,[1] it was still necessary to examine the sensitivity of the Cotton-effect curve, associated with the carbonyl chromophore, to changes in the asymmetric environment. Such information could initially be gathered only by studying empirically a large number of ultraviolet rotatory dispersion curves of closely related substances for which only one variable is changed at a time. This type of work had been done only to a very limited extent with aliphatic aldehydes,[2] and the experimental difficulties prior to 1950 had precluded similar extensive investigations among other organic compounds.

The first systematic studies performed by our group were in the steroid series. This was also the first area of organic chemistry in which rotatory dispersion was accepted quite rapidly as a routine tool. Since the asymmetry of a given spatial arrangement can be affected not only by structural changes but also by alterations in conformation, it was necessary to select a group of substances in which the conformation is essentially fixed—a challenge met admirably by steroids.

[1] See T. M. Lowry, "Optical Rotatory Power," Longmans, Green & Co., Ltd., London, 1935.

[2] For a summary see P. A. Levene and A. Rothen in H. Gilman (ed.), "Organic Chemistry," vol. 2, chap. 21, John Wiley & Sons, Inc., New York, 1938.

4-2.   Saturated [3] Steroid Ketones and Aldehydes

A. Structural Applications. The first variation to be examined [4] systematically was that of keeping all stereochemical and structural features as undisturbed as possible and placing an isolated keto group into the eleven possible ring locations of an A/B *trans*-fused steroid skeleton, usually the cholestane system.

Eleven typical members are represented in structural formulas I to XI and their rotatory dispersion curves are collected in Figs. 4-1 to 4-4. Even a cursory inspection of the figures will lead to the conclusion that there exist very substantial differences among these dispersion curves,

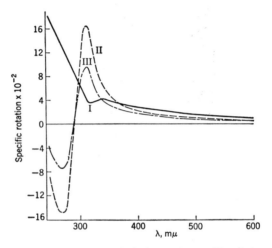

Fig. 4-1. RD curves (methanol) of cholestan-1-one (I), cholestan-2-one (II), and cholestan-3-one (III).

ranging all the way from opposite-sign Cotton effect curves to limited differences in amplitude.

In Fig. 4-1 are reproduced the rotatory dispersion curves of cholestan-1-one (I), cholestan-2-one (II), and cholestan-3-one (III). The first compound shows a very unusual Cotton effect curve, almost approaching that of a plain curve, and immediately serves to distinguish a ketone group in this location from that of all the others (II to XI). The difference between a 2-keto (II) and a 3-keto (III) steroid is limited to the amplitude, as both substances exhibit positive Cotton effects. Since the

[3] "Saturated" in this case implies only that there is no double bond in close proximity to the carbonyl group.

[4] C. Djerassi, W. Closson, and A. E. Lippman, *J. Am. Chem. Soc.,* **78,** 3163 (1956).

amplitudes may vary at times, depending upon the presence of other substituents or radically different background curves (Sec. 2-3), this would not be too satisfactory a criterion, but fortunately the detection of ketal formation by rotatory dispersion means (Sec. 11-4) is decisive in this case.

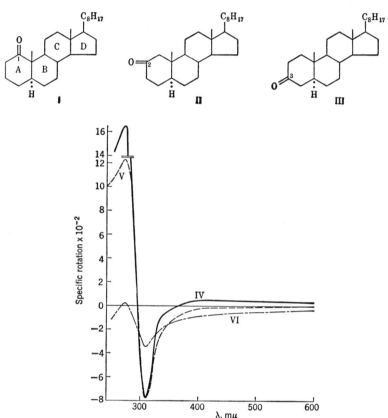

Fig. 4-2. RD curves (methanol) of cholestan-4-one (IV), cholestan-6-one (V), and cholestan-3β-ol-7-one acetate (VI).

No simple differentiation between a 4-ketone (cholestan-4-one) (IV) and a 6-ketone (cholestan-6-one) (V) with the 5α orientation is possible, but on the other hand these two types represent the only positions in the cholestane series for which a carbonyl group in a six-membered ring produces a rather symmetrical negative Cotton effect (Fig. 4-2). A 7-keto-5α steroid such as cholestan-3β-ol-7-one acetate (VI) also has a negative Cotton effect (Fig. 4-2) but with the very characteristic feature of the peak appearing near the zero rotation line.

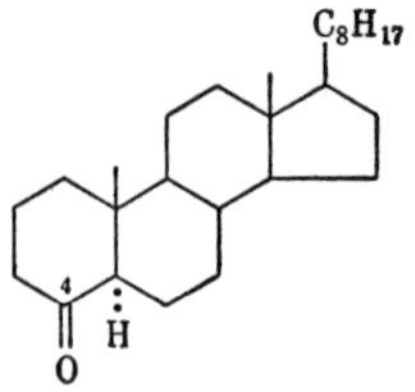

IV 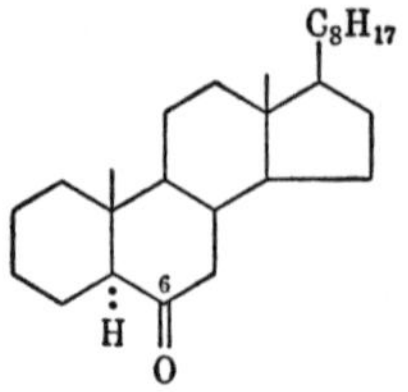   V 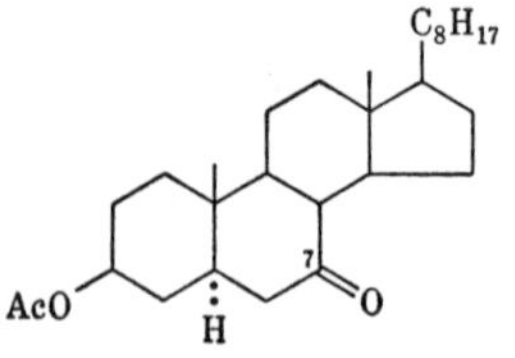   VI

A distinction between an 11-(VII) and a 12-(VIII) keto steroid (ergostan-3β-ol-11-one and ergostan-3β-ol-12-one acetates) is again possible (Fig. 4-3) since the former always shows [5,6,7] a Cotton effect of rather reduced amplitude compared with its C-12 isomer.

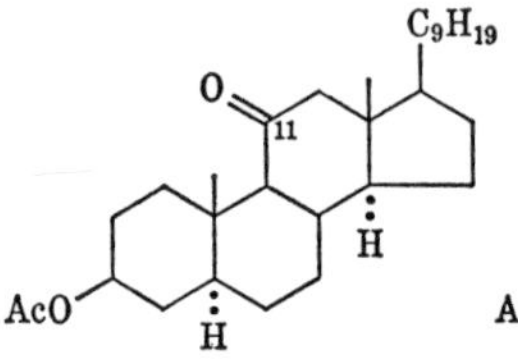

VII 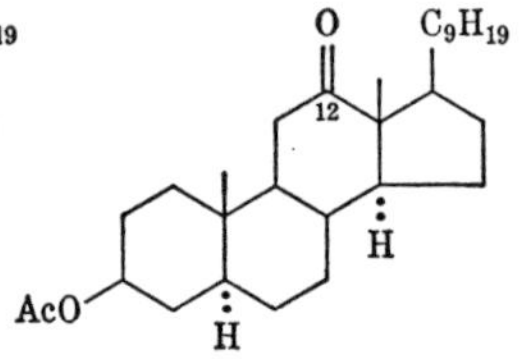   VIII

In Fig. 4-4 are given the rotatory dispersion curves of C/D *trans* steroids with a keto group in the three possible locations of the cyclopentane ring. It can be seen that a keto function at C-16 as in cholestan-16-one (X) is characterized by an enormous negative Cotton effect curve, which serves to distinguish it not only from its two ring-D-substituted partners, cholestan-3β-ol-15-one (IX) and androstan-17-one (XI), but in fact from all the other keto steroids as well.

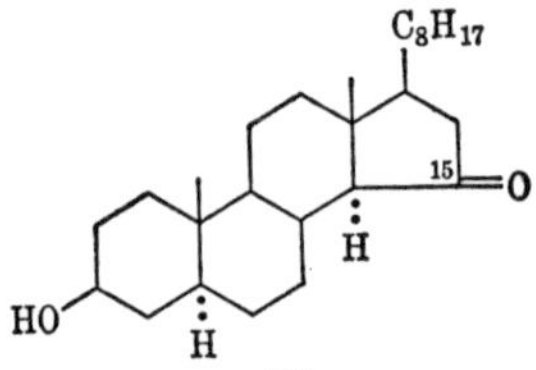

IX 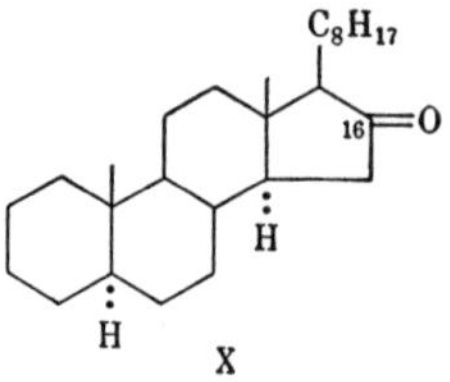   X 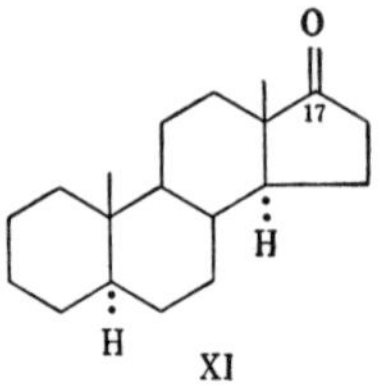   XI

The rotatory dispersion information collected in these four figures indicates that for most alternate locations of a keto group in the A/B *trans* steroid skeleton there will be found substantial differences in sign, shape, and/or amplitude. It remains to be seen how these character-

[5] E. W. Foltz, A. E. Lippman, and C. Djerassi, *J. Am. Chem. Soc.*, **77**, 4359 (1955).

[6] C. Djerassi and W. Closson, *J. Am. Chem. Soc.*, **78**, 3761 (1956).

[7] C. Djerassi, J. Osiecki, R. Riniker, and B. Riniker, *J. Am. Chem. Soc.*, **80**, 1216 (1958).

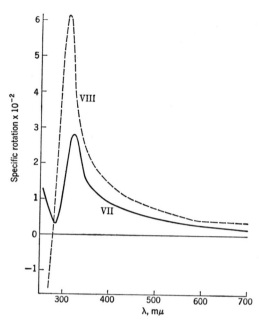

Fig. 4-3. RD curves (methanol) of ergostan-3β-ol-11-one acetate (VII) and ergostan-3β-ol-12-one acetate (VIII).

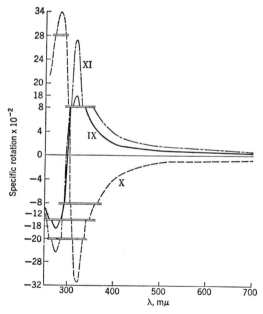

Fig. 4-4. RD curves (methanol) of cholestan-3β-ol-15-one (IX), cholestan-1(·· one (X), and androstan-17-one (XI).

istic rotatory dispersion features, associated with a particular location of the keto chromophore, are affected by other structural changes.

Extensive rotatory dispersion studies with steroidal ketones possessing the spiroketal system (XII) of the sapogenins,[8] substituents with carboxylic acid functions at C-17 (XIII and XIV) typical of the bile acids,[6] or the butenolide grouping (XV) characteristic of the cardiac aglycones [9]

XII   XIII   XIV

showed that these modifications played no important role in influencing the distinguishing features of these Cotton effect curves.   The α-pyrone system (XVI) of the toad poisons interfered [9] because of its strong ultraviolet absorption near 300 mμ.   However, this could be overcome readily by catalytic hydrogenation to the corresponding tetrahydro derivative (XVII), which is transparent in that spectral region.

XV   XVI   XVII

Other changes which were examined and which were found to be of no importance, in so far as the rotatory dispersion picture associated with a given carbonyl group is concerned, were acylation of alcohols,[6] esterification of acid functions,[6] and introduction [10] of double bonds in various positions (XVIII) of a 3-keto-5α steroid.   Another striking

XVIII

[8] C. Djerassi and R. Ehrlich, *J. Am. Chem. Soc.,* **78,** 440 (1956).

[9] C. Djerassi, O. Halpern, V. Halpern, O. Schindler, and C. Tamm, *Helv. Chim. Acta,* **41,** 250 (1958).

[10] C. Djerassi, O. Halpern, V. Halpern, and B. Riniker, *J. Am. Chem. Soc.,* **80,** 4001 (1958).

illustration of the qualitative and quantitative unimportance of different substituents, far away from the chromophore, upon the Cotton effect, is illustrated in Table 4-1 with a series of 3-substituted androstan-17-ones.

Table 4-1

RD Curves (MeOH) of Androstan-17-ones*

Substituent	Peak		Trough		Molecular amplitude $\times 10^{-2}$
	Mol. rot.	λ, mμ	Mol. rot.	λ, mμ	
Unsubstituted	+7550°	315	−7050°	272	145°
3α-Hydroxy	+7250°	312	−7150°	275	144°
3β-Hydroxy	+7350°	312	−7500°	275	148°
3α-Mercapto	+6100°	315	−7800°	272	139°
3β-Mercapto	+7550°	312	−6000°	272	136°
3β-Hydroxy-5-ene	+5920°	312	−8350°	275	143°

* Most of these data are unpublished ones obtained through the courtesy of W. Klyne, Postgraduate Medical School, London.

The implications of these observations are important: To the extent that a Cotton effect is typical of a given location of a carbonyl group in a 5α steroid system (and Figs. 4-1 to 4-4 show that this is the case to an appreciable degree), these standard curves can be used to locate an unknown carbonyl group or hydroxyl function (oxidizable to the ketone) in this group of steroids. Admittedly, a rigorous decision cannot be made in each case, as is, for instance, possible with a 1-keto-5α steroid (I) (Fig. 4-1) or a 16-ketone (X) (Fig. 4-4), but at least the possible structures can be narrowed down to two alternatives and these can then be handled readily by chemical means. It should be recalled that at the present time no other physical method can even approach rotatory dispersion in this respect. Ultraviolet absorption spectroscopy of saturated ketones is of very limited use in this area [11] and even infrared

[11] See, for example, O. Schindler and T. Reichstein, *Helv. Chim. Acta,* **37,** 667 (1954); F. Sallmann and C. Tamm, *ibid.,* **39,** 1340 (1956).

spectral data [12] are largely limited to defining the size of the ring to which the ketone group is attached rather than to establishing its precise location.   Since this type of rotatory dispersion work is largely of qualitative significance, it is possible—by sacrificing accuracy—to conduct most of these measurements with less than 1 mg of material, which can be recovered with precious samples.

A pertinent example of this application of rotatory dispersion is the structure determination of the steroidal alkaloid rubijervine (XIX),[13] for which there existed some doubt as to the precise location of one of the hydroxyl functions.   The problem could be settled to a large extent by examining the rotatory dispersion of the derived ketone rubijervone-12 (XX), since its curve proved to be of the 12-keto steroid type.

XIX   XX

Steroidal aldehydes are of particular interest in the cardiac aglycone series, and the dispersion curves of a number of typical representatives have been examined.[9]   With the use of these standard curves, Reichstein and colleagues [14] were able to reduce the structural possibilities for the toad poison bufotalinin (XXI).   The two uncertainties in its structure were the location of the aldehyde group and the points of attachment of the oxide ring.   By hydrogenating the α-pyrone chromophore, which prevented rotatory dispersion measurements below 320 mμ, to the tetrahydro derivative (XXII) and examining its rotatory dispersion

XXI   XXII

[12] See R. N. Jones and F. Herling, *J. Org. Chem.*, **19**, 1252 (1954); G. Roberts, B. S. Gallagher, and R. N. Jones, "Infrared Absorption Spectra of Steroids," vol. 2, Interscience Publishers, Inc., New York, 1958.

[13] S. W. Pelletier and D. M. Locke, *J. Am. Chem. Soc.*, **79**, 4531 (1957).

[14] H. Schröter, C. Tamm, and T. Reichstein, *Helv. Chim. Acta*, **41**, 720 (1958).

curve, it was found that this was virtually superimposable upon that of tetrahydrohellebrigenin acetate (XXIII), whose constitution had been established earlier.   This suggested that the aldehyde function of XXI was attached to C-19 rather than to C-18.   A similar approach was employed in locating the aldehyde group in the cardiac aglycone pachy-genin.[15]

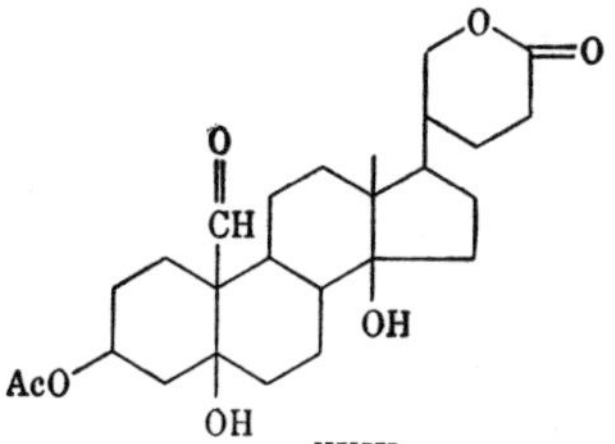

XXIII

B. Stereochemical Applications.   Another manner in which the asymmetric environment of a carbonyl group in such a polycyclic system can be altered is to retain the ketone function in the same place and to change some stereochemical feature of the molecule.   Here again, steroids represent nearly perfect test cases since one can find among them many pairs of isomers differing only in the orientation of one center.

A pertinent example is afforded by dihydrotestosterone (androstan-17β-ol-3-one) (XXIV) and its C-5 isomer, 5β-androstan-17β-ol-3-one

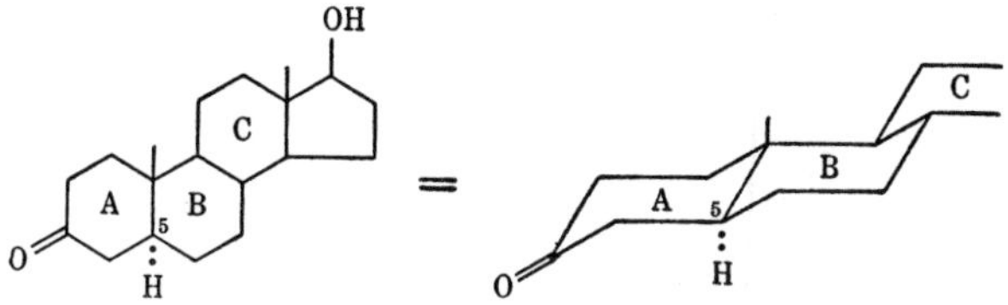

XXIV   XXIVa

(XXV).   These two ketones differ only in the nature of the A/B ring juncture, but this change has a major effect on the molecular geometry of the bicyclic environment of the carbonyl group, as is apparent from

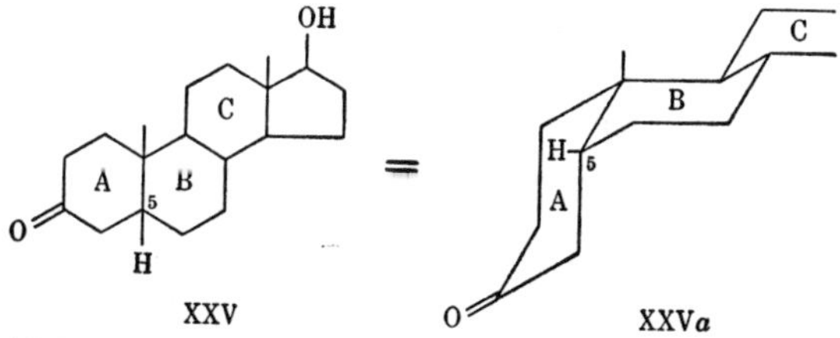

XXV   XXVa

[15] W. Schmid, H. P. Uehlinger, C. Tamm, and T. Reichstein, *Helv. Chim. Acta,* **42,** 72 (1959).

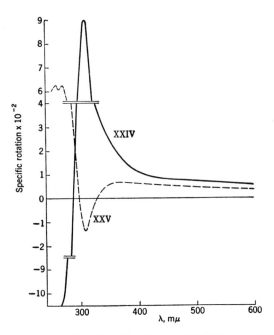

Fig. 4-5. RD curves (methanol) of androstan-17β-ol-3-one (XXIV) and 5β-androstan-17β-ol-3-one (XXV).

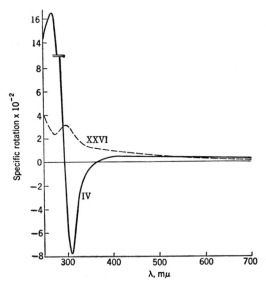

Fig. 4-6. RD curves (methanol) of cholestan-4-one (IV) and coprostan-4-one (XXVI). (*Reproduced from C. Djerassi, Bull. soc. chim. France,* **1957,** 741, *by permission of the editor.*)

the conformational representations XXIV*a* and XXV*a*.   It is not surprising, therefore, that their respective rotatory dispersion curves (Fig. 4-5) are completely different, as was observed [6] for several such pairs irrespective of additional, "nonchromophoric" substituents.

Other illustrations of the marked sensitivity of Cotton effect curves to such stereochemical alterations are provided by the following pairs: cholestan-4-one (IV) [4] versus coprostan-4-one (XXVI) [16] (Fig. 4-6); cholestan-3β-ol-7-one acetate (VI) [4] versus 3α-hydroxy-7-ketocholanic acid (XXVII) [6] (Fig. 4-7); and pregnan-3α-ol-20-one acetate (XXVIII) [17] versus 17α-pregnan-3α-ol-20-one acetate (XXIX) (Fig.

XXVI   XXVII

4-8).   In the last pair, the stereochemical change does not involve a ring juncture but rather the orientation of an acetyl group, and additional substituents [9] at C-17, such as hydroxy or acetoxy functions, do not affect qualitatively the characteristic rotatory dispersion picture.   The strong positive Cotton effect associated [5,9,17] with the 20-keto group of a pregnane derivative with the 17β-oriented side chain (e.g., XXVIII) has been employed recently [18] in locating the carbonyl group in the sodium-excreting factor of adrenal glands, 5α-pregnane-3β,16α-diol-20-one (XXX).

XXVIII   XXIX   XXX

Currently, no other physical tool can approach rotatory dispersion in its utility for settling stereochemical problems in the steroid field; this

[16] C. Djerassi, R. Riniker, and B. Riniker, *J. Am. Chem. Soc.*, **78**, 6362 (1956).
[17] C. Djerassi, *Bull. soc. chim. France*, **1957**, 741.
[18] R. Neher, P. Desaulles, E. Vischer, P. Wieland, and A. Wettstein, *Helv. Chim. Acta*, **41**, 1667 (1958).

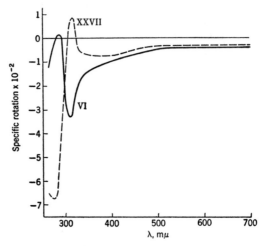

Fig. 4-7. RD curves (methanol) of cholestan-3β-ol-7-one acetate (**VI**) and 3α-hydroxy-7-ketocholanic acid (**XXVII**). (*Reproduced from C. Djerassi, Bull. soc. chim. France,* **1957,** 741, *by permission of the editor.*)

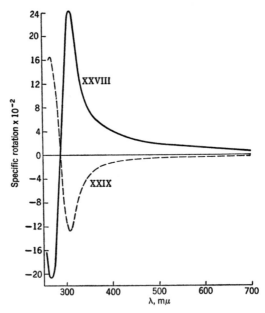

Fig. 4-8. RD curves (methanol) of pregnan-3α-ol-20-one acetate (**XXVIII**) and 17α-pregnan-3α-ol-20-one acetate (**XXIX**). (*Reproduced from C. Djerassi, Bull. soc. chim. France,* **1957,** 741, *by permission of the editor.*)

statement has already been documented by numerous applications in the recent literature.[19]   A few illustrations follow.

Assignment of configuration at C-5 to reduction products of Δ^4-3-ketones has for a long time presented a vexing problem in steroid chemistry and usually involved an investigation of the course of monobromination *cum* dehydrobromination.[20]   Since the remarkable differences (see Fig. 4-5) in the rotatory dispersion curves of 3-keto steroids, epimeric at C-5 (e.g., XXIV versus XXV), are retained in the presence of other substituents, it is now a simple matter to establish the stereochemistry at C-5 by obtaining the Cotton effect curve of the ketone.   This has been used [21] with particular success in settling the steric course of the reduction of Δ^4-3-keto 19-nor steroids, such as 19-nortestosterone (XXXI), which was shown to yield the *trans* isomer 19-nor-5α-androstan-17β-ol-3-one (XXXII) when chemical reducing agents were employed.   On the other hand, catalytic hydrogenation [22] with a ruthenium dioxide catalyst provided 19-nor-5β-androstan-17β-ol-3-one (XXXIII), as demonstrated by the close similarity of its rotatory dispersion curve with that (Fig. 4-5) of its higher homologue, 5β-androstan-17β-ol-3-one (XXV).

XXXI   XXXII   XXXIII

The above example from the 19-nor steroid series shows that the nature of the angular substituent does not play a major role (see also Sec. 4-3D)—provided the carbonyl group is not adjacent to it.   This assumption was utilized in assigning the β orientation to the hydrogen atom at C-10 of 5-methyl-19-norcoprostan-6β-ol-3-one acetate (XXXIV),[23] since its rotatory dispersion curve was of the 3-keto-5β (e.g., XXV) rather than 3-keto-5α (e.g., III and XXIV) type (see Fig. 4-5).   A similar argument was employed for the stereochemistry at C-5 of the steroidal sapogenin kogagenin (XXXV) by examining the rota-

[19] See C. Djerassi, *Record Chem. Progr.*, **20**, 101 (1959).

[20] For relevant literature see L. F. Fieser and M. Fieser, "Steroids," chap. 8, Reinhold Publishing Corporation, New York, 1959.

[21] A. Bowers, H. J. Ringold, and E. Denot, *J. Am. Chem. Soc.*, **80**, 6115 (1958).

[22] R. T. Rapala and E. Farkas, *J. Am. Chem. Soc.*, **80**, 1008 (1958).

[23] H. Aebli, C. A. Grob, and E. Schumacher, *Helv. Chim. Acta*, **41**, 774 (1958).

tory dispersion curve [24] of the derived ketone (XXXVI). Although even the size of the adjacent ring can be ignored (see Sec. 5-2C) in settling stereochemical problems of this type by rotatory dispersion means, there are limitations that must be taken into consideration. An example of the correct as well as incorrect use of this approach can be found in two articles that appeared side by side and dealt with the stereochemistry at C-5 of the hydroformylation products of Δ^5-unsaturated steroids.

XXXIV

XXXV   XXXVI

Nussbaum and collaborators [25] established the 5α stereochemistry of 6α-hydroxymethyl-5α-pregnane-3β,20β-diol diacetate (XXXVIII), the hydroformylation product of Δ^5-pregnene-3β,20β-diol diacetate (XXXVII), by converting the former to 6α-methyl-5α-pregnan-20β-ol-3-one acetate (XXXIX). This substance exhibited a positive Cotton

XXXVII   XXXVIII   XXXIX

[24] Unpublished measurements by Mrs. T. Nakano on specimens supplied by K. Takeda, Shionogi Research Laboratory, Osaka.

[25] A. L. Nussbaum, T. L. Popper, E. P. Oliveto, S. Friedman, and I. Wender, J. Am. Chem. Soc., **81**, 1228 (1959).

effect curve, typical of 3-keto-5α steroids (Fig. 4-5), thus settling unequivocally the 5α orientation in the ketone (XXXIX) and also, therefore, in its precursor (XXXVIII).

Essentially the identical problem was investigated by Beal et al.,[26] who attacked it by examining the rotatory dispersion curve of 6α-methyl-5α-pregnane-3,20-dione (XL). Since this substance also possessed a positive Cotton effect curve, they concluded that the diketone (XL) belonged to the 5α series. This conclusion is not warranted on the basis of their rotatory dispersion evidence, since a *di*ketone was used, and the 20-keto function itself happens to show a very strong positive Cotton effect (see Fig. 4-8). For this evidence to be of stereochemical validity, it would, first of all, be necessary to determine the difference, if any, in the rotatory dispersion curves of 5α-(XLI) and 5β-(XLII) pregnane-3,20-dione. In fact, both diketones exhibit a

strong positive Cotton effect curve,[27a] as could have been anticipated from the earlier recorded [28] rotatory dispersion curves of 5α- and 5β-androstane-3,17-dione. It is apparent, therefore, that stereochemical conclusions of this type can be made in diketones only if one of the carbonyl chromophores shows a very weak Cotton effect and produces no other interactions, a fact which must first be demonstrated with known model compounds (see compounds IL and L in Sec. 4-2C).

C. Analytical Applications. One general observation [29] that emerges from the above data is that in the ultraviolet region the rotation values of a carbonyl-containing substance are by virtue of the Cotton effect invariably greater than those of the corresponding compound lacking this

[26] P. F. Beal, M. A. Rebenstorf, and J. E. Pike, *J. Am. Chem. Soc.,* **81,** 1231 (1959).

[27] Unpublished observation by (*a*) L. A. Mitscher or (*b*) Mrs. T. Nakano in this laboratory.

[28] C. Djerassi, E. W. Foltz, and A. E. Lippman, *J. Am. Chem. Soc.,* **77,** 4354 (1955).

[29] K. Freudenberg, *Ber.,* **66,** 177 (1933), has already called attention to this phenomenon.

chromophore. In this connection several analytical applications come to mind.

The first and most obvious one is simply to take advantage of the information offered by a rotatory dispersion curve in analyses based subsequently on monochromatic polarimetry. If the rotation at only one wavelength is to be selected as a criterion in an analytical or control procedure, it would be most advantageous to choose a wavelength from the rotatory dispersion curve—usually the position of the peak or trough —at which the rotatory power is particularly high and where measurements could be conducted on a microscale.

The second situation is one in which the composition of a mixture is to be determined by polarimetric procedures. This becomes particularly attractive if one of the components possesses a keto group and the second one does not. Two concrete examples, of potential industrial importance, can be offered from sapogenin chemistry. Hecogenin is a sapogenin that is employed on a commercial scale in the manufacture of cortisone. It is usually accompanied in the plant source by tigogenin, and it is desirable to determine the proportion of this sapogenin in a mixture. The rotatory dispersion curves of tigogenin acetate (XLIII) and hecogenin acetate (XLIV) are reproduced in Fig. 4-9;

XLIII

XLIV

their specific rotations at the sodium D line (589 mμ) differ only by 53°. Once the rotatory dispersion curves of the two pure substances are available, one can select a wavelength—in this case the position of the peak of hecogenin acetate (XLIV) at 312.5 mμ—at which their respective rotations differ by 1050°; this is clearly the most advantageous wavelength at which analytical monochromatic polarimetry should be performed.

Figure 4-10 contains the rotatory dispersion curves of diosgenin acetate (XLV), a very important raw material for hormone synthesis, and kryptogenin diacetate (XLVI), a frequent contaminant of diosgenin. Here again, their specific rotations differ by only 70° at the sodium D line, while at the wavelength (320 mμ) corresponding to the trough of kryptogenin diacetate (XLVI), this difference amounts to nearly 2600°.

The above examples involved situations where only one of the com-

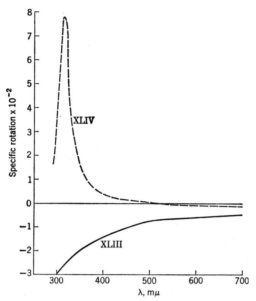

Fig. 4-9. RD curves (dioxane) of tigogenin acetate (XLIII) and hecogenin acetate (XLIV).

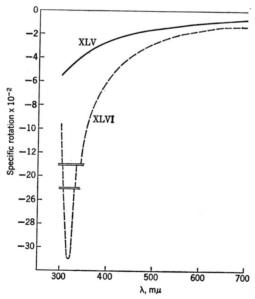

Fig. 4-10. RD curves (dioxane) of diosgenin acetate (XLV) and kryptogenin diacetate (XLVI). (*Reproduced from C. Djerassi, Bull. soc. chim. France,* **1957,** 741, *by permission of the editor.*)

ponents exhibited a Cotton effect curve. Clearly, the same approach can be employed with two ketones, which show Cotton effects of opposite sign. A striking illustration is given in Fig. 4-8, the specific rotations of the two C-17 isomeric ketones differing by over 3600° at 307.5 mμ, the wavelength where XXVIII shows a peak and its isomer XXIX

XLV   XLVI

a trough. Treatment of either one of these ketones with base leads to an equilibrium mixture, the composition of which can now be determined readily by measuring the rotation at 307.5 mμ. The applications of such observations to kinetic measurements are obvious.

Another interesting pair of isomers is represented by 5α-spirostan-15-one (XLVII) and 5α,14β-spirostan-15-one (XLVIII), whose rotatory

XLVII   XLVIII

dispersion curves [27b] (Fig. 4-11) are again of mirror-image type. Advantage is currently being taken of this fact in our laboratory in studying the kinetics of the base-catalyzed isomerization of XLVII to its *cis* isomer (XLVIII).

The amplitudes of these Cotton effect curves are so large that they are able to overcome the relatively weak one (see Fig. 6-1) associated with a 3-keto-4,4-dimethyl function. This is shown in Fig. 4-12, which con-

IL   L

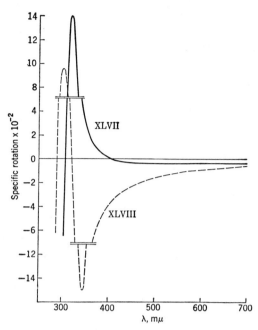

Fig. 4-11. RD curves (dioxane) of 5α-spirostan-15-one (XLVII) and 5α,14β-spirostan-15-one (XLVIII).

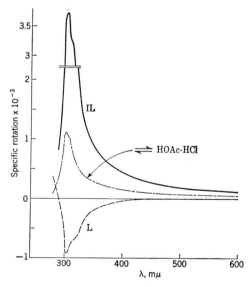

Fig. 4-12. RD curves (acetic acid) of 13β-octanordammarane-3,17-dione (IL), 13α-octanordammarane-3,17-dione (L), and of equilibrium mixture in acetic acid containing hydrochloric acid. (*Courtesy of G. Ourisson, University of Strasbourg.*)

tains the rotatory dispersion curves [30] of 13β-(IL) and 13α-(L) octa-nordammarane-3,17-dione in acetic acid as well as that of the equilibrium mixture produced by addition of hydrochloric acid, a situation that can again be useful in kinetic investigations.

4-3.   α,β-Unsaturated Steroid Ketones

A. Introduction.   Cyclic α,β-unsaturated ketones show maximal absorption of such high intensity between 220 and 260 mμ as to preclude for all practical purposes at present rotatory dispersion measurements through this region of absorption.   In addition, they exhibit another absorption band,[31] owing to the carbonyl group, above 300 mμ.   This band is of low intensity just as it is for the saturated ketones.   The second absorption band, if optically active (see Sec. 1-2), should lend itself to the same type of rotatory dispersion analysis as has been discussed in Sec. 4-2 for saturated ketones.   The only relevant measurements in the literature, prior to our work, have dealt with cortisone acetate (LI) and indicated [32] a plain curve.   This erroneous conclusion

LI

was due to an unfortunate choice of solvent and of too few intervals between readings; in fact, this substance exhibits [5] a multiple Cotton effect curve in which contributions from all three ketone functions (3, 11, and 20) could be discerned.   In order to examine properly the character of the optically active absorption bands of α,β-unsaturated ketones as well as the sensitivity of the resulting Cotton effect curves to structural or stereochemical alterations, it was again necessary to carry out a systematic investigation of the type described in Sec. 4-2 for saturated ketones and to perform this with a wide variety of examples, which contain no other interfering chromophores.

[30] Private communication from G. Ourisson, University of Strasbourg.
[31] See R. C. Cookson and S. H. Dandegaonker, *J. Chem. Soc.*, **1955**, 1651, and references cited therein.
[32] E. Brand, E. Washburn, B. F. Erlanger, E. Ellenbogen, J. Daniel, F. Lippmann, and M. Scheu, *J. Am. Chem. Soc.*, **76**, 5037 (1954).

B. Solvent Effects.   The low-intensity, long-wavelength absorption band of α,β-unsaturated ketones is very sensitive to the polarity of the solvent; [31] the best resolution and the greatest bathochromic shift is observed with nonpolar solvents.   To investigate the existence of such a solvent effect in rotatory dispersion work, the dispersion curve of a typical Δ[4]-3-keto steroid, Δ[4]-cholesten-3-one (LII),[33] was examined [34]

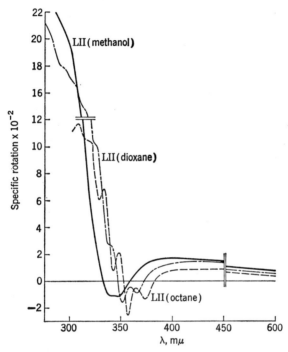

Fig. 4-13. RD curve of Δ[4]-cholesten-3-one (LII) in methanol, dioxane, and octane solution. [*Reproduced from C. Djerassi, R. Riniker, and B. Riniker, J. Am. Chem. Soc., 78, 6377 (1956), by permission of the editor.*]

in three solvents of different polarity—methanol, dioxane, and octane. The results are collected in Fig. 4-13 and are summarized below.

1. The long-wavelength absorption band of a Δ[4]-3-keto steroid—indeed of virtually all α,β-unsaturated ketones examined by us (see Sec. 7-4 for an exception)—is optically active.   The multiple Cotton effect curve indicates the existence of several optically active absorption bands in the 300 to 380 mμ region, and this could be confirmed (see Fig. 5-8)

[33] A. E. Lippman, E. W. Foltz, and C. Djerassi, *J. Am. Chem. Soc.*, **77,** 4364 (1955).

[34] C. Djerassi, R. Riniker, and B. Riniker, *J. Am. Chem. Soc.*, **78,** 6377 (1956).

by careful parallel ultraviolet rotatory dispersion and spectral measurements.[35,36]   In fact, one of the applications of such rotatory dispersion studies may be to call attention to ultraviolet spectral fine structure, likely to be overlooked in a cursory scanning of the spectrum.

2. The polarity of the solvent has the same effect upon the rotatory dispersion picture as upon the ultraviolet absorption spectrum.   The resolution of the fine structure is most pronounced in a nonpolar medium (e.g., octane) and almost completely obliterated in the polar solvent methanol.   Similarly, the position of the peaks and troughs is shifted toward a longer wavelength in a nonpolar solvent.   It is obvious, therefore, that for α,β-unsaturated ketones methanol is a completely unsatisfactory solvent.   In order to strike a compromise between solvent power on the one hand and nonpolarity on the other, dioxane has been selected [34] as the solvent of choice.   Unless noted otherwise, all subsequent discussion relative to α,β-unsaturated ketones refers to rotatory dispersion measurements conducted in that solvent.

C. Conformational and Structural Factors.   As is to be anticipated, structural alterations in a distant part of the molecule do not affect the characteristic rotatory dispersion features of a given α,β-unsaturated ketone.   Thus, the dispersion curves of Δ^4-cholesten-3-one (LII) and of testosterone (LIII, $R = R_1 = H$) are virtually superimposable.

LII   LIII

Furthermore, considerable structural manipulation adjacent to the keto group is possible without causing major changes in the rotatory dispersion picture.   This has been demonstrated [34] by an examination of various testosterone derivatives, where the substituents on the double bond (LIII, R_1 = halogen or alkyl) included [34] chlorine, bromine, methyl, or ethyl; [37] of the corresponding Δ^1 isomers; [34] and of analogues of testosterone in which the C-2 position was substituted by acetoxy or methyl functions (LIII, $R = CH_3$ or AcO).

On the other hand, the rotatory dispersion curve of a Δ^4-3-ketone is extremely sensitive to alterations in the adjacent ring (see also Sec.

[35] Unpublished observations by A. N. James and B. Sjöberg in this laboratory.

[36] W. A. Struck, E. C. Olson, and R. L. Houtman, Abstracts of the American Chemical Society Meeting, Boston, April, 1959, p. 23–0.

[37] C. Djerassi, M. Cais, and L. A. Mitscher, *J. Am. Chem. Soc.,* **81**, 2386 (1959).

5-3B). This seems to be due largely to conformational factors,[10] although electronic ones also play a role, especially in halogenated derivatives (Chap. 9).

This sensitivity of the rotatory dispersion curve to conformational alterations represents one of the important applications of this method in organic chemistry, and further reference is made to it in Chaps. 5 and 6. A telling illustration is provided by Fig. 4-14, where it is shown

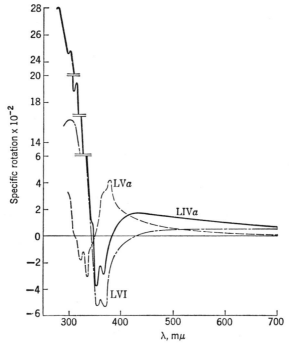

Fig. 4-14. RD curves (dioxane) of 6α-methyltestosterone (LIV*a*), 6β-methyltestosterone (LV*a*), and 2,2-dimethyltestosterone acetate (LVI). [*Reproduced from C. Djerassi, O. Halpern, V. Halpern, and B. Riniker, J. Am. Chem. Soc.,* **80,** 4001 (1958), *by permission of the editor.*]

that the rotatory dispersion curve of the equatorially substituted 6α-methyltestosterone (LIV*a*) is essentially identical to that of an unsubstituted Δ⁴-3-ketone (see Fig. 4-13), whereas introduction of an axial substituent as in 6β-methyltestosterone (LV*a*) results in a completely changed dispersion curve. This has been ascribed [10] to conformational distortion produced by the nonbonded interaction of the axial 6β-methyl group with the angular methyl group at C-10. Complete experimental confirmation of these views has recently been provided by the observation [38] that removal of the angular methyl group leads to two isomers, 6α-(LIV*b*) and 6β-(LV*b*) methyl-19-nortestosterone, whose rotatory dispersion curves are now essentially identical with those of C-6 unsubstituted Δ^4-3-keto steroids (e.g., Fig. 4-13). Such 1,3-diaxial interactions are not serious when they occur in the same ring, since the rotatory dispersion curve (Fig. 4-14) of 2,2-dimethyltestosterone acetate (LVI) is again of the testosterone (LIII, $R = R_1 = H$) type.

LIV*a* R=CH₃
LIV*b* R=H

LV*a* R=CH₃
LV*b* R=H

LVI

An interesting instance of the response of the multiple Cotton effect curve to conformational changes in the adjacent ring is given in Fig. 4-15, where the rotatory dispersion curve of 8-isotestosterone (LVII) is found to be completely different from that of testosterone (LIII, $R = R_1 = H$). It has been suggested [34] that this may be ascribed to the fact that ring B in 8-isotestosterone (LVII) exists as a boat because of the B/C *cis* ring juncture.

A final illustration of the changes that ring A but not ring B can suffer without consequences to the dispersion curve is contained in Fig. 4-16. A-Nortestosterone (LVIII) possesses a rotatory dispersion curve [27b] that is substantially identical with that of its six-membered homologue, testosterone (LIII) (Fig. 4-15). On the other hand, contraction of ring B as in B-nor-Δ^4-cholesten-3-one (LIX) leads to a curve [34] (Fig. 4-16) that is practically antipodal to that (Fig. 4-13) of its parent, Δ^4-cholesten-3-one (LII).

LVII

LVIII

LIX

D. Configurational Assignments to Angular Substituents. The main thesis of this section may be summarized by stating that, on the whole, the nature of the angular substituent in polycyclic α,β-unsaturated ketones is of no particular significance but that the orientation of it will

[38] R. Villotti, C. Djerassi, and H. J. Ringold, *J. Am. Chem. Soc.*, **81**, 4566 (1959).

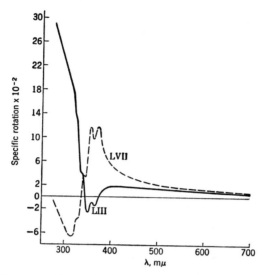

Fig. 4-15. RD curves (dioxane) of testosterone (LIII, $R = R_1 = H$) and 8-iso-testosterone (LVII).

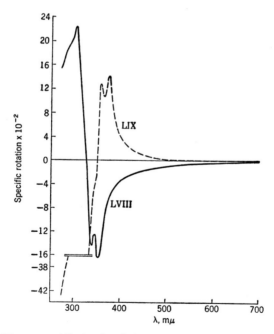

Fig. 4-16. RD curves (dioxane) of A-nortestosterone (LVIII) and B-nor-Δ^4-cholesten-3-one (LIX).

govern the sign of the Cotton effect.   Once established, this premise offers a most convenient means of establishing the configuration of angular substituents in certain steroid and related systems and *ipso facto* of providing a very simple device for assigning absolute configurations to a variety of bicyclic and polycyclic natural products.   This latter aspect will be covered in detail in Chap. 10.

Experimental support [34] for the above statement is provided in part in Fig. 4-17, where it is shown that the rotatory dispersion curves of 10β-hydroxy-19-nortestosterone   (LX)   and   of   19-nortestosterone

LX   R=OH
XXXI R=H

(XXXI) are practically identical with that (Fig. 4-15) of testosterone (LIII, R= R_1 = H).   In fact, this coincidence of the multiple Cotton effect curves represents one of the most cogent arguments in favor of the β orientation of the angular hydrogen atom of 19-nortestosterone (XXXI) and of the 10-hydroxyl group in its microbiological hydroxylation product (LX).[39]   These examples show that the above generalization holds at least for the range of angular substituents covered by hydrogen versus hydroxyl versus methyl.

This information was very helpful in assigning the α orientation to the angular hydrogen atom at C-5 of 19-nor-Δ$^{1(10)}$-androsten-17β-ol-2-one (LXI), since its dispersion curve [40] was identical to that (Fig. 4-17)

LXI   LXII

of 19-nortestosterone (XXXI).   By turning over the structure of LXI by 180°, it will be noted that the absolute stereochemistry of XXXI and LXI is identical in so far as rings A and B are concerned.   As

---

[39] R. L. Pederson et al., *J. Am. Chem. Soc.*, **78**, 1512 (1956); see also J. Perez, J. Iriarte, F. Kincl, and C. Djerassi, *J. Org. Chem.*, **23**, 1744 (1958).

[40] J. Fishman, *Chem. & Ind. (London)*, **1958**, 1556.

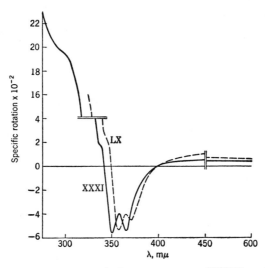

Fig. 4-17. RD curves (dioxane) of 19-nortestosterone (XXXI) and 10β-hydroxy-19-nortestosterone (LX).

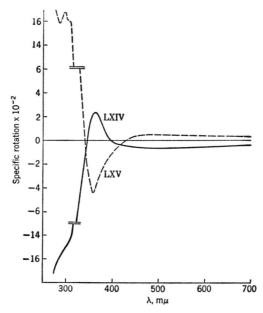

Fig. 4-18. RD curves (dioxane) of Δ⁵-cholesten-4-one (LXIV) and Δ⁴-cholesten-6-one (LXV).

discussed further in Chaps. 5 and 10, this condition is sufficient, in the absence of conformational distortion, to produce similar rotatory dispersion curves.   This approach was also employed in settling the stereochemistry at C-10 of 19-nor-14β,17α-progesterone (LXII), an unknown point of some significance because of the high progestational activity of this substance.[41]   The rotatory dispersion curve of the substance itself would not have been of any significance because of interference by the powerful 20-keto chromophore, but by finding that its precursor, 19-nor-14β,17α-Δ⁴-3-ketoetienic acid (LXIII), showed [42] a curve of the 19-nortestosterone (XXXI) type (see Fig. 4-17), the 10β orientation could be assigned with certainty to LXII and LXIII.

LXIII   LXIV

Rigorous evidence, devoid of conformational complications, will be presented in Chap. 5 for the statement that the orientation of the angular substituent controls the sign of the Cotton effect.   An example from the steroid series bearing on this point is shown in Fig. 4-18, where it is seen that the rotatory dispersion curves [16] of Δ⁵-cholesten-4-one (LXIV) and Δ⁴-cholesten-6-one (LXV) are of mirror-image type.   By turning a model of LXV through 180°, it can be written as LXVa, and it is thus readily seen that as far as rings A and B are concerned, LXIV and LXVa represent antipodal octalone systems as defined by the orientation

LXV   LXVa

of the angular methyl group.   It is not surprising, therefore, that their dispersion curves are also of enantiomeric type.   Some caution has to be exercised in "dissecting" appropriate bicyclic systems in such polycyclic molecules, since it is indispensable that the relevant asymmetric

[41] G. W. Barber and M. Ehrenstein, *Ann.,* **603,** 89 (1957).
[42] C. Djerassi, M. Ehrenstein, and G. W. Barber, *Ann.,* **612,** 93 (1958).

environment (i.e., the conformations of the two systems) be identical. An instructive case is represented by the rotatory dispersion curves of Δ^5-cholesten-3β-ol-7-one acetate (LXVI) and $\Delta^{7,22}$-ergostadien-3β-ol-

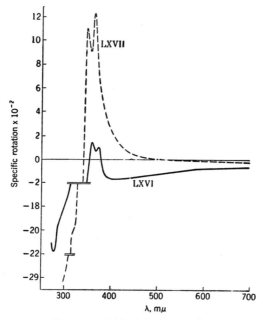

6-one acetate (LXVII) shown in Fig. 4-19.   By equating the angular methyl group between rings A and B of LXVI with the angular hydrogen atom between rings B and C of LXVII (an operation that is surely

Fig. 4-19.   RD curves (dioxane) of Δ^5-cholesten-3β-ol-7-one acetate (LXVI) and $\Delta^{7,22}$-ergostadien-3β-ol-6-one acetate (LXVII).

justified in the light of the above discussion), it will be seen that rings A and B of LXVI and rings B and C of LXVII can be represented by the partial structure LXVIII (R = CH_3 for LXVI; R = H for LXVII). This structure represents the antipode of rings A and B of testosterone (LIII) and 19-nortestosterone (XXXI).   It is understandable, therefore, that the two rotatory dispersion curves of LXVI and LXVII in Fig. 4-19 are enantiomeric to those reproduced in Fig. 4-17.

Figure 4-20 shows that the orientation of the angular substituent between rings C and D plays the same role, since the rotatory dispersion

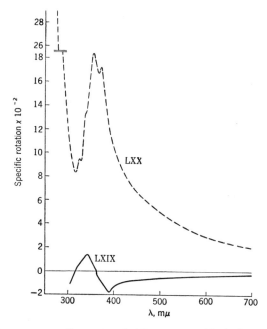

Fig. 4-20. RD curves (dioxane) of Δ^{15}-androsten-3β-ol-17-one (LXIX) and 14β-Δ^{15}-androsten-3β-ol-17-one (LXX). (*Courtesy of F. Sondheimer, Weizmann Institute of Science, Israel.*)

curves [43] of Δ^{15}-androsten-3β-ol-17-one (LXIX) and of 14β-Δ^{15}-androsten-3β-ol-17-one (LXX) bear an antipodal relationship to each other.

Reference curves of many other α,β-unsaturated keto steroids can be found in earlier papers [5,10,16,17,28,33,34] from our laboratory.

[43] Private communication from F. Sondheimer, Weizmann Institute of Science, Israel.

4-4.   Steroidal Diketones.   Calculation of Composition Curves

A. Diketones with Widely Separated Absorption Bands. Virtually all the examples discussed in this chapter have dealt with substances possessing only one carbonyl group. The situation is considerably more complicated when two such groups are present, unless their relevant absorption bands are situated in distant parts of the spectrum. A particularly striking instance is noted in Chap. 14 and Fig. 14-1 with Δ^4-pregnen-3-one-20-thione; the two principal, optically active absorption bands are separated by about 200 mμ. In diketones, the situation can usually still be handled in compounds such as progesterone (LXXI)[5] and some of its relatives,[34] in which the contribution of both the saturated 20-keto steroid (strong positive Cotton effect with peak near 310 mμ) and the Δ^4-3-keto moiety (multiple Cotton effect in the 380 to 350 mμ region; see Fig. 4-13) can be discerned. Indeed in favorable cases, this assignment of rotatory dispersion contributions can be accomplished even in triketones, this having been achieved with cortisone (LI) by comparing[5] its rotatory dispersion curve with that of hydrocortisone (LXXII), the difference being attributable to the 11-keto function.

LXXI   LXXII

At the present stage of development, rotatory dispersion curves of diketones, particularly if both chromophores absorb in essentially the same region of the spectrum, are useful largely for "fingerprinting." A detailed study[6] of saturated, steroidal diketones consisting of various combinations with carbonyl substituents at positions 3, 6, 7, 11, 12, and 17 has demonstrated that in those cases in which there exists vicinal interaction, the dispersion curve will not represent the summation of the rotatory dispersion curves of the two individual monoketones, but rather will acquire a distinct new appearance. This new dispersion curve can then be used for purposes of characterization.

B. Vicinal Interaction in Diketones. From a theoretical standpoint, the rotatory dispersion curve of a diketone offers the most precise means of determining the presence and amount of "vicinal interaction." [44] This is done by obtaining the molecular rotatory dispersion curves of the two monoketones and comparing the calculated curve [45] with the observed molecular rotatory dispersion curve of the diketone. In steroids, vicinal interaction is largely a function of distance, and the sum of the molecular rotatory dispersion curves of cholestan-3-one (III) and cholestan-6-one (V), for example, is quite different from the observed [6] curve of cholestane-3,6-dione (LXXIII). On the other hand, no vicinal interaction is noted by this procedure in androstane-3,17-dione (LXXIV), and other examples can be found in the original

LXXIII   LXXIV

literature.[6]   That structure as well as distance enters into this picture is illustrated in Sec. 5-2D with *trans*-8-methylhydrindane-2,5-dione, for which no vicinal interaction was observed in spite of the close proximity of the two carbonyl chromophores.

Reference should also be made to Sec. 11-3A, where it is shown that the rotatory dispersion curves of certain diketones can be analyzed by taking into consideration the differential reactivity of the two ketone groups toward ketal formation.

[44] See, for example, W. Kuhn and K. Freudenberg, Drehung der Polarisationsebene des Lichtes, "Handbuch und Jahrbuch der chemischen Physik," vol. 8, part 3, Akademische Verlagsgesellschaft, Leipzig, 1932.

[45] Represented by the sum of the two rotatory dispersion curves of the respective monoketones. It should be noted that in Ref. 6 all values were by mistake divided by one-half.

5 | BICYCLIC KETONES

5-1. Introduction

The discussion and especially the figures of Chap. 4 have shown that an empirical analysis of rotatory dispersion curves of steroidal ketones offers a rather wide scope with important applications to structural and stereochemical problems. The question now arises as to what portion of the steroid molecule is responsible for the characteristic features of a given Cotton effect curve associated with a carbonyl group in a certain location of the steroid nucleus. This is answered most readily by dissecting a steroid and noting how far the structure can be simplified without affecting the main character of the dispersion curve.

Initial studies with tricyclic ketones [1,2]—especially α,β-unsaturated ones [1]—indicated that the limiting factor would be reached principally in the area of bicyclic ketones. Since these also offered some interesting conformational problems, not necessarily present among steroids, a considerable synthetic effort was expended in our laboratory to provide the necessary optically active reference compounds. The results will be discussed in detail in Secs. 5-2 and 5-3, but they can be abstracted briefly by stating that with certain exceptions, *qualitatively* the characteristic rotatory dispersion picture (sign and over-all shape, although not necessarily amplitude) is governed by the bicyclic spatial environment (structural, stereochemical, and conformational) surrounding the carbonyl chromophore. Indeed, the subject can be introduced best by considering a specific example from the recent literature where advantage is taken of this conclusion.

[1] C. Djerassi, R. Riniker, and B. Riniker, *J. Am. Chem. Soc.*, **78**, 6362 (1956).
[2] C. Djerassi and W. Klyne, *Chem. & Ind. (London)*, **1956**, 988.

One of the unsolved problems of the structure of lumisterol (I), an irradiation product of ergosterol, has been the stereochemistry at C-9. This has been settled recently [3] by degradation to *des*-A-Δ^{22}-lumisten-5-one (II), which could also be obtained from 9β-ergosterol.   By taking

cognizance of the observation that the nature of the angular substituent (Sec. 4-2B) has no important effect, one can now compare the rotatory dispersion curve of the tricyclic ketone II with that [4] of 4β-methylcoprostan-3-one (IV), a reference ketone of known stereochemistry.   As shown in Fig. 5-1, the two dispersion curves are of mirror-image type, and if one rewrites the structure of the tricyclic ketone (II) from lumisterol as III, it will be noted that the relevant bicyclic environments of III and IV bear in fact an antipodal relationship to each other, thus affording independent evidence for the stereochemistry at C-9 of lumisterol (I).

5-2.   Saturated Bicyclic Ketones

A. Structural Factors.   We shall first consider certain diverse structural types from the bicyclic series [5] and compare their rotatory dispersion curves with those of relevant steroid models.

In Fig. 5-2 are reproduced the rotatory dispersion curves of *trans*-10-methyl-2-decalone (V) [1] and *cis*-10-methyl-2-decalone (VI),[6] and it

[3] J. Castells, E. R. H. Jones, G. D. Meakins, and R. W. J. Williams, *J. Chem. Soc.*, **1959**, 1159.

[4] C. Djerassi, O. Halpern, V. Halpern, and B. Riniker, *J. Am. Chem. Soc.*, **80**, 4001 (1958).

[5] For the sake of simplicity, each of the compounds is shown as that enantiomer which has the same absolute configuration as the steroids, even though in several cases the antipode is described in the literature (see Refs. 1, 6, and 16).

[6] C. Djerassi and D. Marshall, *J. Am. Chem. Soc.*, **80**, 3986 (1958).

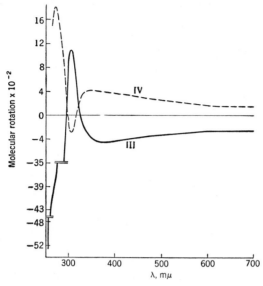

Fig. 5-1. RD curves (methanol) of *des*-A-Δ^{22}-lumisten-5-one (III) and 4β-methylcoprostan-3-one (IV).

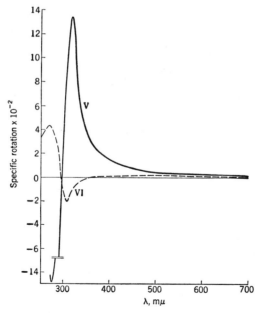

Fig. 5-2. RD curves of *trans*-10-methyl-2-decalone (V) (dioxane) and *cis*-10-methyl-2-decalone (VI) (methanol).

will be noted that in terms of shape and sign of the Cotton effect curve they are virtually identical with those of the relevant 3-keto-5α and 3-keto-5β steroids (Fig. 4-5). A similar statement can be made about the dispersion curves [1] (Fig. 5-3) of *trans*-8-methylhydrindan-1-one (VII) and *trans*-8-methylhydrindan-2-one (VIII), since these show again a great similarity when compared with the appropriate steroidal 17- and 16-ketones (Fig. 4-4).

Trans-9-methyl-1-decalone (IX), on the other hand, exhibits a fairly strong positive Cotton effect (Fig. 5-4)—completely different from the unusually shaped one (Fig. 4-1) of a 1-keto steroid—from which one can conclude that the rest of the molecule in a 1-keto steroid plays an important role.[7]

In connection with a systematic examination of the rotatory dispersion curves of tetracyclic triterpenes (Sec. 6-2), it was observed [4] that introduction of a *gem*-dimethyl function into position 4 of a 3-keto-5α steroid (positive Cotton effect) caused inversion of the sign of the Cotton effect. The analogous structural change in the bicyclic series [6] involves the conversion of *trans*-10-methyl-2-decalone (V) to *trans*-1,

V   VI   VII

1,10-trimethyl-2-decalone (X), and here also the former's positive Cotton effect curve (Fig. 5-2) is inverted to a negative one (Fig. 5-4). Regardless of the explanation [4,8] for this phenomenon, it is obvious that the responsible factor is already present in the bicyclic system (X).

VIII   IX   X

A gross, visual comparison of the rotatory dispersion curves of bicyclic versus polycyclic ketones, as carried out above, will indicate whether "dissection" of a bicyclic unit from the polycyclic model is justified. This information is of utmost importance for assignments of

[7] For further discussion on this point see W. Klyne in R. A. Raphael (ed.), "Advances in Organic Chemistry: Methods and Results," vol. 1, Interscience Publishers, Inc., New York, 1960, pp. 239–348.

[8] W. Moffitt, A. Moscowitz, R. B. Woodward, W. Klyne, and C. Djerassi, unpublished; for further discussion, see Chap. 13.

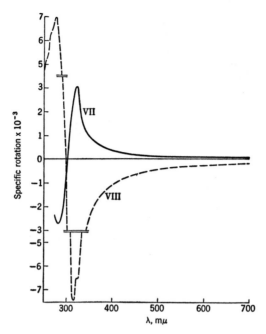

Fig. 5-3. RD curves of *trans*-8-methylhydrindan-1-one (VII) (dioxane) and *trans*-8-methylhydrindan-2-one (VIII) (methanol).

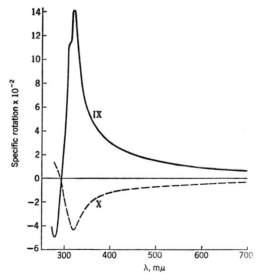

Fig. 5-4. RD curves of *trans*-9-methyl-1-decalone (IX) (dioxane) and *trans*-1,1,10-trimethyl-2-decalone (X) (methanol).

absolute configurations (Chap. 10) and for conformational problems (Sec. 5-2B). More precise conclusions of a quantitative nature with respect to the contribution of distant substituents or rings beyond the bicyclic sphere can be reached by conducting comparisons of molecular rotatory dispersion curves of bicyclic versus polycyclic ketones. Molecular amplitudes for a wide variety of such systems have been recorded [7] and these should be consulted for more extensive comparisons, but two examples are given here to illustrate the information that can be derived from such comparisons.

The molecular amplitude of the rotatory dispersion curve of *trans*-10-methyl-2-decalone (V) is of substantially the same order of magnitude as that of androstan-3-one (XI) and other 3-keto-5α steroids, thus indicating that rings C and D of the steroid do not contribute to any extent to the rotatory dispersion curve. On the other hand, a similar comparison between *trans*-8-methylhydrindan-1-one (VII) and androstan-17-one (XII) shows that the molecular amplitude of VII is only about 50 per cent that of XII, leading to the conclusion that in this instance rings A and B of androstan-17-one (XII) exert a quantitative effect.

B. Conformational Factors. Attention has already been called in Sec. 4-3C to the importance of conformational factors, and these will be considered further in Chap. 13. Since conformational distortion or inversion changes the spatial situation of a chromophore to a marked extent, it is apparent that secure comparisons between bicyclic and polycyclic substances can only be made when the conformational picture is identical. This can hardly be overemphasized, and two examples will be given here to introduce this point, which will again recur with bicyclic α,β-unsaturated ketones in Sec. 5-3B.

The most important area of application will be among *cis*-fused decalones, since these can exist in two all-chair conformations,[9] as illustrated by XIII and XIV for *cis*-10-methyl-2-decalone (VI). In the

[9] For pertinent references see W. G. Dauben and K. S. Pitzer in M. S. Newman (ed.), "Steric Effects in Organic Chemistry," chap. 1, John Wiley & Sons, Inc., New York, 1956.

steroid series this is unambiguous, since the additional B/C *trans* juncture fixes the molecule in conformation XIII, which will be referred to as *steroid-like*. This restriction does not exist in decalones, and more subtle factors have to be taken into consideration [10] to decide between the steroid-like (XIII) and the nonsteroid (XIV) conformations.   In fact, it has been suggested [10] that *cis*-10-methyl-2-decalone (VI) probably exists in the nonsteroid form XIV.

A decision can be reached on the basis of the great similarity of the rotatory dispersion curve (Fig. 5-2) of *cis*-10-methyl-2-decalone (VI) to that of 3-keto-5β steroids (see Fig. 4-5), which shows that the steroid-like conformation XIII is favored.   Intuitively, one would expect a differently shaped Cotton effect curve from conformation XIV, and this has now been confirmed by theoretical and experimental observations (see Chap. 13).

A more ambiguous example is provided by *cis*-10-methyl-1-decalone (XV), whose rotatory dispersion [6] is characterized by a symmetrical Cotton effect curve, identical in sign but quite distinct in shape from that of the steroid analogue coprostan-4-one (see Fig. 4-6).   This raises

XIII   XIV   XV

considerable doubt as to whether XV exists in the steroid-like conformation.   Theoretical considerations [8] by the octant rule (Chap. 13) suggest that the nonsteroid form is preferred.

C. Stereochemical Applications.   The conclusion that the bicyclic environment usually represents the governing factor is of the greatest significance for absolute configurational studies (Chap. 10) but can also prove very useful for the solution of stereochemical problems, as shown below by two concrete examples.

Hydrogenation of the two double bonds of the sesquiterpene (−)-α-santonin (XIX) can lead to four possible tetrahydrosantonins, of which three (XVI, XVII, and XVIII) are rather readily available.   Their rotatory dispersion curves [1] are reproduced in Fig. 5-5.   When compared with the standard curves (Fig. 5-2) of *trans-* (V) and *cis-* (VI) 10-methyl-2-decalones, it can be stated immediately that isomer

[10] W. Klyne, *Experientia,* **12,** 119 (1956).

XVI must have the *trans* and isomer XVIII the *cis* ring juncture.   The third isomer (XVII) exhibited a positive Cotton effect curve (Fig. 5-5), whose trough showed a positive rotation value.   When this substance was treated with acid, it was converted to the *trans*-tetrahydrosantonin

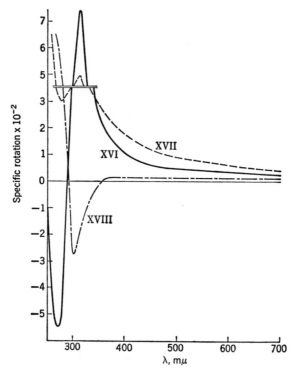

Fig. 5-5.   RD curves (dioxane) of isomeric tetrahydrosantonins (XVI, XVII, and XVIII).   [*Reproduced from C. Djerassi, Record Chem. Progr.,* **20,** 101 (1959), *by permission of the editor.*]

XVI.   Since these conditions could not have affected the ring juncture but could only have caused epimerization of the methyl group adjacent to the keto group, it follows that the third isomer has a *trans* ring fusion and an axially oriented methyl group, leading to stereoformula XVII. When these stereochemical assignments were made [1] on the basis of such a rotatory dispersion analysis, they were contrary to the then-existing conclusions [11] but were shown subsequently [12] to be correct.

The rotatory dispersion results contained in Fig. 5-5 were also useful in settling the stereochemistry of certain hydrogenation products of a C-11 isomeric santonin,[13] and they represented decisive evidence in

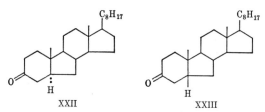

XIX XX XXI

settling the outstanding stereochemical details of the hydrogenation products [14] of artemisin (XX).

The second example shows how at times rotatory dispersion data accumulated with bicyclic ketones can be of assistance in first uncovering and then solving a problem in steroid chemistry.

Hydrogenation of B-norcholesterol (XXI) can give two dihydro derivatives (rings A/B *trans*- or *cis*-fused); the predominant product was assigned [15] the *trans* fusion on very reasonable analogy to reactions of cholesterol itself (XXI with ring B six-membered) and on infrared spectroscopic grounds. The hydrogenation product was oxidized to the corresponding ketone, which should then have been represented by stereoformula XXII. However, its rotatory dispersion curve [16] (XXIII

XXII XXIII

in Fig. 5-6) indicated that it should be represented by XXIII, thus implying that the hydrogenation of B-norcholesterol (XXI) had proceeded unexpectedly by adsorption on the β face of the molecule. A conclusion

[11] M. Yanagita and A. Tahara, *J. Org. Chem.*, **20**, 959 (1955).

[12] M. Yanagita and R. Futaki, *J. Org. Chem.*, **21**, 949 (1956); M. Yanagita and H. Ogura, *ibid.*, **22**, 1092 (1957); W. Cocker and T. B. H. McMurry, *J. Chem. Soc.*, **1956**, 4549.

[13] W. Cocker, N. J. H. Dodds, and T. B. H. McMurry, *Tetrahedron*, **3**, 160 (1958).

[14] M. Sumi, *J. Am. Chem. Soc.*, **80**, 4869 (1958).

[15] W. G. Dauben and G. J. Fonken, *J. Am. Chem. Soc.*, **78**, 4736 (1956).

[16] C. Djerassi, D. Marshall, and T. Nakano, *J. Am. Chem. Soc.*, **80**, 4853 (1958).

based on rotatory dispersion comparisons with six-membered homologues (Fig. 4-5) involves the assumption that contraction of the adjacent ring (as in XXII or XXIII) does not affect the Cotton effect, a premise which had to be proved, especially in view of the increased strain in a *trans*-hydrindane system.

Synthesis [16] of the bicyclic analogue *trans*-8-methylhydrindan-5-one (XXIV) [5] and comparison of its rotatory dispersion curve (Fig. 5-6)

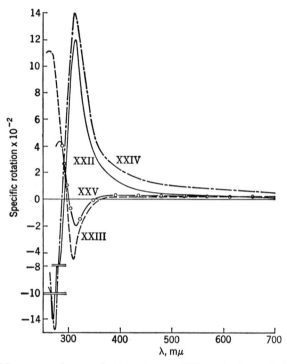

Fig. 5-6. RD curves of B-norcholestan-3-one (XXII) (methanol), B-norcoprostan-3-one (XXIII) (methanol), *trans*-8-methylhydrindan-5-one (XXIV) (methanol), and *cis*-8-methylhydrindan-5-one (XXV) (dioxane).

with that (Fig. 5-2) of its higher homologue V demonstrated that the size of the adjacent ring was of no consequence. Since this appears also to be the case with the corresponding *cis*-8-methylhydrindan-5-one (XXV) [17] (Fig. 5-6), it seemed very likely that the original [15] stereochemical assignment had to be reversed.[16] These conclusions have recently been verified completely by chemical reactions [18] and by the

[17] H. Conroy and E. Cohen, *J. Org. Chem.,* **23,** 616 (1958); W. Acklin and V. Prelog, *Helv. Chim. Acta,* **42,** 1239 (1959).

[18] T. Goto and L. F. Fieser, *J. Am. Chem. Soc.,* **81,** 2276 (1959).

isolation [19] of a second isomer (XXII), whose rotatory dispersion curve (Fig. 5-6) is completely consistent with a *trans* ring juncture.   A similar revision [20] of stereochemistry is required with the hydrogenation products [21] of B-nor-Δ^5-androsten-3β-ol-17-one.

XXIV   XXV   XXVI

D. Summation Curve in a Bicyclic Diketone.   A very good criterion of the presence or absence of interaction between two isolated carbonyl groups in a diketone is to compare the summation curve, derived from the experimental rotatory dispersion curves of the two monoketones, with the rotatory dispersion curve of the diketone.   In the steroid series (Sec. 4-4B) this interaction appeared to be largely a function of distance, and an interesting test case among bicyclic compounds is *trans*-8-methylhydrindane-2,5-dione (XXVI).[16]

The choice is a particularly fortunate one, because the corresponding monoketones,   *trans*-8-methylhydrindan-2-one   (VIII)   and   -5-one (XXIV) show opposite-sign Cotton effect curves (Figs. 5-3 and 5-6). Addition of these two curves yielded a calculated dispersion curve for the diketone XXVI which was virtually identical with the experimental one of this substance.   It follows that there exists no perceptible vicinal interaction between the two carbonyl groups in *trans*-8-methylhydrindane-2,5-dione (XXVI).

5-3.   α,β-Unsaturated Bicyclic Ketones

A. Standard Rotatory Dispersion Curves.   Solvent Effects.   The rotatory dispersion curve [6] of 10-methyl-$\Delta^{1(9)}$-2-octalone (XXIX)— structurally the simplest analogue of a Δ^4-3-keto steroid—showed a multiple Cotton effect curve, which in terms of rotation was somewhat displaced from that of the corresponding steroid (see Fig. 4-13) although the peaks and troughs occurred at practically the same wavelengths.   An especially instructive example is offered in Fig. 5-7 with the rotatory dispersion curves [22] of (5S,10S)-(XXVII) and (5S,10R)-(XXVIII) 5-hydroxy-10-methyl-$\Delta^{1(9)}$-2-octalone.[23]   The   curve   of

[19] Private communication from W. G. Dauben, University of California.

[20] Based on unpublished rotatory dispersion measurements by Mrs. T. Nakano in our laboratory with samples kindly provided by F. Sorm.[21]

[21] J. Joska, J. Fajkos, and F. Sorm, *Chem. & Ind. (London)*, **1958**, 1665.

[22] C. Djerassi, J. Osiecki, and W. Herz, *J. Org. Chem.*, **22**, 1361 (1957).

[23] V. Prelog and W. Acklin, *Helv. Chim. Acta*, **39**, 748 (1956).

XXVII is very similar to that of standard Δ^4-3-keto steroids, thus showing that the latter's multiple Cotton effect is largely a reflection of the
octalone system.   Even more important is the observation that the dispersion curves of XXVII and XXVIII are virtual mirror images, even
though the two octalones are not exact antipodes, which demonstrates

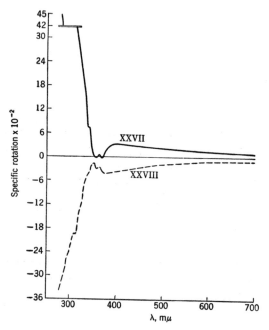

Fig. 5-7.   RD curves (dioxane) of (5S,10S)-5-hydroxy-10-methyl-$\Delta^{1(9)}$-2-octalone
(XXVII) and (5S,10R)-5-hydroxy-10-methyl-$\Delta^{1(9)}$-2-octalone (XXVIII).

quite conclusively that the stereochemistry at the angular position controls the sign of the Cotton effect (see Sec. 4-3D).   This conclusion is
of particular utility in the solution of problems of absolute configurations
(Chap. 10), and two additional examples [24] will be cited here.

OH   R

XXVII   XXVIII   R=OH
               XXIX   R=H

The naturally occurring sesquiterpene carissone (XXX) exhibits a
multiple Cotton effect curve very similar to that of XXVII or of Δ^4-3-

[24] C. Djerassi, R. Riniker, and B. Riniker, *J. Am. Chem. Soc.,* **78,** 6377 (1956).

keto steroids (Fig. 4-13), which is completely consistent with the β orientation of the angular methyl group established earlier by chemical interconversions.[25]

The absolute configuration of 1,14-dimethyl-2-keto-$\Delta^{1(11),6}$-decahydrophenanthrene (XXXI) is known [26] and, if rewritten as XXXI*a,* it

XXX   XXXI   XXXI*a*

will be seen that the angular substituent of the octalone system (the controlling factor as far as the sign of the Cotton effect is concerned) is α-oriented and that the rotatory dispersion curve should, therefore, be of the same sign as the octalone XXVIII in Fig. 5-7. Experimentally [24] this was found to be the case.

Before turning to specific applications of these observations, attention should be called to Fig. 5-8, which contains a portion of the rotatory dispersion curve [24] of *trans*-10-methyl-$\Delta^{3,6}$-2-hexalone (XXXII) meas-

XXXII

ured in three solvents (methanol, dioxane, and octane) of varying polarity. The situation is the same as in Fig. 4-13, except that the resolution of fine structure in the nonpolar medium octane is particularly well emphasized when contrasted with the curve obtained in methanol. The appropriate ultraviolet absorption spectral data in these same three solvents are included also in order to show the intimate relationship in the solvent dependency of rotatory dispersion and ultraviolet absorption of α,β-unsaturated ketones.

In octane solution, the ultraviolet absorption spectrum of the hexalone XXXII exhibits (Fig. 5-8) well-resolved shoulders or maxima at 372, 354, 341, and 330 mμ. If we assume that the corresponding rotatory dispersion curve plotted immediately above the absorption spectrum in Fig. 5-8 consists of a series of Cotton effects superimposed upon a negative background rotation, then excellent correspondence between the

[25] W. A. Ayer and W. I. Taylor, *J. Chem. Soc.,* **1955,** 3027; F. J. McQuillin and J. D. Parrack, *ibid.,* **1956,** 2973.

[26] L. B. Barkley, M. W. Farrar, W. S. Knowles, H. Raffelson, and Q. E. Thompson, *J. Am. Chem. Soc.,* **76,** 5014 (1954).

rotatory dispersion extrema and the ultraviolet spectral maxima and shoulders will be noted. The highest wavelength extremum at 386 mμ is then not a trough of a Cotton effect but rather the point at which the influence of the negative background is superseded by the first Cotton effect, which is positive with a peak at 377 mμ and a trough at 367 mμ. The mid-point (372 mμ) of this positive Cotton effect corresponds extremely well with the first ultraviolet spectral shoulder at 372 mμ. An equally good agreement will also be obtained by a similar analysis

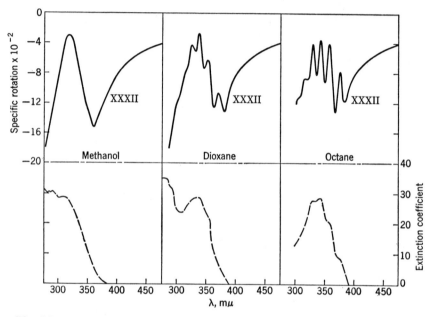

Fig. 5-8. RD curves and ultraviolet absorption spectra of *trans*-10-methyl-Δ³,⁶-2-hexalone (XXXII) in methanol, dioxane, and octane solution.

of the remainder of the multiple Cotton effect curve, which can then be considered as consisting of four principal positive Cotton effects. The hexalone would represent an interesting case for a detailed circular dichroism study and would also demonstrate whether the above assumption about the extremum at 386 mμ is justified.

Figure 5-8 also offers an excellent illustration of the advantage of rotatory dispersion over ultraviolet spectroscopy in examining such fine structure. The latter is not only much better resolved in the rotatory dispersion curve than in the ultraviolet spectrum, but the low extinction of the absorption spectrum requires at least 5 to 10 times as much material for satisfactory measurement.

B. Detection of Conformational Distortion. The special sensitivity of α,β-unsaturated steroid ketones to conformational alterations has already been noted in Sec. 4-3C.

A very relevant example of this phenomenon in the bicyclic series can probably be correlated with a similar one from the steroid series. The sesquiterpene α-cyperone (XXXIII) possesses [1] the expected multiple Cotton effect associated with this particular octalone system (see XXVII in Fig. 5-7). Epi-α-cyperone (XXXIV),[27] on the other hand, which differs from α-cyperone (XXXIII) only in that its isopropenyl substituent has the axial orientation, shows [1] a completely different multiple Cotton effect curve which resembles greatly that (Fig. 4-15) of 8-isotestosterone (XXXV). In the latter, either ring B or ring C must exist as a boat in order to accommodate the B/C *cis* ring juncture. Since the only common structural features between epi-α-cyperone (XXXIV) and 8-isotestosterone (XXXV) are rings A and B, it is sug-

XXXIII   XXXIV   XXXV

gested that ring B of epi-α-cyperone (XXXIV) exists partly or completely in a boat conformation in order to relieve the steric strain imposed by the axial isopropenyl group.

Another illustration of the dramatic response of the rotatory dispersion curve to conformational factors is presented by the dispersion curves [24] of the sesquiterpenes α- and β-vetivone (XXXVI), differing only in the orientation of the methyl group. Their respective multiple Cotton effect curves, characterized by an abundance of fine structure, are completely distinct.

XXXVI   XXXVII

C. Applications to Structural Studies. Several examples of the use of rotatory dispersion measurements in sesquiterpene chemistry have already been presented in this chapter. A case in which the dispersion

[27] F. J. McQuillin, *J. Chem. Soc.*, **1955**, 528.

curve was of some utility in helping to distinguish between two structural alternatives can be selected from the guaianolide group of sesquiterpenes.

The structure of helenalin (XXXVII), especially with regard to the cyclopentenone ring, is secure.[28]   On the other hand, some doubt had

XXXVIII   XXXIX

been expressed [29] about the structure XXXVIII proposed [30] for tenulin, the alternative XXXIX being presented for consideration.   Although several objections were put forward against the last proposal, rotatory dispersion [22] was of some aid in settling this point, since the curves of helenalin (XXXVII) and tenulin (XXXVIII) showed a great similarity, which should not have been expected if the alternative constitution XXXIX had been the correct one.

[28] G. Büchi and D. Rosenthal, *J. Am. Chem. Soc.*, **78**, 3860 (1956).
[29] B. H. Braun, W. Herz, and K. Rabindran, *J. Am. Chem. Soc.*, **78**, 4423 (1956).
[30] D. H. R. Barton and P. De Mayo, *J. Chem. Soc.*, **1956**, 142.

6 | TRITERPENOIDS

6-1. Introduction. Importance of Conformational Factors

The initial rotatory dispersion studies with steroid ketones might have suggested a complete and direct application of these results to polycyclic triterpenes. As it soon became apparent that the Cotton effect curve is often very sensitive to conformational alterations, a factor bound to be operative in triterpenes with so many axial methyl groups, it was necessary to undertake detailed dispersion studies [1,2] within this group and compare the results with the ones derived from the steroid series, thus uncovering the presence of conformational distortion.

6-2. Tetracyclic Triterpenes and Polymethylated Steroids

Since tetracyclic triterpenes [3] can be considered to be trimethyl steroids, a systematic examination was undertaken [1] of the effect of methylation upon the Cotton effect curve of a 3-keto-5α steroid such as cholestan-3-one (I). It was observed that the sign of the Cotton effect was not altered in the four possible α-methyl ketones, 2α-, 2β-, 4α-, and 4β-methylcholestan-3-one, nor was this the case with 2,2-dimethylcholestan-3-one. The differences in amplitude associated with

[1] C. Djerassi, O. Halpern, V. Halpern, and B. Riniker, *J. Am. Chem. Soc.,* **80,** 4001 (1958).

[2] C. Djerassi, J. Osiecki, and W. Closson, *J. Am. Chem. Soc.,* **81,** 4587 (1959).

[3] For review see R. M. Gascoigne and J. J. H. Simes, *Quart. Revs. (London),* **9,** 328 (1955); E. R. H. Jones and T. G. Halsall in L. Zechmeister (ed.), "Progress in the Chemistry of Organic Natural Products," vol. 12, pp. 14–130, Springer-Verlag, Vienna, 1955.

methylation have already been considered [4] in the light of the octant rule (see Chap. 13). However, when two methyl groups are introduced into position 4, as in 4,4-dimethylcholestan-3-one (II), then its Cotton

I   II

effect curve is inverted (Fig. 6-1) by comparison with the unmethylated parent ketone (I). This was an important observation since the 3-keto-4,4-dimethyl grouping with the A/B *trans* juncture represents a structural unit found in nearly all tetracyclic triterpenes. That this inversion in the sign of the Cotton effect is not due to diaxial interaction between the axial methyl groups at C-4 and C-10 could be demonstrated [1] easily since this effect was still noted with 19-nor-4,4-dimethyl-3-keto steroids, where the angular methyl group at C-10 was lacking. In part, this "4,4-dimethyl effect," which is also found (Sec. 5-2A) in the decalone series, may be attributed [1] to a combination of two conformational interactions—the 2-alkyl ketone effect [5] as well as interference between the equatorial methyl group at C-4 and the hydrogen atoms at C-6. It is pertinent to note that the effect does not persist when ring A is five-membered,[6] since A-nor-3,3-dimethylcholestan-2-one (III) has a very strong positive Cotton effect.

Even a cyclopropane ring does not alter the gross features of this rotatory dispersion relationship. Cycloartenone (IV) shows (Fig. 6-2) the typical negative Cotton effect of a 4,4-dimethyl-3-keto steroid,

III   IV   V

whereas the related 4α-monomethyl triterpene, cycloeucalenone (V), exhibits a positive one, characteristic of 3-keto-5α steroids (e.g., I).

A second structural variable of importance in the tetracyclic triter-

---

[4] W. Moffitt, A. Moscowitz, R. B. Woodward, W. Klyne, and C. Djerassi, unpublished observation.

[5] W. Klyne, *Experientia*, **12**, 119 (1956).

[6] Private communication from G. Ourisson, University of Strasbourg.

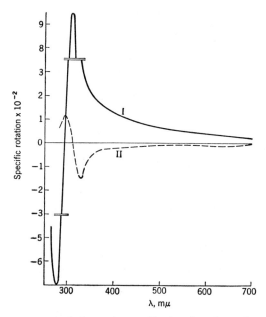

Fig. 6-1. RD curves of cholestan-3-one (I) (methanol) and 4,4-dimethylcho-lestan-3-one (II) (dioxane).

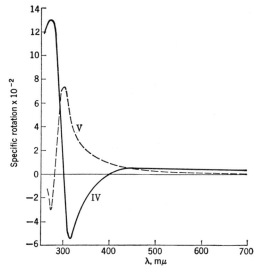

Fig. 6-2. RD curves (methanol) of cycloartenone (IV) and cycloeucalenone (V).

pene series is the absence or presence of double bonds in ring B.   The situation is best illustrated [1] with three derivatives of lanosterol, lanostan-3-one (VI), Δ^7-lanosten-3-one (VII), and Δ^8-lanosten-3-one (VIII).   As can be seen from Fig. 6-3, the first two ketones exhibit negative Cotton effect curves, although their shapes differ considerably, whereas Δ^8-lanosten-3-one (VIII) possesses a positive Cotton effect.

The sensitivity of the rotatory dispersion curve of such 4,4-dimethyl-3-keto steroid types to double bonds in the adjacent ring has a direct bearing on pentacyclic triterpenes and will be discussed in Sec. 6-3.

These specific rotatory dispersion features are not influenced to any extent by rings C and D.   Dihydrobutyrospermone (IX) and masticadienonic acid (X), in spite of the fact that their C/D ring juncture

bears an antipodal relationship to that of Δ^7-lanosten-3-one (VII), have Cotton effect curves which resemble closely that of Δ^7-lanosten-3-one (VII).   This resemblance offers welcome additional evidence for the 9α orientation of dihydrobutyrospermone (IX), long a subject of debate.[7]   Similarly, isomasticadienonic acid (XI) and elemenonic acid

[7] M. C. Dawson, T. G. Halsall, E. R. H. Jones, G. D. Meakins, and P. C. Phillips, J. Chem. Soc., 1956, 3172; W. Lawrie, W. Hamilton, F. S. Spring, and H. S. Watson, ibid., 1956, 3272.

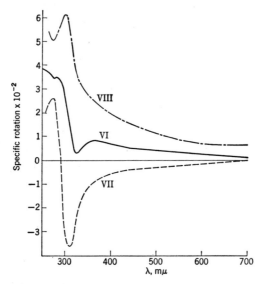

Fig. 6-3. RD curves (methanol) of lanostan-3-one (VI), Δ^7-lanosten-3-one (VII), and Δ^8-lanosten-3-one (VIII).

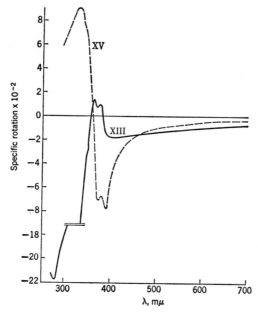

Fig. 6-4. RD curves (dioxane) of Δ^5-cholesten-3β-ol-7-one acetate (XIII) and 3β-acetoxy-Δ^5-lanosten-7-one (XV).

(XII) exhibit curves of the Δ^8-lanosten-3-one (VIII) type, even though rings C and D again possess the enantiomeric ring fusion.

In Sec. 4-3C it was pointed out that conformational distortions in the adjacent ring manifest themselves in the rotatory dispersion of steroidal α,β-unsaturated ketones. Further examples can now be presented among tetracyclic triterpenes. A Δ^5-7-keto steroid such as Δ^5-cholesten-3β-ol-7-one acetate (XIII) shows the expected multiple Cotton effect curve (Fig. 6-4) of enantiomeric sign (Sec. 4-3D) to that (Fig. 4-13) of Δ^4-3-keto steroids. As soon as two methyl groups are introduced in position 4, as in 4,4-dimethyl-Δ^5-cholesten-3β-ol-7-one acetate (XIV) or 3β-acetoxy-Δ^5-lanosten-7-one (XV), the rotatory dispersion

XIII

XIV R=H
XV   R=CH$_3$

curve [1] becomes inverted (XV in Fig. 6-4). In other words, the conformational interaction and the resulting rotatory dispersion change are exactly analogous to the pair testosterone versus 6β-methyltestosterone (see Fig. 4-14). This sensitivity to conformational interactions appears to exist only when the α,β-unsaturated carbonyl chromophore is involved in the juncture to that ring, which is implicated in terms of conformational interferences. This is illustrated by the rotatory dispersion curve [1] of 3β-benzoyloxy-Δ^8-lanosten-7-one (XVI), which is essentially identical to that of Δ^8-cholesten-3β-ol-7-one acetate (XVII), even though the former contains two methyl groups in position 4.

XVI

XVII

6-3. Pentacyclic Triterpenes

In this group of natural products, different locations of isolated double bonds have an important effect on the slope and even on the sign of the plain dispersion curve (in the absence of a carbonyl group). The use of such plain curves is covered in Chap. 16. In a proper evaluation of the Cotton effect curves of carbonyl-containing triterpenes, these plain "background" curves (see Sec. 2-3 and Fig. 2-3) ought to be taken into consideration.

A. Application in Structural Studies.   A very considerable amount of work is still being conducted on the structure elucidation of penta-cyclic triterpenes.   Since these belong to only very few, fundamentally distinct, structural types, most of the investigations are concerned with interconversions of an unknown triterpene with a member of the same

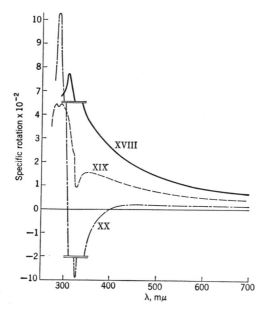

Fig. 6-5.   RD curves (dioxane) of β-amyrone (XVIII), sumaresinonic acid methyl ester 3-acetate (XIX), and Δ^{12}-oleanen-3β-ol-16-one (XX).

class whose constitution is known.   Reduced to its simplest denominator, the problem resolves itself to one of the recognition and especially the location of the various oxygen functions.   These are most frequently carbonyl or hydroxyl substituents and, since the latter can be oxidized to the former, any physical tool that aids in the placement of carbonyl groups will be of great importance.   In this respect, rotatory dispersion is the method par excellence, and a series of reference curves has been accumulated [2] which can be used for comparison with the dispersion curves of unknown monoketones or aldehydes, belonging to the major groups of pentacyclic triterpenes.   For solubility reasons, the solvent of choice, even with nonconjugated carbonyl compounds, is dioxane.

As an illustration, there are collected in Fig. 6-5 the rotatory dispersion curves of three members of the β-amyrin (oleanane) series, the most widely distributed one in nature.   The examples encompass location of a keto group in position 3 [β-amyrone (XVIII)], position 6 [sumaresinonic acid methyl ester 3-acetate (XIX)], and position 16 [Δ^{12}-oleanen-3β-ol-16-one (XX)]; standard curves for other locations may be found in the original literature.[2] These characteristically shaped curves are not affected to any marked extent (provided the background rotation of the system is always taken into consideration) by "nonchromophoric" substituents in other parts of the molecule.   For instance, the positive Cotton effect curve (XVIII in Fig. 6-5) associated with a keto group in position 3 of a β-amyrin triterpene will be of the same type in the two other major groups of pentacyclic triterpenes, the ursane [e.g., α-amyrone (XXI)] and lupane [e.g., lupenone (XXII)] series.

XVIII   XIX   XX

XXI   XXII

Attention has been called [1,2] to the interesting observation that although the rotatory dispersion curves (Fig. 6-3) of the two closely related ketones, Δ^7-(VII) and Δ^8-(VIII) lanosten-3-one, are completely distinct and even of opposite sign, two such structurally dissimilar ketones as β-amyrone (XVIII) and Δ^8-lanosten-3-one (VIII) resemble each other considerably in terms of their rotatory dispersion behavior.   This would point toward a common, conformational denominator, and in that connection it is appropriate to note that Barton and collaborators [8] have found that β-amyrone (XVIII) and Δ^8-lanosten-

[8] D. H. R. Barton, A. J. Head, and P. J. May. *J. Chem. Soc.*. **1957**. 935.

3-one (VIII) condense at virtually identical rates with benzaldehyde, in contrast to Δ^7-lanosten-3-one (VII), for which the rate is greatly reduced.

Advantage can be taken of these observations in supporting recent structural assignments [9] of the biogenetically intriguing triterpene bauerenol (XXIII). Rotatory dispersion measurements on samples of bauerenone (XXIV) and isobauerenone (XXV), kindly supplied by

XXIII   XXIV   XXV

F. N. Lahey [9] of the University of Queensland, showed that their dispersion curves bore the same relationship to each other as do those (Fig. 6-3) of Δ^7-lanosten-3-one (VII) and Δ^8-lanosten-3-one (VIII).

B. Stereochemical Applications. The complete stereochemistry of the lupane skeleton (e.g., XXII) is known.[10] This is not necessarily the case with its degradation product trisnorlupanonyl acetate (XXVI), since the newly formed keto group is adjacent to an invertible center (C-18). Using as a reference standard the strongly positive Cotton effect curve of A-nor-3-ketocholanic acid (XXVII), whose A/B ring

XXVI   XXVII

juncture is known to be *cis,* it was found [2] that the trisnor ketone (XXVI) showed a similar dispersion curve, from which it can be concluded that inversion must have occurred at C-18 during its preparation. Similarly, the positive Cotton effect of trisnorhopan-21-one (XXVIII) [11]

[9] F. N. Lahey and M. V. Leeding, *Proc. Chem. Soc.,* **1958,** 342.

[10] T. G. Halsall, E. R. H. Jones, and G. D. Meakins, *J. Chem. Soc.,* **1952,** 2862, and references cited therein.

[11] W. J. Dunstan, H. Fazakerley, T. G. Halsall, and E. R. H. Jones, *Croat. Chem. Acta,* **29,** 173 (1957).

demonstrated that inversion must have been involved at C-17 in its preparation from hydroxyhopanone (XXIX).[12]

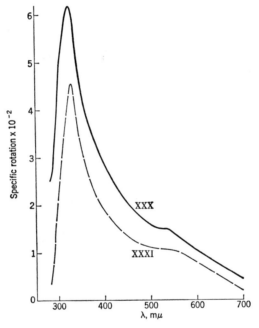

The stereochemical identity in ring A of the triterpenes gypsogenin and quillaic acid was only demonstrated [13] after laborious multistage chemical interconversions. The ease with which this problem could

Fig. 6-6. RD curves (dioxane) of gypsogenin methyl ester (XXX) and quillaic acid methyl ester (XXXI).

have been settled by rotatory dispersion is illustrated in Fig. 6-6. The great similarity of the curves of gypsogenin methyl ester (XXX) and

[12] K. Schaffner, L. Caglioti, D. Arigoni, O. Jeger, H. Fazakerley, T. G. Halsall, and E. R. H. Jones, *Proc. Chem. Soc.,* **1957,** 353.

[13] See L. Ruzicka, B. Bischof, E. C. Taylor, A. Meyer, and O. Jeger, *Collection Czech Chem. Commun.,* **15,** 893 (1950).

of quillaic acid methyl ester (**XXXI**) can be used as strong, presumptive evidence for identical stereochemical attachments of the aldehyde function.

When applied with caution, rotatory dispersion evidence can also be employed for supporting stereochemical assignments of methyl groups adjacent to carbonyl functions.

The dispersion curve [14] of friedelin (**XXXII**) is compared in Fig. 6-7 with those of 17$a\alpha$-methyl-D-homoandrostan-3β-ol-17-one

XXX   R=H
XXXI R=OH

XXXII

(**XXXIII**) and 17$a\beta$-methyl-D-homoandrostan-3β-ol-17-one (**XXXIV**), the configuration of the methyl groups in these two D-homo steroids having been established previously.[15]   Since the curve of friedelin (**XXXII**) corresponded closely to that of the equatorially oriented 17$\alpha\beta$-

XXXIII

XXXIV

methyl ketone (**XXXIV**) and since the stereochemistry and conformation of the relevant bicyclic nuclei (rings A and B of **XXXII** versus rings C and D of **XXXIII** and **XXXIV**) were identical, it is safe to conclude that the C-4 methyl group of friedelin also has the equatorial orientation, which is in accord with chemical evidence.[16]

The rotatory dispersion curve [1] of 20-bisnor-Δ^{12}-oleanen-3β-ol-20-one benzoate (**XXXV**) [17] is very similar to that of coprostan-3-one (**XXXVII**), from which the correct conclusion can be drawn that rings D and E of the triterpene degradation product **XXXV** are *cis*-fused. On the other hand, the similarity of the rotatory dispersion curve of 20-nor-Δ^{12}-ursen-3β-ol-20-one   benzoate   (**XXXVI**),   a   methylation

[14] C. Djerassi, R. Riniker, and B. Riniker, *J. Am. Chem. Soc.*, **78**, 6362 (1956).

[15] F. Ramirez and S. Stafiej, *J. Am. Chem. Soc.*, **78**, 644 (1956).

[16] E. J. Corey and J. J. Ursprung, *J. Am. Chem. Soc.*, **78**, 5041 (1956).

[17] E. J. Corey and E. W. Cantrall, *J. Am. Chem. Soc.*, **81**, 1745 (1959).

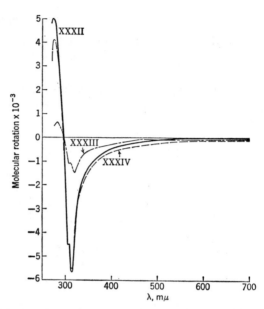

Fig. 6-7. RD curves (dioxane) of friedelin (XXXII), 17*a*α-methyl-D-homo-androstan-3β-ol-17-one (XXXIII), and 17*a*β-methyl-D-homoandrostan-3β-ol-17-one (XXXIV). [*Adapted from C. Djerassi, R. Riniker, and B. Riniker, J. Am. Chem. Soc.,* **78**, 6362 (1956), *by permission of the editor.*]

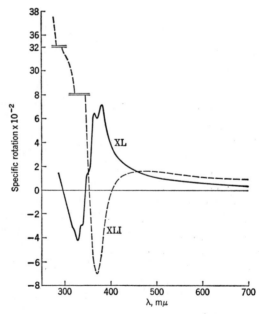

Fig. 6-8. RD curves (dioxane) of $\Delta^{9(11)}$-oleanen-3β-ol-12-one acetate (XL) and $\Delta^{9(11)}$-18α-oleanen-3β-ol-12-one acetate (XLI).

product of **XXXV**, with that of coprostan-3-one (**XXXVII**) cannot be used as evidence for the location of the methyl group in **XXXVI**, since the dispersion curves [1] of both 2β-methyl-(**XXXVIII**) and 4β-methyl-(**XXXIX**) coprostan-3-one closely resemble that of the methyl-free parent compound, coprostan-3-one (**XXXVII**).

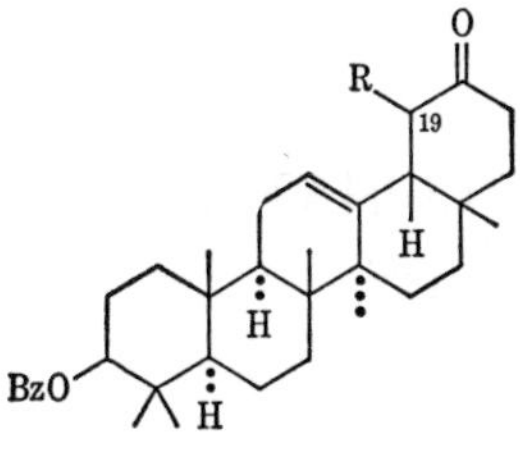

XXXV R=H
XXXVI R=CH₃

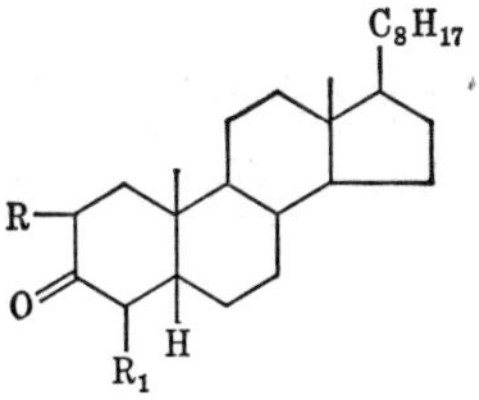

XXXVII R=R₁=H
XXXVIII R=CH₃; R₁=H
XXXIX   R=H; R₁=CH₃

C. α,β-Unsaturated Ketones. The rotatory dispersion curves of a variety of α,β-unsaturated, pentacyclic triterpenoid ketones have been measured [2] and the expected (see Secs. 4-3C and 5-3B) sensitivity to stereochemical and conformational alterations has been noted. This can be particularly helpful in settling stereochemical problems in this field, and a single example should suffice.

Figure 6-8 contains the rotatory dispersion curves of $\Delta^{9(11)}$-oleanen-3β-ol-12-one acetate (**XL**) and of $\Delta^{9(11)}$-18α-oleanen-3β-ol-12-one acetate (**XLI**); these were found to be of mirror-image type even though the only stereochemical difference between the two isomers resides in the orientation of the hydrogen atom attached to C-18. Using these

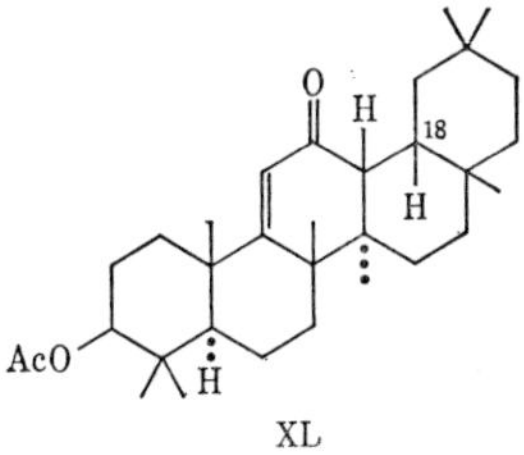

XL 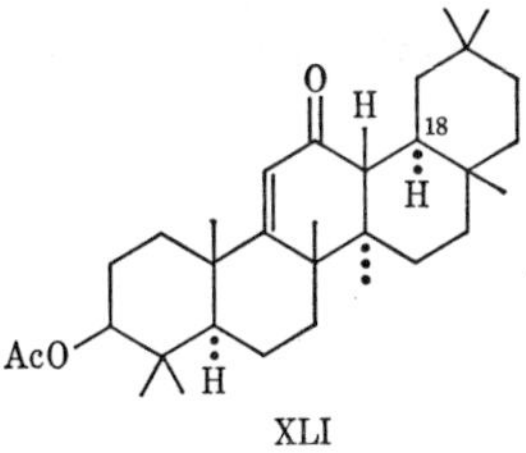   XLI 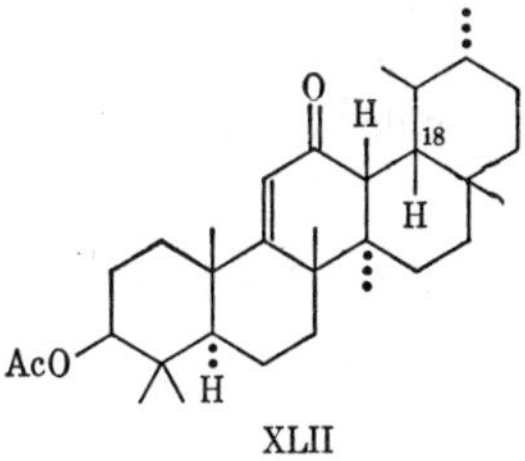   XLII

authentic reference curves, it is a simple matter to assign the correct stereochemistry (18β) to the corresponding α-amyrin derivative, $\Delta^{9(11)}$-ursen-3β-ol-12-one acetate (**XLII**),[18] by noting that its dispersion curve closely resembles that of the 18β isomer (**XL**).

[18] See A. Meisels, O. Jeger, and L. Ruzicka, *Helv. Chim. Acta,* **33,** 700 (1950).

7 | MONOCYCLIC AND ALIPHATIC CARBONYL COMPOUNDS

7-1. Conformational Mobility

A proper correlation between rotatory dispersion and structure of monocyclic or aliphatic carbonyl compounds is beset by several difficulties, the most serious of which is the possibility of conformational or free-rotational isomerization. Indeed in many instances the substance will exist in solution as a mixture of conformational isomers, and, although this problem can at times be attacked effectively by rotatory dispersion (see Sec. 9-3E), it is first necessary to accumulate a considerable amount of basic information. As will be shown below, research in this area has only just started and much must be done before secure generalizations can be made. Nevertheless, one can predict even at this early stage that rotatory dispersion will become a very important tool for the solution of conformational problems among flexible molecules.

7-2. Effect of Ring Size

Clearly one way in which the environment around a carbonyl group in a cyclic ketone can be affected is by altering the size of the ring, and this may be expected to reflect itself in the rotatory dispersion curve. The first investigation bearing on this point is one [1] in which the dispersion curves of a series of 3-methylcycloalkanones (I to V) were measured; because the stereochemistry of the single asymmetric center was kept constant, the only variable was the size of the ring. The generalization that cyclic compounds show larger rotations than their

[1] C. Djerassi and G. W. Krakower, *J. Am. Chem. Soc.,* **81,** 237 (1959).

open-chain analogues has been known for some time,[2] but no information has been available on the role that the size of the ring may play.

(+)-3-Methylcyclopentanone (I) and (+)-3-methylcyclohexanone
(II) both show positive Cotton effect curves, the amplitude of the former
being nearly five times as large as that of the six-membered ketone.   Increase of the ring size by one more carbon atom now leads to (−)-3-
methylcycloheptanone (III), which exhibits a negative Cotton effect
(Fig. 7-1), and this feature was retained through the nine-(IV) and

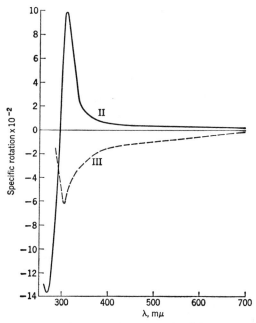

Fig. 7-1.   RD curves (methanol) of (+)-3-methylcyclohexanone (II) and (−)-3-
methylcycloheptanone (III).

fifteen-(V) membered homologues.   The negative Cotton effect makes
itself felt already in the visible region, so that these ketones exhibit
negative rotations at the sodium D line.   This explains, for instance,
why (+)-3-methylcyclohexanone (II) and (−)-muscone (3-methyl-
pentadecanone) (V) belong to the same stereochemical series but exhibit $[\alpha]_D$ of opposite sign; their identity in terms of absolute configuration had to be established [3] by synthesis.

[2] See W. J. Kauzmann, J. E. Walter, and H. Eyring, *Chem. Revs.,* **26,** 339 (1940),
especially pp. 376–380; K. Mislow and C. L. Hamermesh, *J. Am. Chem. Soc.,* **77,**
1590 (1955), and references cited therein.

[3] S. Ställberg-Stenhagen, *Arkiv Kemi,* **3,** 517 (1951).

This inversion of the Cotton effect curve in going from 3-methylcyclo-hexanone (II) to 3-methylcycloheptanone (III) can be interpreted by means of the octant rule (Chap. 13) as indicating the preponderance [in the case of the seven-membered ketone (III)] of a conformation other than the chair form.   This appears to be in agreement with recent energy calculations [4] of cycloheptanone.

$$O = \underset{\underset{\substack{\text{I} \quad n=1 \\ \text{II} \quad n=2 \\ \text{III} \quad n=3 \\ \text{IV} \quad n=5 \\ \text{V} \quad n=11}}{}}{\overset{\overset{CH_3}{\cdots}}{\bigwedge}} (CH_2)_n$$

Another type of investigation, which would lead to interesting data for theoretical calculations and might also be fruitful from an empirical standpoint, would be one in which the size of a given medium- or large-ring ketone is kept constant and the distance of the asymmetric center (methyl group with identical absolute configuration in each case) from the carbonyl chromophore is varied.   Unfortunately, the synthetic problem is sufficiently formidable to preclude rapid progress in this area in the very near future.

7-3.   Alkylated Cyclohexanones

(+)-3-Methylcyclohexanone (II) presumably exists almost entirely in conformation VI, rather than in the alternate chair form VII, and its positive Cotton effect (Fig. 7-1) may therefore be used as a suitable reference point.   Although the equilibrium between the two conformationally isomeric forms, VI and VII, may be expected to lie almost completely on the side of VI (with an equatorial methyl group), introduction of other substituents may well alter this picture.   If the conformational reversal is attended by changes in the rotatory dispersion curve, an interesting approach to the study of conformational equilibria among cyclohexanones would be available.   Indeed the octant rule (Chap. 13) predicts a positive Cotton effect curve for conformer VI and a strongly negative one for the alternate chair form, VII.

Extensive investigations are now under way in our laboratory [5] to provide suitably substituted, optically active model compounds for such

---

[4] N. L. Allinger, *J. Am. Chem. Soc.*, **81**, 5727 (1959).

[5] E. J. Eisenbraun, J. Osiecki, F. Burian, and C. Djerassi, to be published. See also E. J. Eisenbraun and J. Osiecki, Abstracts of the American Chemical Society Meeting, Chicago, September, 1958, p. 25-P.

rotatory dispersion measurements. Fortunately, some of the naturally occurring monoterpenes are equally adequate and an example will be given below.

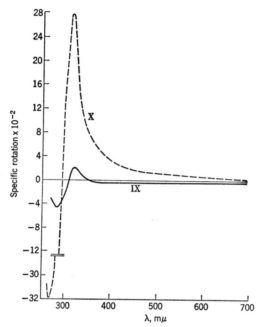

Fig. 7-2. RD curves (methanol) of (−)-menthone (IX) and (+)-isomenthone (X).

(−)-Menthone (IX) exhibits [6] (Fig. 7-2) a positive Cotton effect curve of essentially the same amplitude as that [6] of *trans*-2,5-dimethyl-cyclohexanone (VIII), and this ketone would be expected to exist predominantly in that conformation in which both methyl groups are

equatorially oriented. Similarly, (−)-menthone (IX) would be predicted [7] to favor conformation IX*a* (two equatorial alkyl groups) rather than IX*b* (two axial alkyl groups).

[6] Unpublished measurements by Mrs. V. Halpern and Mrs. J. Osiecki. See also T. M. Lowry and R. E. Lishmund, *J. Chem. Soc.*, **1935**, 709.

[7] See W. Klyne, *Experientia*, **12**, 119 (1956).

Isomerization of (−)-menthone (IX) leads to (+)-isomenthone (X), characterized by a strongly positive Cotton effect curve (Fig. 7-2), thus affording another illustration of the inadequacy of configurational prefixes based on $[\alpha]_D$ values, since in the case of (−)-menthone (IX) the positive rotatory dispersion curve starts on the negative side in the visible spectral range.

IX   IXa   IXb

X   Xa   Xb

Two all-chair conformations can be written for (+)-isomenthone (X), and in each of them one of the alkyl substituents is axial and the other equatorial. The octant rule (Chap. 13) predicts a positive Cotton effect curve (experimentally observed—Fig. 7-2) for conformation Xa and a negative one for conformation Xb, which leads to the interesting suggestion that the energy difference between an axial versus an equatorial isopropyl group adjacent to a ketone in a cyclohexanone is smaller than that [7] (ca. 0.9 kcal) existing between axial and equatorial methyl functions β to such a keto group. At this stage, when precise quantitative applications of the octant rule are not yet available, this should only be considered as a very tentative suggestion. Thus, intermediate forms between chairs and boats are not taken into consideration and free rotation of the isopropyl group complicates the use of the octant rule. All that can be said is that even in its present very crude form, rotatory dispersion measurements can raise—if not completely solve—conformational problems that merit further examination by other methods.

7-4. Aliphatic Carbonyl Compounds

In principle, a systematic investigation of rotatory dispersion among aliphatic ketones and aldehydes can be defined as providing the answer to the effect of distance between the asymmetric center and the carbonyl chromophore upon the dispersion curve. The "insulating" effect of distance has already been examined by Tschugaeff [8] with certain xanthates and has been considered in general terms as the phenomenon of "vicinal action" by Kuhn and Freudenberg.[9]

Turning to the specific area of aliphatic carbonyl compounds, there is now encountered the experimental difficulty that the rotations of such aliphatic compounds are considerably smaller [2] than those of the corresponding cyclic analogues and the error, especially in the ultraviolet, correspondingly larger.   Nevertheless, generalizations based on sign and shape of Cotton effect can be made.   The first systematic study in this area has been described in a classic paper by Levene and Rothen,[10] who measured the rotatory dispersion curves of a homologous series of aldehydes (XI, $n = 0$ to 3).   They observed that when the aldehyde function was adjacent to the asymmetric center ($n = 0$), a positive Cotton effect curve was exhibited, while separation by one carbon atom (XI, $n = 1$) resulted in a negative Cotton effect.   With the higher homologues, a positive rotatory dispersion curve was obtained, the existence of a Cotton effect being demonstrated by Drude's equation (Sec. 1-3), since the experimental measurements in the ultraviolet did not suffice for this purpose.

$$\begin{array}{cc}
\text{(CH}_2)_n\text{CHO} & \text{(CH}_2)_n\overset{\overset{\text{O}}{\|}}{\text{C}}\text{CH}_3 \\
\vdots & \vdots \\
\text{CH}_3-\!\!-\text{C}-\!\!-\text{H} & \text{CH}_3-\!\!-\text{C}-\!\!-\text{H} \\
\vdots & \vdots \\
\text{C}_2\text{H}_5 & \text{C}_2\text{H}_5 \\
\text{XI} & \text{XII}
\end{array}$$

Recently, the synthesis and rotatory dispersion measurements (using a modern spectropolarimeter) of this series of aldehydes (XI, $n = 0$ to 3) were repeated,[11] and the relevant dispersion curves are reproduced in Fig. 7-3.   Similar results were encountered [11] with a homologous series of methyl ketones (XII, $n = 0$ to 4), thus leading to the following conclusions.

1. The dispersion curves assume a progressively more plain character (see Sec. 2-2) as the distance between the asymmetric center and the carbonyl chromophore is increased.   Separation by more than two carbon atoms affords a dispersion curve that is substantially plain within the experimental limits of presently available spectropolarimeters.

2. There exists a marked inversion in sign of the Cotton effect be-

[8] L. Tschugaeff and A. Ogorodnikoff, *Z. physik. Chem. (Leipzig)*, **85**, 481 (1913).

[9] See W. Kuhn, K. Freudenberg, and I. Wolf, *Ber.*, **63**, 2367 (1930); W. Kuhn and H. Biller, *Z. physik. Chem. (Leipzig)*, **(B)29**, 1 (1935).

[10] P. A. Levene and A. Rothen, *J. Chem. Phys.*, **4**, 48 (1936).

[11] C. Djerassi and L. E. Geller, *J. Am. Chem. Soc.*, **81**, 2789 (1959).

tween a compound whose carbonyl chromophore is adjacent to the asymmetric center and its next higher homologue (XI or XII, $n = 0$ versus $n = 1$). Eventually, this observation may be correlated with the predominance of a certain free-rotational, spatial situation of the carbonyl group, as has already been attempted with some steroidal α-halo ketones (see Sec. 9-3E).

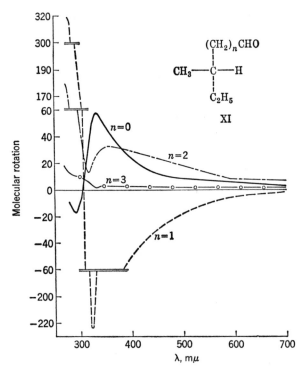

Fig. 7-3. RD curves (octane) of (+)-2-methylbutanal (XI, $n = 0$), (−)-3-methylpentanal (XI, $n = 1$), (+)-4-methylhexanal (XI, $n = 2$), and (+)-5-methylheptanal (XI, $n = 3$). [*Reproduced from C. Djerassi and L. E. Geller, J. Am. Chem. Soc.,* **81,** 2789 (1959), *by permission of the editor.*]

At the present time, the conclusions outlined under (2) can probably be used for certain assignments of absolute configuration,[12] since the actual substituent attached to the asymmetric center can be varied. An example is provided by the antibiotic actidione (XIII), which has been

[12] This approach has recently been employed for establishing the absolute configuration of phytol (P. Crabbé, C. Djerassi, E. J. Eisenbraun, and S. Liu, *Proc. Chem. Soc.,* **1959,** 264).

degraded [13] to (+)-4-methyl-6-oxoheptanoic acid (XIV).   If the propionic acid substituent of XIV can be equated with the ethyl substituent
of the reference ketone (+)-4-methylhexanone-2 (XV) (XII, $n = 1$),
one would have a means of establishing the absolute configuration of the
asymmetric center of XIV and hence of one of the centers of the antibiotic actidione (XIII).   Indeed, the *positive* Cotton effect of the acid

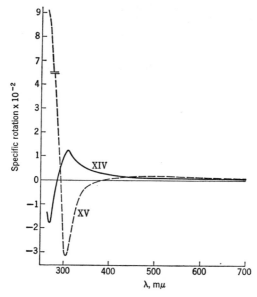

Fig. 7-4. RD curves (methanol) of (+)-4-methyl-6-oxoheptanoic acid (XIV)
and (+)-4-methylhexanone-2 (XV).

XIV when compared (Fig. 7-4) with the *negative* one of (+)-4-methyl-
hexanone-2 (XV), of known absolute configuration, leads to the con-

clusion that the two substances belong to enantiomeric series; this was
confirmed [13] by independent degradation.   It should be noted that
specific rotation measurements at the sodium D line would not have

[13] E. J. Eisenbraun, J. Osiecki, and C. Djerassi, *J. Am. Chem. Soc.*, **80**, 1261
(1958).   Further rotatory dispersion studies with related antibiotics are reported
by T. Okuda, *Chem. Pharm. Bull. (Japan)*, **7**, 137 (1959).

been very helpful, since both ketones (XIV, XV) exhibit a small, positive rotation.

Another area of considerable potential promise lies among the sugars. Although in general the carbonyl function (aldehyde or ketone) is completely masked because of acetal or ketal formation (see Chap. 11), showing only plain dispersion curves, this is not the case when the hydroxyl groups are protected.   Thus, it was found [14] that pentaacetyl fructose and various polyacetylated aldehydo sugars all showed Cotton effect curves of substantial amplitudes, the first extremum occurring near 310 mμ and the second around 265 mμ.   More extensive rotatory dispersion studies with carbonyl-containing sugars appear to be warranted and may prove to be of possible stereochemical value.

$$CH_3CCH_2—C—CH_2CH_3$$

XV   XVI

Insufficient dispersion data are available to make any generalizations on α,β-unsaturated aliphatic carbonyl compounds, but it is pertinent to note that dihydropseudoionone (XVI) shows [15] only a plain dispersion curve with very low rotation values throughout the measurable spectral region.

[14] W. C. G. Baldwin, M. L. Wolfrom, and T. M. Lowry, *J. Chem. Soc.*, **1935,** 696.

[15] Unpublished measurements by Dr. and Mrs. Pierre Crabbé.

8 | α-HYDROXY KETONES

8-1. Effect of Axial and Equatorial Hydroxyl Substituents

Extensive studies in the steroid series [1,2] have shown that the ultraviolet absorption maximum of a saturated ketone in a six-membered ring is affected in a predictable manner by an adjacent hydroxyl substituent. An *axial* hydroxyl group produces a *bathochromic* shift of 14 to 20 mμ, while an *equatorial* substituent results in a *hypsochromic* change (9 to 13 mμ). This generalization has been tested in a variety of steroidal ketols of the cholestane, bile acid, and cardiac aglycone series.

In view of the relationship existing between rotatory dispersion and absorption (Sec. 1-2), it was of interest to see whether such shifts could also be observed experimentally in the Cotton effect curves of the appropriate ketols, and uniform, qualitative agreement was indeed found.[3]

The results are most easily presented in tabular form and while it would have been preferable to list the position of the "optically active absorption band" (i.e., the mean of the rotatory dispersion peak and trough), this was not possible because in many cases only one extremum (Sec. 2-3) (i.e., peak *or* trough) could be measured. Consequently, the wavelength of the first extremum of the Cotton effect curve is compared with the position of the ultraviolet absorption maximum. For the sake of simplicity, only a few examples are listed in Table 8-1, and these support the following two generalizations.

[1] R. C. Cookson and S. H. Dandegaonker, *J. Chem. Soc.,* **1955**, 352.
[2] G. Baumgartner and C. Tamm, *Helv. Chim. Acta,* **38**, 441 (1955).
[3] C. Djerassi, O. Halpern, V. Halpern, O. Schindler, and C. Tamm, *Helv. Chim. Acta,* **41**, 250 (1958).

1. Introduction of a hydroxyl function adjacent to the ketone group usually does not affect the sign of the Cotton effect.[4]

2. An equatorial hydroxyl group shifts the position of the first extremum by 5 to 10 mμ toward a lower wavelength as compared to the unsubstituted ketone. An axial hydroxyl group, on the other hand, results in a bathochromic shift of 12 to 23 mμ of the peak (or trough).

Although ultraviolet absorption and rotatory dispersion offer the same answer as far as assigning an equatorial or axial orientation to a hydroxyl group in an α-hydroxy ketone is concerned, the latter method may often be preferable. Rotatory dispersion peaks and troughs are usually much sharper than the corresponding ultraviolet absorption maxima, a problem that is particularly serious in the spectra of certain ketols.[5] Furthermore, smaller amounts of material are required.

Table 8-1

Ultraviolet and Rotatory Dispersion Data of Some Steroidal α-Hydroxy Ketones

Substance	UV max,* mμ	$\Delta\lambda_{ax.}$	$\Delta\lambda_{eq.}$	RD first extremum,† mμ	$\Delta\lambda_{ax.}$	$\Delta\lambda_{eq.}$
Bile acid:						
12-Ketone:	290			305		
11β-OH	307	+17		327.5	+22.5	
11α-OH	278		−12	300		− 5
11-Ketone:	298			320		
12β-OH	285		−13	315		− 5
Sapogenin:						
11-Ketone:	ca. 299			325‡		
12α-OH	ca. 313	+14		337.5‡	+12.5	
12β-OH	290		− 9	315‡		−10
Cholestane:						
6-Ketone:	280			306		
5α-OH	299.5	+19.5		322.5	+16.5	

* Ethanol.
† Methanol.
‡ Dioxane.

Another area in which rotatory dispersion can be useful is in helping to locate a hydroxyl group adjacent to a steroidal 20-ketone function.

[4] Some exceptions have been observed in certain cardiac aglycones.[3]

[5] See J. Elks, G. H. Phillipps, T. Walker, and L. J. Wyman, *J. Chem. Soc.*, **1956**, 4330.

This is illustrated [3] by considering the position of the rotatory dispersion peaks of Δ^5-pregnen-3β-ol-20-one (I, 307.5 mμ), Δ^5-pregnene-3β,21-diol-20-one (II, 305 mμ), and Δ^5-pregnene-3β,17α-diol-20-one (III,

320 mμ). It can be concluded that introduction of a hydroxyl group at C-21 has a small hypsochromic effect, while hydroxylation at C-17 is accompanied by a considerable bathochromic shift.

8-2. Effect of Axial and Equatorial Acetoxyl Substituents

A comparative study has also been carried out [1,2,5] between the ultraviolet absorption spectra of steroidal six-membered ketones and their corresponding α-acetoxy derivatives. Here again, an axial acetoxy group produces a bathochromic (ca. 10 mμ), and an equatorial acetoxy function a hypsochromic (ca. 5 mμ), shift, the only difference being that the quantitative effects are not so large as observed with the corresponding alcohols (Sec. 8-1). In Table 8-2 are summarized the ultraviolet spectral as well as rotatory dispersion [3] results, and the same conclusions can be reached as have already been stated above for the corresponding α-hydroxy ketones. Noteworthy is the fact that the axial acetoxy ketones show an increase in the rotatory dispersion amplitude of at least 100 per cent, and an appreciable increase can be observed also in the extinction coefficients of their ultraviolet absorption maxima.

Although the concepts "axial" and "equatorial" lose much of their meaning in cyclopentanones, some striking wavelength shifts—qualitatively of the same order of magnitude in the rotatory dispersion and ultraviolet absorption—accompany [3] the introduction of acetoxy functions at C-17 of 16-keto steroids (IV), and at C-16 of 17-keto steroids (V); these are summarized in Table 8-3.

Table 8-2

**Ultraviolet and Rotatory Dispersion Data of Some Steroidal
α-Acetoxy Ketones**

Substance	UV max,* mμ	$\Delta\lambda_{ax.}$	$\Delta\lambda_{eq.}$	RD first extremum,† mμ	$\Delta\lambda_{ax.}$	$\Delta\lambda_{eq.}$
Bile acid:						
11-Ketone:	298			320		
12α-AcO	308	+10		335	+15	
12β-AcO	293		−5	313		−7
Sapogenin:						
11-Ketone:	ca. 299			325‡		
12α-AcO	310	+11		340‡	+15	
12β-AcO	293		−6	322.5‡		−2.5
Cholestane:						
6-Ketone:	280			306		
5α-AcO	290	+10		310	+ 4	

* Ethanol.
† Methanol.
‡ Dioxane.

Table 8-3

**Ultraviolet and Rotatory Dispersion Data of Some Steroidal
α-Acetoxy Cyclopentanones ***

Substance	UV max for dioxane, mμ	$\Delta\lambda$	RD first extremum for dioxane, mμ	$\Delta\lambda$
16-Ketone (IV):	298		322	
17α-AcO	314	16	345	23
17β-AcO	298	0	325	3
17-Ketone (V):	295.5		320	
16α-AcO	305	9.5	330	10
16β-AcO	307.5	12	337.5	17.5

* From C. Djerassi, O. Halpern, V. Halpern, O. Schindler, and C. Tamm, *Helv. Chim. Acta*, **41,** 250 (1958).

9 | α-HALOKETONES

9-1. Introduction. Wavelength Shifts Associated with Orientation of the Halogen Atom

Numerous spectroscopic studies have been performed with α-halogenated ketones. Most of the important generalizations have first come from investigations in the steroid series, for which the location as well as the orientation of the halogen atom is known with certainty. In the infrared region, the field effect of the C-halogen and C=O dipoles is involved, the electrostatic repulsion being greatest when the halogen atom is equatorial and least when it occupies the axial orientation. On the basis of extensive measurements [1] of polycyclic as well as monocyclic cyclohexanones, it was concluded that an equatorial halogen atom shifts the infrared carbonyl band to a lower wavelength, while practically no effect is noted with an axially oriented halogen atom.

Of particular interest to rotatory dispersion are the results accumulated [2] with ultraviolet spectroscopic measurements, which demonstrated that the maximum associated with an isolated carbonyl group in a six-membered ring is subjected to a hypsochromic shift of about 5 mμ by an adjacent equatorial bromine atom, but is moved to a longer wavelength by approximately 28 mμ when the bromine atom possesses an axial orientation. It has already been shown in Chap. 8 that the ultraviolet spectroscopic shifts involved with axial or equatorial hydroxy or acet-

---

[1] (a) R. N. Jones, D. A. Ramsay, F. Herling, and K. Dobriner, *J. Am. Chem. Soc.*, **74**, 2828 (1952); (b) E. J. Corey, *ibid.*, **75**, 2301 (1953), and later papers; (c) E. G. Cummins and J. E. Page, *J. Chem. Soc.*, **1957**, 3847.

[2] R. C. Cookson, *J. Chem. Soc.*, **1954**, 282; R. C. Cookson and S. H. Dandegaonker, *ibid.*, **1955**, 352.

oxy groups find their parallel in the rotatory dispersion picture, and it is, therefore, not surprising that this also holds true with α-halogenated ketones.

Just as with the spectroscopic data,[1,2] most of the initial rotatory dispersion measurements were accumulated [3,4] in the steroid field. The conclusions are given below.

A. Equatorial Halogen. Considering first the effect of varying the nature of the halogen atom, it will be seen from Table 9-1 that by comparison with cholestan-3-one (I), introduction of equatorial fluorine (II), chlorine (III), or bromine (IV) produces a slight bathochromic shift of practically the same magnitude (2 to 3 mμ), while an iodine atom results in a somewhat larger change (8 mμ).

With one exception (iodine), the range of wavelength shifts is roughly comparable with that observed [2] in the corresponding ultraviolet absorption spectra (hypsochromic shift of 4 to 7 mμ). Thus a slight bathochromic change (+3 mμ) is noted (Table 9-1) in going from cholestan-3-one (I) to 2α-bromocholestan-3-one (IV), but a hypsochromic one of 10 mμ is noted when comparing the position of the trough of cholestan-3β-ol-7-one acetate (VI, 310 mμ) with that of 6α-bromocholestan-3β-ol-7-one acetate (VII, 300 mμ). Intermediate values ranging from −10 to +4 mμ will be found in the literature [3] (see also Fig. 9-1). A second characteristic feature associated with the introduction of an equatorial halogen atom is that the rotatory dispersion amplitude of the parent ketone is not affected to a marked extent.

I	X=H
II	X=F
III	X=Cl
IV	X=Br
V	X=I

VI	X=H
VII	X=Br

Iodine appears to be an exception, since in the two cases studied [4] there was encountered a move to a longer wavelength in the rotatory dispersion peak, while the ultraviolet absorption maximum suffered a change to a lower wavelength ranging from 20 to 30 mμ. This ap-

[3] C. Djerassi, J. Osiecki, R. Riniker, and B. Riniker, *J. Am. Chem. Soc.,* **80,** 1216 (1958).

[4] C. Djerassi, I. Fornaguera, and O. Mancera, *J. Am. Chem. Soc.,* **81,** 2383 (1959).

Table 9-1

Rotatory Dispersion and Ultraviolet Absorption Data of Equatorial 2-Halocholestan-3-ones *

Substance	RD peak, mμ	Mol. rot. MeOH	UV absorption max for MeOH, mμ
Cholestan-3-one (I) :	307	3710°	286†
2α-Fluoro (II)	309	2650°	280
2α-Chloro (III)	310	3130°	279†
2α-Bromo (IV)	310	3190°	282†
2α-Iodo (V)	315	4400°	258

* From C. Djerassi, I. Fornaguera, and O. Mancera, *J. Am. Chem. Soc.,* **81,** 2383 (1959).

† In ethanol, because the substance was insufficiently soluble in methanol for satisfactory measurement.

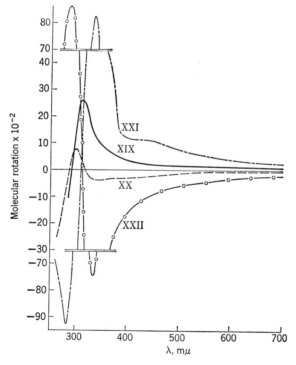

Fig. 9-1. RD curves (methanol) of 2α-bromoandrostan-17β-ol-3-one acetate (XIX), 4α-bromoandrostan-17β-ol-3-one acetate (XX), 2β-bromoandrostan-17β-ol-3-one acetate (XXI), and 4β-bromoandrostan-17β-ol-3-one acetate (XXII).

parent discrepancy can be rationalized as follows.   The absorption band at 258 mμ is due to the iodine atom and apparently is not optically active (see also Sec. 14-5), whereas the Cotton effect is associated with a second ultraviolet absorption maximum in the 290-mμ region—of sufficiently low intensity as to be masked by the iodine absorption and not detectable under the experimental conditions employed—which is optically active and which corresponds to the carbonyl group.   Circular-

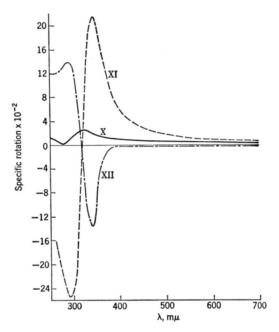

Fig. 9-2. RD curves (methanol) of ergostan-3β-ol-11-one acetate (X), 9α-bromoergostan-3β-ol-11-one acetate (XI), and 12α-bromoergostan-3β-ol-11-one acetate (XII). [*Reproduced from C. Djerassi, J. Osiecki, R. Riniker, and B. Riniker, J. Am. Chem. Soc., **80**, 1216 (1958), by permission of the editor.*]

dichroism studies would be very instructive with such α-iodo ketones, since they would settle this point unambiguously.

B. Axial Halogen.   The most impressive wavelength changes in the ultraviolet spectra were observed [2] with axial bromine, and the same finding was made [3] in rotatory dispersion measurements.   With the exception of axial iodine, where a move to a higher wavelength of 32 mμ was noted (see Table 9-2), axial fluorine, chlorine, and bromine produce a bathochromic shift of 20 ± 5 mμ, as illustrated by several examples in Table 9-2.   Furthermore, the rotatory dispersion amplitude

Table 9-2

Rotatory Dispersion Wavelength Shifts Associated with Axial Halogen Atoms *

Substance	RD first extremum,† mμ	Wavelength shifts of axial halogen			
		Iodine	Bromine	Chlorine	Fluorine
Cholestan-2-one:	310				
3α-Iodo	342	+32			
Ergostan-3β-ol-11-one acetate (X):	322.5				
9α-Bromo (XI)	347.5		+25		
12α-Bromo (XII)	342.5		+20		
Friedelin:	315‡				
2α-Bromo	335‡		+20		
4α-Bromo	335‡		+20		
Cholestan-3-one (I):	307				
2β-Chloro	327			+20	
5α-Spirostan-3β-ol-11-one acetate (XIII):	325‡				
12α-Chloro (XIV)	340‡			+15	
12α-Fluoro (XV)	340‡				+15
11-Ketoprogesterone-3,20-bisketal (XVI):	321.5				
9α-Fluoro (XVII)	340				+18.5

* All data are derived from C. Djerassi, J. Osiecki, R. Riniker, and B. Riniker, *J. Am. Chem. Soc.,* **80,** 1216 (1958), except for 3α-iodocholestan-2-one and 2β-chlorocholestan-3-one (unpublished measurements by W. Klyne, Postgraduate Medical School, London, on samples supplied by R. C. Cookson, University of Southampton).

† Methanol.

‡ Dioxane.

is greatly increased (see Figs. 9-1 and 9-2), and some applications of these generalizations will be given in Sec. 9-3.

The wavelength shifts summarized in Table 9-2 refer to the position of the first extremum, because in several cases the second extremum, occurring at a lower wavelength, could not be measured. Where both the peak and trough could be determined experimentally, the mid-point (corresponding to the position of the optically active absorption band) confirmed the conclusions reached above by just employing the position of the first extremum. For instance, both 6β-bromo-(VIII) and 8β-bromo-(IX) cholestan-3β-ol-7-one acetate exhibit [3] rotatory dispersion extrema at 335 and 287.5 mμ. The mean (311 mμ) of these peaks and troughs corresponds nearly exactly to the point of zero rotation

VIII   X=Br; X'=H
IX   X=H; X'=Br

(312.5 mμ), and this in turn is in excellent agreement with the observed [2] ultraviolet absorption maximum of VIII at 313 mμ.

9-2.   The Axial Haloketone Rule

The sign of the Cotton effect associated with a given cyclohexanone is not altered by introduction of an equatorial bromine atom on either side of the keto group.   On the other hand, this does not apply when the halogen atom exhibits an axial orientation, because in that event a reversal in sign may occur.   The entire situation is summarized in Fig. 9-1, which contains the rotatory dispersion curves [5] of all four possible monobromination products of androstan-17β-ol-3-one acetate (XVIII). The parent ketone XVIII has a single, positive Cotton effect (see Fig. 4-5), and its sign is not altered by introduction of an equatorial halogen atom, as shown by the dispersion curves of 2α-bromo-(XIX) and 4α-bromo-(XX) androstan-17β-ol-3-one acetate.   The shift of the curve of the 4α-bromo isomer toward more negative rotation values is understandable in the light of the octant rule (which is discussed in detail in Chap. 13).

On the other hand, the effect of an axial halogen atom is highly dependent on the site of substitution.   Thus 2β-bromoandrostan-17β-ol-3-one acetate (XXI) exhibits a strongly positive, and 4β-bromoandrostan-17β-ol-3-one acetate (XXII) a strongly negative Cotton effect (Fig. 9-1).   That this is not a fluke observation is shown in Fig. 9-2, the rotatory dispersion curves of ergostan-3β-ol-11-one acetate (X) and 9α-bromoergostan-3β-ol-11-one acetate (XI) being positive, while the other axially substituted isomer, 12α-bromoergostan-3β-ol-11-one acetate (XII), is characterized by a powerful negative Cotton effect.   Nu-

---

[5] Unpublished measurements by Mrs. T. Nakano on specimens provided by F. Sorm [see J. Fajkos and F. Sorm, *Chem. listy*, **52**, 2115 (1958)].

merous other examples of this phenomenon [6] have been recorded in the literature [3] and, as demonstrated in Fig. 9-3, this applies also to axial chlorine, since 5α-spirostan-3β-ol-11-one acetate (11-ketotigogenin acetate) (XIII) has a positive, and 12α-chloro-11-ketotigogenin acetate (XIV) a negative, Cotton effect; an analogous inversion with a 12α-

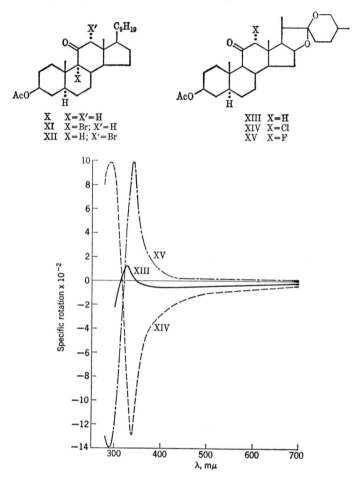

X   X=X'=H
XI   X=Br; X'=H
XII   X=H; X'=Br

XIII   X=H
XIV   X=Cl
XV   X=F

Fig. 9-3. RD curves (dioxane) of 5α-spirostan-3β-ol-11-one acetate (XIII), 12α-chloro-5α-spirostan-3β-ol-11-one acetate (XIV), and 12α-fluoro-5α-spirostan-3β-ol-11-one acetate (XV).

[6] The large amplitudes of the Cotton effects of the axial bromo ketones make themselves felt already at the sodium D line, but this is not the case with the equatorial isomers (see Fig. 9-1). E. J. Corey and J. J. Ursprung, *J. Am. Chem. Soc.,* **78,** 5041 (1956), have noted the change in sign at the D line in the rotations of two pairs of axially substituted bromo ketones and have employed this for a correct assignment of absolute configuration.

bromo-11-keto steroid is contained in Fig. 9-2. It should be noted, however, that axial fluorine behaves anomalously (Fig. 9-3) and that the generalization made below applies to axial bromine, chlorine, and probably also iodine (see Table 9-2) but not to fluorine.

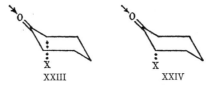

XVI X=H
XVII X=F

XVIII X=X'=H
XIX X=Br; X'=H
XX X=H; X'=Br

XXI X=Br; X'=H
XXII X=H; X'=Br

All the rotatory dispersion data accumulated to date can be encompassed in the "axial haloketone rule," which states: [7]

1. Introduction of equatorial halogen in either adjacent position of a keto group in a cyclohexanone does not alter the sign of the Cotton effect of the halogen-free ketone.

2. The effect of introducing an axial chlorine or bromine (and probably also iodine) atom next to the keto group of a cyclohexanone [8] may affect the sign of the Cotton effect of the parent ketone. This can be predicted by placing a model of the molecule in such a manner that the carbonyl group occupies the "head" of the chair (or boat—see Sec. 9-3D) as in XXIII and XXIV. By looking down the 0=C axis as indicated by the arrow, a cyclohexanone derivative with chlorine or bromine to the left (XXIII) of the observer will exhibit a negative Cotton effect, whereas a positive one will be found when the halogen atom is to the right (XXIV).

XXIII   XXIV

The applications of this rule to stereochemical problems are manifold —some of them unique—and examples are given in the following section.

---

[7] C. Djerassi and W. Klyne, J. Am. Chem. Soc., **79**, 1506 (1957).

[8] Originally (Ref. 7) this was believed to be applicable only to chair forms, but recent work (see Sec. 9-3D) has shown that boat forms also fall within the scope of the axial haloketone rule.

9-3.   Applications of the Axial Haloketone Rule

A. Assignment of Orientation to the Halogen Atom.   The first application, to differentiate between an axial and an equatorial halogen atom, is inherent in the results discussed in Sec. 9-1 and is not unique, because the problem can usually be solved also by infrared[1] or ultraviolet[2]

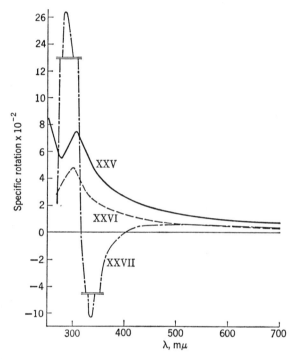

Fig. 9-4.   RD curves (methanol) of 3α-acetoxy-12-ketocholanic acid methyl ester (**XXV**), 11α-bromo-3α-acetoxy-12-ketocholanic acid methyl ester (**XXVI**), and 11β-bromo-3α-acetoxy-12-ketocholanic acid methyl ester (**XXVII**). [*Reproduced from C. Djerassi, J. Osiecki, R. Riniker, and B. Riniker, J. Am. Chem. Soc.,* **80,** 1216 (1958), *by permission of the editor.*]

spectroscopic means.   Nevertheless, it is often desirable to have available a third criterion for settling such a stereochemical problem, as situations can arise in which one or the other of these methods cannot be employed.   Diagnosis by infrared means[1] may fail in compounds that possess carbonyl functions in the form of esters, lactones, etc., because these will interfere or obscure completely interpretation of the relevant infrared spectral region, but no such difficulty will be encountered with rotatory dispersion or ultraviolet spectroscopy.   The latter, on the other hand, suffers from the disadvantage of requiring larger samples than rotatory dispersion; furthermore, maxima, especially of equatorially substituted haloketones, can sometimes not be distinguished because of the broad absorption with a very low extinction coefficient.

An instructive example is given in Fig. 9-4 by the rotatory dispersion curves of 3α-acetoxy-12-ketocholanic acid methyl ester (XXV) and its two C-11 epimeric bromo ketones.   The equatorial isomer, 11α-bromo-3α-acetoxy-12-ketocholanic acid methyl ester (XXVI), shows substantially the same dispersion curve, while the axially oriented 11β-bromo-3α-acetoxy-12-ketocholanic acid methyl ester (XXVII) exhibits a strongly negative Cotton effect with the characteristically large amplitude and bathochromic shift of the first extremum.   It should be noted that infrared spectroscopic analysis is somewhat complicated by the presence of two other carbonyl-containing functions; consideration of $[\alpha]_D$ is worthless in this case, since both epimeric bromo ketones possess practically identical rotations at 589 mμ.

XXV   X=H
XXVI   X=Br

XXVII

XXVIII

Welcome confirmation of the axial nature of a bromine atom was provided recently [9] by the strongly negative Cotton effect of 8β-bromo-cholestan-3β-ol-7-one acetate (IX), because chemical methods failed in this instance.

B. Location of the Halogen Atom.   A corollary of the axial haloketone rule is that if the absolute configuration of the ketone is known, the location of the axial bromine atom follows from the sign of its Cotton effect.   A pertinent example [10] is the bromination of 2,3-*seco*-cholestan-6-one-2,3-dioic acid (XXVIII), which led to an axial mono-bromo derivative.   The location of this bromine atom at C-5 was proved easily by noting that the substance exhibited a strongly negative Cotton effect.   The axial haloketone rule predicts a negative Cotton effect for a 5α-bromo and a positive one for a 7α-bromo derivative of XXVIII.

[9] E. R. H. Jones and D. J. Wluka, *J. Chem. Soc.,* **1959**, 911.

[10] Unpublished measurements by W. Klyne on samples provided by G. H. R. Summers, University of Wales.

C. Demonstration of Conformational Mobility.   Effect of Solvent Polarity.   As mentioned in Chap. 7, the conformational problems in monocyclic ketones are complicated because of the ease with which the molecule can change from one conformation to another.   This field offers an example [11] for which rotatory dispersion measurements and the axial haloketone rule yielded a unique solution not amenable to attack by other physical means.

Chlorination of (+)-3-methylcyclohexanone furnished a mixture from which a pure, crystalline monochloro derivative could be isolated and which by chemical means was shown to be 2-chloro-5-methylcyclo-

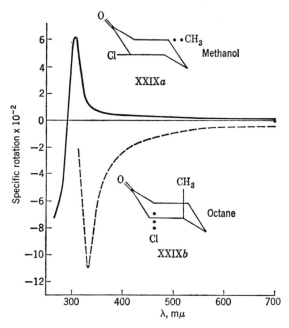

Fig. 9-5.   RD curves of *trans*-2-chloro-5-methylcyclohexanone (XXIX) in methanol and in octane solution.

hexanone.   This substance can exist as a *trans* (XXIX) and a *cis* (XXX) isomer, and each of these can in turn exist in two chair conformations (XXIXa or XXIXb, XXXa or XXXb).   The infrared and ultraviolet spectral properties in an octane solution suggested the presence of an axial chloro ketone (XXIXb or XXXa); the negative Cotton effect (Fig. 9-5) is only consistent with the *trans* form (XXIXb), since

[11] C. Djerassi and L. E. Geller, *Tetrahedron*, **3**, 319 (1958); C. Djerassi, L. E. Geller, and E. J. Eisenbraun, *J. Org. Chem.*, **25**, 1 (1960).

the axial haloketone rule would predict a positive Cotton effect for the *cis* isomer (XXXa).

The conformational equilibrium exemplified by the two chair forms (XXIXa and XXIXb) should be very dependent on the polarity of

the solvent.[12]   A polar solvent (e.g., methanol) favors the equatorial conformer (XXIXa) at the expense of the axial one (XXIXb), while an increased proportion of the latter would be expected in a nonpolar medium (e.g., octane).   Since the axial haloketone rule predicts a positive Cotton effect for conformer XXIXa and a negative one for XXIXb, a change in the rotatory dispersion picture can be anticipated upon varying the solvent.   This is shown in a striking fashion in Fig. 9-5, where the sign of the Cotton effect is actually inverted in going from octane to methanol, thus giving a very convincing demonstration of conformational mobility in this cyclohexanone system.

Similar conclusions could be reached with 2-bromo-5-methylcyclo-hexanone; by utilizing average rotatory dispersion amplitudes from steroidal axial α-bromo ketones, in which conformational mobility is inhibited, the position of the conformational equilibrium could be calculated [13] and found to be in good agreement with values derived from dipole moment and infrared spectral measurements.

D. Demonstration of Boat Form in a Steroid Ketone.   At times rotatory dispersion measurements can uncover conformational inconsistencies that are not apparent from other spectral studies.   A case in point is the monobromination [14] of 2α-methylcholestan-3-one (XXXIa), which was conducted under kinetically controlled conditions.   Infrared and ultraviolet spectral measurements [14] demonstrated the axial orientation of the bromine atom.   As its position at C-2 had been established chemically, the substance was assumed to be 2β-bromo-2α-methyl-

[12] J. Allinger and N. L. Allinger, *Tetrahedron*, **2**, 64 (1958).

[13] N. L. Allinger, J. Allinger, L. E. Geller, and C. Djerassi, *J. Org. Chem.*, **25**, 6 (1960).

[14] Y. Mazur and F. Sondheimer, *J. Am. Chem. Soc.*, **80**, 5220 (1958).

cholestan-3-one (XXXIIa) by analogy to generalizations in the litera-ture [1b] on the mechanism of bromination. When rewritten in the conformational representation XXXIII, it will be seen that the axial haloketone rule predicts a strongly positive Cotton effect, but, experi-mentally, a negative one was observed.[15] The same discrepancy was encountered [15] in the kinetically controlled monobromination of 2α-methylandrostan-17β-ol-3-one acetate (XXXIb). This apparent con-

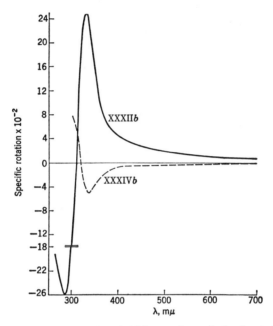

Fig. 9-6. RD curves (methanol) of 2β-bromo-2α-methylandrostan-17β-ol-3-one acetate (XXXIIb) and 2α-bromo-2β-methylandrostan-17β-ol-3-one acetate (XXXIVb) in boat form (XXXV).

tradiction is resolved easily if it is assumed that the initial bromination products are represented by the 2α-bromo-2β-methyl structure (XXXIVa and b). Its chair form (bromine atom equatorial) is inconsistent with the spectral results, which require an axial orientation, but the boat conformation (XXXV) accommodates all the experimental facts—the axial orientation established on spectroscopic grounds as well as the negative Cotton effect (Fig. 9-6) predicted by the axial haloketone rule. Complete confirmation of these views, which now call for modification [16]

[15] C. Djerassi, N. Finch, and R. Mauli, *J. Am. Chem. Soc.,* **81,** 4997 (1959).
[16] R. Villotti, M. J. Ringold, and C. Djerassi, *J. Am. Chem. Soc.,* in press.

of the presently accepted [1b] mechanism of ketone bromination, could be presented by the preparation [15] of authentic 2β-bromo-2α-methyl-3-keto steroids (XXXII) with the anticipated (see XXXIII) strongly positive Cotton effect (Fig. 9-6).

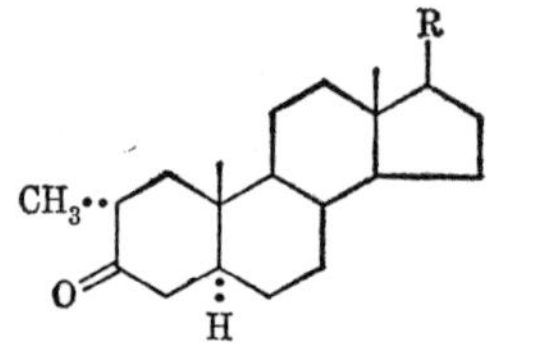

XXXIa R=C₈H₁₇
XXXIb R=OAc

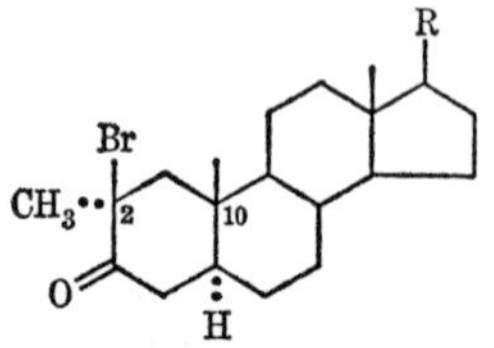

XXXIIa R=C₈H₁₇
XXXIIb R=OAc

This demonstration of the applicability of the axial haloketone rule to boat forms of cyclohexanones increases significantly the scope of such rotatory dispersion measurements to conformational problems.

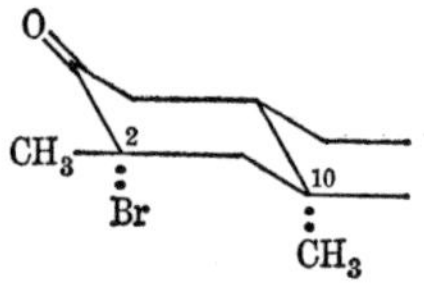

XXXIII

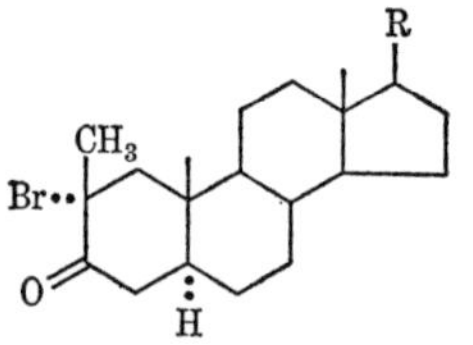

XXXIVa R=C₈H₁₇
XXXIVb R=OAc

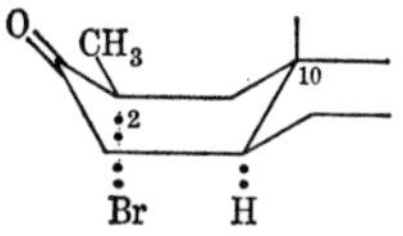

XXXV

E. Examination of Free-rotational Isomerism.   Preliminary studies [4] suggest that the axial haloketone rule may also be applied to certain acyclic α-haloketones and that the results may be used in differentiating between free-rotational isomers.

20-Keto steroids such as 5α-pregnan-3β-ol-20-one acetate (XXXVI) exhibit strongly positive Cotton effect curves (see Fig. 4-8), and this also

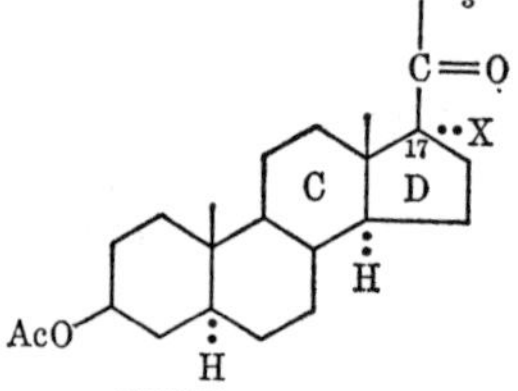

XXXVI X=H
XXXVII X=Br

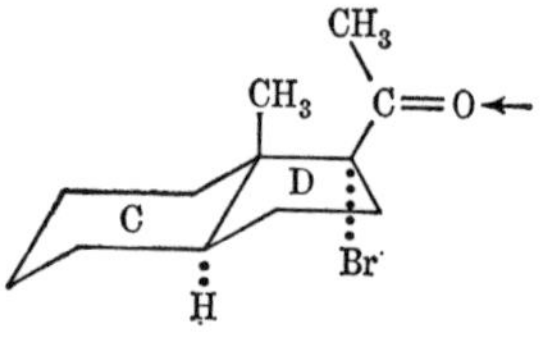

XXXVIIa

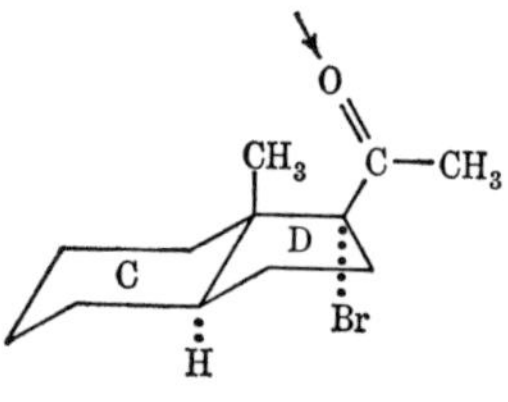

XXXVIIb

applies [4] to their derivatives with halogen atoms at C-21.   Substitution at C-17 by bromine or chlorine, on the other hand, results in an inversion of the dispersion curve, and 17α-bromo-5α-pregnan-3β-ol-20-one acetate (XXXVII) possesses a negative Cotton effect.   Although free rotation around C-17 is theoretically possible, the other substituents will cause the acetyl side chain at C-17 to prefer a certain stereochemical position.   If the axial haloketone rule is applicable to acyclic ketones of this type, then of the two principal, preferred orientations of the side chain, that represented by XXXVIIa (arrow indicating position of observer) would be predicted to exhibit a negative Cotton effect and XXXVIIb should show a positive one.   The experimentally observed negative dispersion curve would suggest that the orientation illustrated in XXXVIIa is the preferred one.

9-4.   Halogen-substituted α,β-Unsaturated Ketones

A. The Halogen Atom Adjacent to a Carbonyl Group.   Although rotatory dispersion measurements of halogenated α,β-unsaturated ketones are not too abundant, studies [17] with the following types of steroids show that placement of a halogen atom adjacent to the ketone does not produce gross abnormalities when compared with the halogen-free parent ketone: 2-bromo-Δ^1-3-ketone (XXXVIII), 2-chloro-Δ^1-3-ketone (XXXIX), 4-bromo-Δ^4-3-ketone (XL), and 2α-bromo-Δ^4-3-ketone (XLI).[18]

XXXVIII   XXXIX   XL   XLI

B. The Halogen Atom Adjacent to a Double Bond.   Presently, the only available data [3] come from 6-substituted Δ^4-3-keto steroids, a group whose ultraviolet absorption spectra [19] have also been studied.   Here again, fluorine is found to behave differently from chlorine and bromine. In Fig. 9-7 are reproduced the rotatory dispersion curves of 6α-fluoro-testosterone (XLII) and of 6β-fluorotestosterone (XLIII).   As is to be expected (see Sec. 4-3C), an equatorial substituent (XLII) does not affect the dispersion picture, which is essentially identical to that (Fig. 4-15) of testosterone, while the axial 6β-fluoro derivative shows a dispersion curve that is shifted considerably toward lower rotation values. A completely distinct situation is observed in Fig. 9-8 by the rotatory

[17] C. Djerassi, R. Riniker, and B. Riniker, *J. Am. Chem. Soc.*, **78**, 6377 (1956), and unpublished measurement by Mrs. R. Riniker.

[18] No information is available on the possible effect of an adjacent axial halogen atom.

[19] C. W. Bird, R. C. Cookson, and S. H. Dandegaonker, *J. Chem. Soc.*, **1956**, 3675.

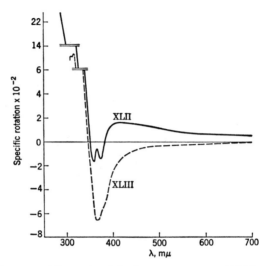

Fig. 9-7. RD curves (dioxane) of 6α-fluorotestosterone (XLII) and 6β-fluoro-testosterone (XLIII).

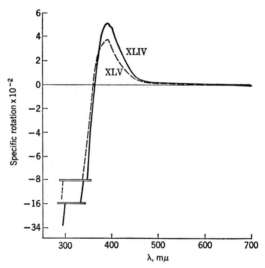

Fig. 9-8. RD curves (dioxane) of 6β-bromotestosterone acetate (XLIV) and 6β-chlorotestosterone acetate (XLV).

dispersion curves of 6β-bromotestosterone acetate (XLIV) and 6β-chlorotestosterone acetate (XLV). The two curves resemble each other greatly—again demonstrating the identical effects of chlorine and bromine already noted in Sec. 9-2—but differ completely from that of 6β-fluorotestosterone (XLIII), since the curves are actually of opposite

sign. A related situation has already been noted in a comparison of an axial α-fluoro versus the corresponding α-chloro ketone (Fig. 9-3).

The rotatory dispersion changes induced by an axial 6β-halogen atom are probably largely of electronic origin,[19] although the operation of some steric effects, of the type noted with 6β-methyltestosterone (Fig. 4-14), cannot be ignored with the limited information presently available.

10 | DETERMINATION OF ABSOLUTE CONFIGURATION

10-1. Introduction

The problem of determining the absolute configuration of an optically active molecule has been of concern since the earliest days of stereochemistry, and a number of chemical and physical methods have been developed for this purpose.[1,2,3] Nevertheless, the armamentarium of the organic chemist is still woefully small in this respect—especially when rapid solutions are required and extensive chemical interrelations are not feasible—and rotatory dispersion appears to satisfy an important need. With very few exceptions (see Chap. 15), this method was not used until 1956; several examples will be given of recent applications.

10-2. Rotatory Dispersion Comparisons of Relevant Chromophoric Systems

The basis of this approach[4] is implicit in the subjects discussed in Chaps. 4 and 5, which led to the conclusion that usually the gross, characteristic features of a Cotton effect curve of a given chromophore (in this instance the carbonyl group) in cyclic compounds are largely gov-

[1] The early literature is covered completely by K. Freudenberg, "Stereochemie," pp. 662–720, F. Deuticke, Leipzig, 1932.
[2] References to more recent studies can be found in J. A. Mills and W. Klyne in W. Klyne (ed.), "Progress in Stereochemistry," vol. 1, chap. 5, Academic Press, Inc., New York, 1954.
[3] A simple description of the X-ray method, together with leading references, is given by J. M. Bijvoet, *Endeavour,* **14,** 71 (1955).
[4] C. Djerassi, R. Riniker, and B. Riniker, *J. Am. Chem. Soc.,* **78,** 6362 (1956).

erned by the immediate bicyclic environment. It was noted also that changes in the stereochemical arrangement or conformation of the system can manifest themselves in a striking manner in the rotatory dispersion curve, and this fact must be taken into careful consideration when employing such curves for assignments of absolute configuration.

Briefly, all that is necessary is to compare the rotatory dispersion curve of the compound in question with that of another substance, whose absolute configuration is known and which contains the identical chromophore in the same stereochemical and conformational environment. Among cyclic ketones steroids represent ideal reference compounds, since an enormous variety of structural alternatives is available. In addition, their absolute configurations have been established securely by classical chemical interconversions [5] as well as by asymmetric syntheses.[6] If we now recall the demonstration (Chaps. 4 and 5) that frequently neither the nature of the angular substituent nor additional nonchromophoric substituents play an important role, it will be understood why the rotatory dispersion approach to absolute configurational problems has found such rapid acceptance in the area of natural products. A simple example [4] of the correct use of this method will suffice before turning to more recent illustrations of the scope and power of rotatory dispersion in assignments of absolute configurations.

19-Nortestosterone (I) can be used as a suitable configurational standard because of its relationship to testosterone (Sec. 4-3D) and thence to the sterols.[5,6] In order to establish the absolute configuration of 8,13-dimethyl-8-methoxycarbonyl-2-oxo-$\Delta^{1(11)}$-dodecahydrophenanthrene (II), a ketone derived from the resin acid neoabietic acid,

I   II   IIa

all that is necessary is to examine its rotatory dispersion curve in relation to that of 19-nortestosterone (I). The ketone II can also be written as IIa, which clarifies the similarity of the relevant bicyclic nuclei

[5] J. W. Cornforth, I. Youhotsky, and G. Popjak, *Nature,* **173,** 536 (1954); B. Riniker, D. Arigoni, and O. Jeger, *Helv. Chim. Acta,* **37,** 345 (1954); M. Viscontini and P. Miglioretto, *ibid.,* **38,** 930 (1955); K. Brenneisen, C. Tamm, and T. Reichstein, *ibid.,* **39,** 1233 (1956).

[6] W. G. Dauben, D. F. Dickel, O. Jeger, and V. Prelog, *Helv. Chim. Acta,* **36,** 325 (1953).

around the carbonyl group and shows why comparison of rotatory dispersion curves is permissible.   As demonstrated in Fig. 10-1, the two multiple Cotton effect curves are so similar that there is no question that the absolute configuration of the ketone is expressed correctly in stereoformula II.   If it had belonged to the enantiomeric series, the two dispersion curves would have been of mirror-image type.

In principle, this comparison approach to the solution of absolute configurational problems is identical to the generalized method of

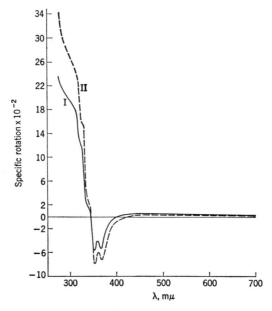

Fig. 10-1. RD curves (dioxane) of 19-nortestosterone (I) and 8,13-dimethyl-8-methoxycarbonyl-2-oxo-$\Delta^{1(11)}$-dodecahydrophenanthrene (II). [*Reproduced from C. Djerassi, R. Riniker, and B. Riniker, J. Am. Chem. Soc., 78, 6362 (1956), by permission of the editor.*]

(monochromatic) molecular rotation differences,[7] except that in the latter comparisons are carried out at only one wavelength (sodium D line), while the rotatory dispersion method involves comparisons at literally hundreds of points.   The reason that results from both methods usually agree is that the sign of the rotation at the D line is frequently a reflection [8] of the sign of the dispersion curve in the ultraviolet.   Discrepancies will be found only if the dispersion curve changes sign some-

[7] See W. Klyne, *J. Chem. Soc.*, **1952**, 2916; *ibid.*, **1953**, 3072.
[8] See W. Kuhn and H. Biller, *Z. physik. Chem. (Leipzig)*, **(B)29**, 1 (1935).

where between the visible and the ultraviolet (see Chap. 16). *It must be emphasized that if comparisons of rotatory dispersion curves are not applicable to a given case, then* ipso facto *there can be no rationale for using calculations of monochromatic molecular rotation differences as an alternative.*

One other general comment worth noting is that if comparisons of rotatory dispersion curves are employed with compounds showing marked Cotton effects, complete resolution is unnecessary provided the charac-

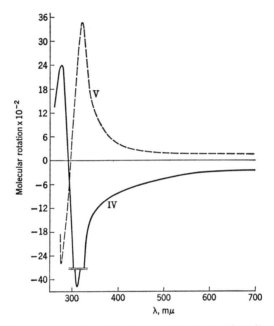

Fig. 10-2. RD curves of ketone IV (from cafestol) (methanol) and 4α-ethyl-cholestan-3-one (V) (dioxane).

teristic shape of the Cotton effect remains noticeable. With many ketones this means that only 10 to 20 per cent resolution may be sufficient. This aspect may become particularly important in examining the extent of racemization of α-amino acids by the use of derivatives outlined in Chap. 15.

A. Cafestol, Iresin, and Related Terpenes. The rotatory dispersion approach has been uniquely useful in recent problems in terpene chemistry, for which other methods have so far not been applicable. Four examples are presented.

Cafestol (III) is an important diterpene from coffee and its presently accepted structure was proposed in 1955.[9a]   In order to attack its absolute configuration,[9b] the substance was degraded to the ketone IV and its rotatory dispersion curve (Fig. 10-2) was compared with that of 4α-ethylcholestan-3-one (V). The antipodal nature of the curves shows that cafestol (III) belongs to the enantiomeric series (rings A and B being used as reference points) from the steroids, an unexpected and rare development in diterpene chemistry.

Similarly, degradation of the sesquiterpene iresin (VI) [10a] to the ketone VII and comparison [10b] of its Cotton effect curve (negative) with the positive one of the reference ketone 4α-methylandrostan-17β-ol-3-one acetate (VIII) led to the conclusion that this sesquiterpene also bears an antipodal relationship to the steroids.

As an alternate approach, which led to the same conclusion, the positive Cotton effect of the 3-ketone of dihydroiresin was compared [10c] with the negative Cotton effect (Fig. 6-1) of the reference ketone 4,4-dimethylcholestan-3-one.   The identical rotatory dispersion analysis with 4,4-disubstituted 3-ketones in the darutigenol [11a] and andrographolide [11b] series showed that these diterpenes also belong to the cafestol and iresin class in terms of absolute configuration.

[9] (a) H. Bendas and C. Djerassi, *Chem. & Ind.* (*London*), **1955**, 1481; (b) C. Djerassi, M. Cais, and L. A. Mitscher, *J. Am. Chem. Soc.*, **80**, 247 (1958); *ibid.*, **81**, 2386 (1959).

[10] (a) C. Djerassi, W. Rittel, A. L. Nussbaum, F. W. Donovan, and J. Herran, *J. Am. Chem. Soc.*, **76**, 6410 (1954); (b) C. Djerassi and S. Burstein, *J. Am. Chem. Soc.*, **80**, 2593 (1958); *Tetrahedron*, **7**, 37 (1959); (c) P. Crabbé, S. Burstein, and C. Djerassi, *Bull. soc. chim. Belges*, **67**, 632 (1958).

[11] (a) J. Pudles, A. Diara, and E. Lederer, *Bull. soc. chim. France*, **1959**, 693; (b) M. P. Cava and B. Weinstein, *Chem. & Ind.* (*London*), **1959**, 851.

B. Gibberellic Acid. The structure of this new plant-growth regulator was established in a series of important degradations [12] without, however, affording any information on the relative or absolute configuration of the molecule. Although some stereochemical speculations (regarding ring A) based on the presumed common biogenetic origin of cafestol (III) and gibberellic acid (IX) have been recorded,[9b] Stork [13] has presented decisive evidence with rotatory dispersion playing an important role.

Allogibberic acid (X), a product of the acid hydrolysis of gibberellic acid (IX), has been transformed [14] to the keto dimethyl ester XI, whose

relative stereochemistry, especially the B/C *trans* juncture, was proved by Stork.[13] Since it had been shown (Chaps. 4 and 5) that cholestan-3-one (XII), cholestan-2-one (XIII), and *trans*-8-methylhydrindan-5-one (XIV) all show a positive Cotton effect curve, this criterion can be used to decide upon the absolute configuration of the dimethyl ester XI.

The latter exhibited [15] a strongly positive Cotton effect and, since the nature of the angular substituent is not important, one is justified in stating that the substance must have the absolute configuration implicit in stereoformula XI. This conclusion is also supported if one applies the octant rule (Chap. 13) to this substance.

C. Bicyclic Microbiological Hydroxylation Products. The extensive microbiological hydroxylations performed in the steroid field during the

[12] B. E. Cross, J. F. Grove, J. MacMillan, T. P. C. Mulholland, and N. Sheppard, *Proc. Chem. Soc.*, **1958**, 221; B. E. Cross, J. F. Grove, J. MacMillan, J. S. Moffatt, T. P. C. Mulholland, J. C. Seaton, and N. Sheppard, *ibid.*, **1959**, 302.

[13] Lecture by G. Stork, VIIth Latinamerican Congress of Chemistry, Mexico City, April 2, 1959. G. Stork and H. Newman, *J. Am. Chem. Soc.*, **81**, 3168 (1959).

[14] T. P. C. Mulholland, *J. Chem. Soc.*, **1958**, 2693.

[15] Unpublished measurements by Mrs. A. James on a specimen provided by G. Stork of Columbia University.

past few years have stimulated similar studies among simpler bicyclic analogues. In the latter case, the starting material is racemic but the microbiological transformation product is resolved, and the problem of attributing an absolute configurational representation to it arises invariably. In the following section (10-2D) there will be given several examples from the decalin series, where rotatory dispersion was of substantial aid in solving this configurational problem.

An interesting illustration is provided by the fungal incubation of racemic 10-ethoxycarbonyl-$\Delta^{1(9)}$-2-octalone (XV), which led [16] to an

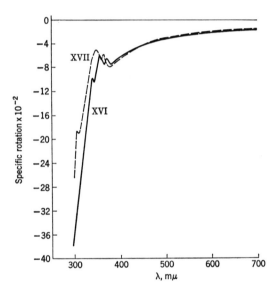

Fig. 10-3. RD curves (dioxane) of 10-ethoxycarbonyl-7-hydroxy-$\Delta^{1(9)}$-2-octalone (XVI) and 10-methyl-$\Delta^{1(9)}$-2-octalone (XVII).

optically active 7-hydroxy analogue whose absolute configuration could not be established with the evidence available. As shown in Fig. 10-3, its rotatory dispersion curve [17] is of the same type and sign as that of 10-methyl-$\Delta^{1(9)}$-2-octalone (XVII) of established absolute configuration,[18] whereupon it follows that the microbiological transformation product should be assigned the absolute configuration implicit in structure XVI. A similar conclusion can be reached by comparing the

[16] A. Schubert, A. Rieche, G. Hilgetag, R. Siebert, and S. Schwarz, *Naturwiss.,* **45,** 623 (1958).

[17] Unpublished measurements by Miss S. Boschma on a sample provided by A. Schubert (VEB Jenapharm, Jena, Germany).

[18] C. Djerassi and D. Marshall, *J. Am. Chem. Soc.,* **80,** 3986 (1958).

rotatory dispersion curve (Fig. 10-3) of 10-ethoxycarbonyl-7-hydroxy-$\Delta^{1(9)}$-2-octalone (XVI) with those (Fig. 5-7) of some 10-methyl-5-hydroxy-$\Delta^{1(9)}$-2-octalones. The newly introduced hydroxyl group is of sufficiently small bulk that it is very unlikely that its orientation (probably [16] axial) will affect the multiple Cotton effect curve to any marked extent, as was observed in the α-cyperone series (Sec. 5-3B).

XV   XVI   XVII

D. Maaliol and α-Cadinol. The synthesis [18] of cis-(XVIII) and trans-(XIX) 10-methyl-1-decalone of established absolute configuration provides two important reference ketones, whose rotatory dispersion curves (Fig. 10-4) can be used for several absolute configurational deductions.

The sesquiterpene maaliol (XX) has been transformed [19] into normaalione (XXI), which exhibited a rather strong positive Cotton effect. If the cyclopropane ring does not have a major effect, the coincidence of the positive Cotton effect of normaalione (XXI) with that

XVIII   XIX   XX   XXI

(Fig. 10-4) of trans-10-methyl-1-decalone (XIX) leads to the conclusion that these decalones possess the same absolute configuration and that maaliol should be represented by stereoformula XX.

The two models XVIII and XIX were of considerable help in settling the absolute configurations of a number of microbiological transformation products, such as trans-10-methyl-5-hydroxy-1-decalone (XXII)[20] (positive Cotton effect), cis-5-hydroxy-1-decalone (XXIII)[20] (negative Cotton effect), trans-5-hydroxy-1-decalone (XXIV)[20] (negative Cotton effect), and trans-4-hydroxy-1-decalone (XXV)[21] (negative Cotton effect).

The rotatory dispersion curves of these substituted decalones (XXII to XXV) and the two model compounds (XVIII and XIX) could then

[19] G. Büchi, M. S. Wittenau, and D. M. White, *J. Am. Chem. Soc.*, **81**, 1968 (1959).

[20] P. Baumann and V. Prelog, *Helv. Chim. Acta*, **41**, 2379 (1958).

[21] *Ibid.*, p. 2362.

be used in turn to establish the absolute configuration of $(-)$-α-cadinol (XXVI),[22] since this sesquiterpene had been transformed into *trans*-4-isopropyl-6-methyl-1-decalone (XXVII) (negative Cotton effect)

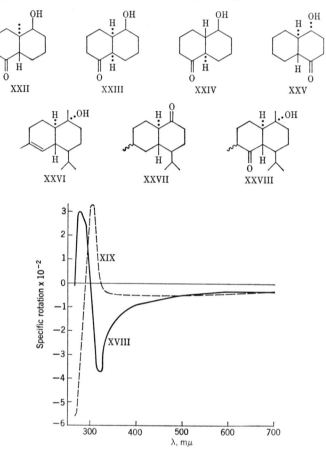

Fig. 10-4. RD curves (methanol) of *cis*-10-methyl-1-decalone (XVIII) and *trans*-10-methyl-1-decalone (XIX) (still contaminated by some cis isomer).

and *trans*-2,5-dimethyl-5-hydroxy-8-isopropyl-1-decalone (XXVIII) (positive Cotton effect).

E. Conclusion. This approach to the solution of absolute configurational problems has been used with a number of diverse substances;[23] in

[22] V. Sykora, V. Herout, and F. Sorm, *Collection Czech Chem. Commun.*, **23,** 2181 (1958); V. Herout and V. Sykora, *Tetrahedron*, **4,** 246 (1958).

[23] For additional examples see Ref. 4 and C. Djerassi, *Record Chem. Progr.*, **20,** 101 (1959).

some cases, rotatory dispersion simply confirmed conclusions already reached by consideration of monochromatic polarimetric data (e.g., longifolene [24]), while in others (e.g., guaianolide group of sesquiterpenes [25]) it afforded the only information currently available.

The method is not limited to cyclic ketones, as demonstrated with degradation products of actidione (Sec. 7-4) nor in fact to ketones (Chap. 15). Indeed even substances with plain dispersion curves (see Chap. 16) can at times be subjected to this type of analysis, where conclusions based on rotations at the sodium D line would not be applicable. Although the deductions often can be accepted as completely rigorous (e.g., Fig. 10-1), there are several cases in which absolute configurational assignments based on rotatory dispersion comparisons should only be considered tentative [e.g., maaliol (XX)] because of possible conformational complications. Nevertheless, the numerous applications in the literature during the past two years show that the use of rotatory dispersion curves is fulfilling a real need in this field and that it already represents an important adjunct to stereochemical methodology.

10-3.   The Axial Haloketone Rule and the Octant Rule

The rotatory dispersion comparison method depends always on a suitable model compound, but this is not the case in the following approach, which utilizes empirical rules for predicting the sign of the Cotton effect curve. Although these were based originally on models whose absolute configuration was established by an independent method, such reference compounds are not required for further applications of these rules and potentially their scope is much greater as far as assignments of absolute configurations are concerned.

The axial haloketone rule [26] (Sec. 9-2) can distinguish between antipodal representations. If, for instance, 2-bromocyclohexanone were resolved, it could be represented by either XXIX or XXX, since it is

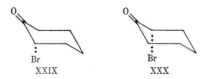

[24] G. Jacob, G. Ourisson, and A. Rassat, *Bull. soc. chim. France,* **1959,** 1374.

[25] C. Djerassi, J. Osiecki, and W. Herz, *J. Org. Chem.,* **22,** 1361 (1957); L. Dolejs, M. Soucek, M. Horak, V. Herout, and F. Sorm, *Collection Czech Chem. Commun.,* **23,** 2195 (1958).

[26] C. Djerassi and W. Klyne, *J. Am. Chem. Soc.,* **79,** 1506 (1957).

known [27] that the bromine atom exists predominantly in the axial orientation in a nonpolar solvent.   The axial haloketone rule predicts a positive Cotton effect curve for XXIX and a negative one for XXX. Therefore, all that is required to arrive at an assignment of absolute configuration is to measure the rotatory dispersion curve of the resolved antipode and compare the resulting curve with the predictions.   As was pointed out in Sec. 10-2, complete resolution is not necessary for the application of this approach.

It must be emphasized that to use this method, the structure and especially the location of the halogen atom must be known.   Its axial orientation must then be confirmed spectroscopically, if it does not follow already from the mode of synthesis; only then are the necessary conditions met for use of this rule.   It is apparent that only micro-quantities are required for these spectral and rotatory dispersion meas-urements.   Although this approach will be most useful in the area of ketones, olefins in which the double bond forms part of a six-membered ring should not be neglected.   These can be transformed into epoxides and thence by treatment with hydrogen halide to the diaxial halohydrin. Oxidation of the resulting alcohol group under suitable conditions will then provide an axial α-halo cyclohexanone, whose absolute configura-tion can be investigated by rotatory dispersion means.

The octant rule will be discussed in Chap. 13.   As will be shown there, it represents an extension of the axial haloketone rule, which per-mits the prediction of the sign of a Cotton effect curve for a wide variety of cyclohexanones without requiring an axial α-halogen sub-stituent.   Therefore, if the structure and conformation of the cyclo-hexanone is known, its absolute configuration follows in many instances from the sign of its anomalous rotatory dispersion curve.   Examples of this approach will be given in Chap. 13, but it is already obvious that further refinements of such empirical rules, especially if they also become applicable to aliphatic compounds and to derivatives of alcohols and amines of the type mentioned in Chap. 15, will represent an enormous advance in stereochemistry.

[27] J. Allinger and N. L. Allinger, *Tetrahedron*, **2**, 64 (1958); see also E. J. Corey, *J. Am. Chem. Soc.*, **75**, 2301 (1953).

11 | DETECTION AND IMPLICATION OF KETAL FORMATION

11-1. Introduction

A carbonyl chromophore absorbing near 300 mμ becomes transparent in this spectral region when it is converted into an alcohol, hemiketal (or hemiacetal), or ketal (or acetal). Recently [1] advantage has been taken of this fact to measure quantitatively the reaction of certain monocyclic ketones with methanol in the presence of acid. The kinetics were interpreted in terms of hemiketal rather than ketal formation; lowering of the ultraviolet extinction coefficient between 280 and 290 mμ was used as the relevant criterion.

Translated into rotatory dispersion terms, this would imply that conversion of a carbonyl compound (with an anomalous Cotton effect curve) into its ketal or acetal derivative should result in a plain dispersion curve. Experimental verification for this observation is provided by the plain dispersion curves [2] of various carbohydrates in which the carbonyl function is masked by acetal formation and the contrasting Cotton effect curves noted [3] with polyacetylated aldehydo sugars and fructose in which acetal or ketal formation is prevented.

Since steric factors among cyclic ketones appear to affect [1] greatly

[1] O. H. Wheeler, *J. Am. Chem. Soc.,* **79,** 4191 (1957); O. H. Wheeler and J. L. Mateos, *Anal. Chem.,* **29,** 538 (1957).

[2] T. L. Harris, E. L. Hirst, and C. E. Wood, *J. Chem. Soc.,* **1932,** 2108; R. W. Herbert, E. L. Hirst, and C. E. Wood, *ibid.,* **1934,** 1151.

[3] W. C. G. Baldwin, M. L. Wolfrom, and T. M. Lowry, *J. Chem. Soc.,* **1935,** 696.

the extent of (hemi)ketal [4] formation, it was of obvious interest to examine this phenomenon more closely by means of rotatory dispersion. Just as was noted in Chap. 8 with α-ketols, ultraviolet absorption measurements of saturated ketones are often unsatisfactory because of unsharp maxima and, most importantly, because of the low extinction coefficient, which precludes work with insoluble or rare compounds. None of these objections apply to dispersion studies with such substances.

The problem was attacked [5] by measuring the rotatory dispersion of the ketone in methanol solution, adding a drop of hydrochloric acid, and after a suitable time interval [6] repeating the rotatory dispersion determination.   By assuming that the (hemi)ketal will have a negligible rotation at the wavelength where the ketone exhibits a peak or trough, the diminution in the amplitude of this extremum can then be used as a semiquantitative index of (hemi)ketal formation.   More precise values can be derived by determining the rotatory dispersion curve of the corresponding alcohol and equating these rotation values to 100 per cent (hemi)ketal production.

11-2.   Effect of Solvent

Using (+)-3-methylcyclohexanone (I) as a test case, it was found that in methanol solution the amplitude of its positive Cotton effect curve (Fig. 7-1) was reduced by 93 per cent upon the addition of hydrochloric acid, indicating nearly complete conversion to the (hemi)-ketal (II).   In ethanol solution, hydrochloric acid caused a diminution of only 33 per cent, while no change was observed in isopropyl alcohol after addition of acid.

These results are in excellent agreement with those [1] based on ultraviolet spectroscopy, which also demonstrated that (hemi)ketal forma-

---

[4] Throughout this chapter the term "(hemi)ketal" will be used to emphasize that in most instances it was not established whether the ketal or hemiketal was formed. Wheeler's experiments [1] with cyclohexanone and related ketones seem to indicate hemiketal formation, but on the other hand dimethylketals have actually been isolated by us on occasion with certain ketones. For the purposes of this discussion, it is immaterial whether a ketal, hemiketal, or a mixture of both is produced, since all these compounds would be expected to show plain dispersion curves.

[5] C. Djerassi, L. A. Mitscher, and B. J. Mitscher, *J. Am. Chem. Soc.*, **81**, 947 (1959).

[6] This time interval is governed by two factors. The most significant one is that equilibrium should be reached between the ketone and (hemi)ketal forms; this can be determined by observing the change in rotation at one of the rotatory dispersion extrema until the value is constant. The second factor was a "blanking-out" phenomenon, which often did not permit measurements for a certain time. This has been found to be due largely to a refractive index gradient (see Sec. 3-3C).

tion was greatly dependent on the steric requirements of the alcohol. Consequently for routine use of the type outlined below, methanol is the only feasible solvent.

11-3.   Ring Size.   Effect of α-Alkyl Substituents

Addition reactions to the carbonyl group of cyclic ketones are greatly dependent upon ring size,[7] a six-membered ketone being considerably more reactive than its next higher or lower homologues.   This has now been confirmed by rotatory dispersion means, since the amplitudes of the Cotton effect curves of (+)-3-methylcyclopentanone (III) and of (−)-3-methylcycloheptanone (IV) were reduced by 24 and 21 per cent, respectively, as compared with 93 per cent for (+)-3-methylcyclohexanone (I).

Another factor that reduces (hemi)ketal formation is the presence of alkyl substituents, and numerous examples have been found [5] of this retarding effect.   A single example should suffice, such as the amplitude reduction of *trans*-2,5-dimethylcyclohexanone (V), which occurred only to the extent of 25 per cent as compared to 93 per cent for the ketone (I) lacking the α-methyl group.   Two α substituents [e.g., 2,2,5-trimethylcyclohexanone (VI)] completely inhibit any acid-catalyzed reaction with methanol.

A. Differential Recognition of Diketones.   In certain instances, the above information can be used to good advantage in gaining information about the nature of two carbonyl groups in a diketone, providing the steric environments of the two ketones are nonequivalent.

Androstane-3,17-dione (VII) is an excellent example since there exists essentially no interaction between the two ketone groups (see Sec. 4-4B).   Its molecular rotatory dispersion curve represents [5] almost

[7] See, for example, H. C. Brown, *J. Chem. Soc.,* **1956,** 1248.

exactly the sum of the individual contributions of androstan-17-one (VIII) and androstan-3-one (IX). Furthermore, these two keto groups differ greatly in reactivity; androstan-3-one (IX) forms over 80 per cent of (hemi)ketal (X), as demonstrated in Fig. 11-1. The 17-ketone, on the other hand, in androstan-17-one (VIII) is completely

unreactive, since it not only forms part of a cyclopentanone ring, already shown (cf. III) to exhibit greatly reduced reactivity, but in addition is completely substituted on one side. As a consequence, it is possible to demonstrate the presence and calculate rather precisely the rotatory dispersion amplitude of two separate carbonyl groups by this rather simple device.

Experimentally,[5] androstane-3,17-dione (VII) exhibits a specific rotation of $+4000°$ at the peak (312.5 mμ), and this is reduced to $+2625°$ in the presence of hydrochloric acid. This reduction should be due exclusively to removal of the rotatory contribution of the 3-keto group—now present largely as the (hemi)ketal (X)—and this is indeed the case, since the observed rotation of androstan-17-one (VIII) at 312.5 mμ is $+2695°$.

11-4.   Effect and Recognition of New 1,3-Diaxial Interactions

The sensitivity of (hemi)ketal formation to steric effects is demonstrated very strikingly when the effect of hydrochloric acid upon the rotatory dispersion curves in methanol solution of a 3-keto steroid versus a 2-ketone is being considered. In the former [e.g., androstan-3-one (IX)], no major new steric interactions are set up in the derived (hemi)-ketal (X), and the equilibrium lies largely on the side of the latter (see Fig. 11-1). On the other hand, in a 2-keto steroid such as androstan-17β-ol-2-one propionate (XI), the corresponding (hemi)ketal (XII)

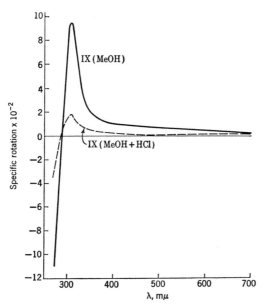

Fig. 11-1. RD curve of androstan-3-one (IX) in methanol and in methanol–hydrochloric acid.

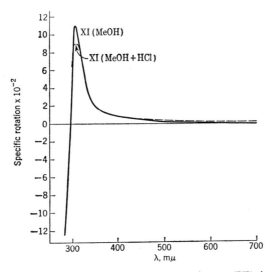

Fig. 11-2. RD curve of androstan-17β-ol-2-one propionate (XI) in methanol and in methanol–hydrochloric acid.

now possesses a new 1,3-diaxial interaction between the oxygenated substituent at C-2 and the angular methyl group at C-10. It is not surprising, therefore, that the equilibrium in the presence of acid remains almost entirely on the side of the ketone (XI). This is illustrated in Fig. 11-2, where it is seen that the amplitude of the Cotton effect curve of the ketone is hardly changed. Identical observations were made [5] with analogous decalone derivatives.

11-5. Application to Structural and Stereochemical Problems

A. Differentiation of 2- and 3-Keto-5α Steroids. It has already been stated in Sec. 4-2A that a secure differentiation between a 2-keto (e.g., XI) and a 3-keto (e.g., IX) steroid of the 5α series (rings A/B *trans*-fused) is not possible by inspection of the rotatory dispersion curve, since both structural types present positive Cotton effect curves. As noted in the preceding paragraph, the problem can now be solved very simply by conducting the rotatory dispersion measurement in methanol solution—first without and then with hydrochloric acid—and noting whether a considerable reduction in amplitude is observed.

B. Lophenol. The presence of adjacent alkyl groups was also shown [5] to have a strong inhibitory effect upon (hemi)ketal formation and advantage was taken of this observation in the structure elucidation [8] of lophenol (XIII), a novel type of biogenetically important plant sterol. Reduction of its double bond and oxidation provided lophanone (XIV), whose rotatory dispersion curve was very similar to that of cholestan-3-one (XV), except that there was noted only a slight reduc-

[8] C. Djerassi, G. W. Krakower, A. J. Lemin, L. H. Liu, J. S. Mills, and R. Villotti, *J. Am. Chem. Soc.*, **80**, 6284 (1958).

tion in amplitude upon the addition of hydrochloric acid, in contrast to the marked one (64 per cent) suffered by cholestan-3-one (XV). This behavior, coupled with other observations, strongly suggested the presence of a methyl group adjacent to the oxygen function, and this helped greatly in the identification of lophanone (XIV) as 4α-methyl-cholestan-3-one.

C. Determination of the Stereochemistry of a Methyl Group. In connection with synthetic work [9] in the eremophilone series, it was essential to demonstrate the stereochemistry at C-4 of *trans*-4,10-dimethyl-2-decalone (XVII) produced in the hydrogenation of the hexalone XVI. This was accomplished by noting that the rotatory dispersion curve of the ketone XVII in methanol solution underwent a marked reduction in

amplitude upon addition of hydrochloric acid, which would only be compatible with an equatorial orientation of the methyl group. The axial isomer would almost certainly have inhibited the formation of the (hemi)ketal.

11-6. Conclusion and Experimental Recommendation

The above examples show some of the areas in which a study of (hemi)ketal formation may be of utility, and further illustrations have been collected elsewhere.[5,10]

In view of the experimental ease with which these measurements can be performed, it is recommended that any rotatory dispersion measurement of a saturated ketone [11] be first performed in methanol and that the curve be repeated in the presence of hydrochloric acid, since such differential treatment is often of considerable structural or stereochemical diagnostic value. Determinations conducted with proper care can also be of utility for kinetic investigations of the rate of (hemi)ketal production.

[9] L. H. Zalkow, F. X. Markley, and C. Djerassi, *J. Am. Chem. Soc.*, **81**, 2914 (1959).

[10] C. Djerassi, *Record Chem. Progr.*, **20**, 101 (1959).

[11] This will be limited largely to saturated ketones, since the few α,β-unsaturated ketones that have been examined [5] did not react. Furthermore, the rotatory dispersion curves of such unsaturated ketones are routinely obtained in a nonpolar solvent (see Chap. 3) and thus do not lend themselves to this type of study unless a methanolic solution is examined separately.

12 | THEORY AND ANALYSIS OF ROTATORY DISPERSION CURVES *

12-1. Introduction

A modern organic chemistry laboratory invariably contains a variety of colored boxes that bear such labels as Ultraviolet Spectrometer, Nuclear Magnetic Resonance Spectrometer, and the like. These machines are there because organic chemists have come to appreciate the value of light, electromagnetic radiation, as a molecular probe, and these same chemists have learned how to translate the multishaped curves produced by these machines into useful chemical information.

During the past few years, a polarimeter that covers the visible and near ultraviolet regions of the spectrum has become commercially available. This means another species of curve that requires interpretation from the organic chemical point of view, and it is toward this end that this chapter is written. Our viewpoint here will be quite narrow. We shall be interested mainly in what new information is contained in a rotatory dispersion curve that is unavailable elsewhere, and how this information may be most conveniently extracted and economically catalogued. Although much of what we say will be applicable to optical activity in general, we shall deal specifically with the polarimetry of molecules of relatively low molecular weight in homogeneous, isotropic liquids. The unique effects attributable to aggregation into larger forms, such as helical proteins,[1] or to the orientation produced by external fields [2] will not be our concern here.

* The entire chapter is a contribution by Albert Moscowitz.
[1] See Chap. 17.
[2] See, for example, I. Tinoco and W. G. Hammerle, *J. Phys. Chem.,* **60,** 1619 (1956); I. Tinoco, *J. Chem. Phys.,* **26,** 1356 (1957); I. Tinoco, *J. Am. Chem. Soc.,* **81,** 1540 (1959).

12-2. Macroscopic Considerations

A. Circular Birefringence. Any beam of light has associated with
it time-dependent electric and magnetic fields. It is the interaction of
these fields with material media that gives rise to the many phenomena
that are included in the word "spectroscopy." If the light beam be
monochromatic and *linearly polarized,* the associated electric field will
oscillate sinusoidally in time with a definite frequency v along a single
direction in space. This behavior of the electric field as a function of
the time *t* may be represented by the vector **E,** as shown in Fig. 12-1.
Here we have taken the *x* axis as the direction of vibration.

If the wave be traveling in the *z* direction, the *xz* plane is said to be
the *plane of vibration,* and such a wave is also said to be *plane-polarized.*

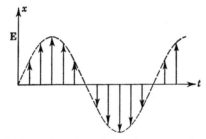

Fig. 12-1.   Electric field as a function of time in a monochromatic linearly polarized wave.

To an observer standing on the *z* axis and looking in the negative *z*
direction, **E** might appear as in Fig. 12-2 during the course of one cycle
of the oscillation.

It will be noted from Fig. 12-3 that each of the vectors **E** in Fig. 12-2
may be thought of as the resultant of two vectors of equal length, call
them $\mathbf{E}_L$ and $\mathbf{E}_R$. If $\mathbf{E}_R$ rotates clockwise and $\mathbf{E}_L$ rotates counterclock-
wise with frequency v such that both vectors make equal angles with
the *x* axis, their resultant **E** will perform the requisite harmonic motion
for a plane-polarized wave whose electric field oscillates along the *x*
direction.

Actually, the behavior we have described for $\mathbf{E}_R$ is the same as that
of the electric field for a so-called *right circularly polarized* wave of
frequency v. Similarly, $\mathbf{E}_L$ represents the electric field of a *left circularly polarized* wave. Therefore, one may look upon a plane-polarized
wave as a superposition of a right and a left circularly polarized wave
of the same frequency. Such a viewpoint is not just a convenient fic-
tion, for experimentally one can break down a plane-polarized wave into

its circularly polarized components or, conversely, superpose these components to form a plane-polarized wave.

In drawing Fig. 12-3 we always required that $\mathbf{E}_R$ and $\mathbf{E}_L$ make equal angles with the x axis. If this were not the case, then, although the

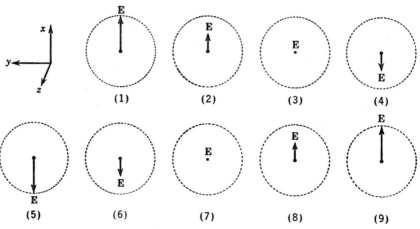

Fig. 12-2. Variation of the electric field vector **E** with time as seen by an observer standing at a fixed point on the z axis and looking in the negative z direction.

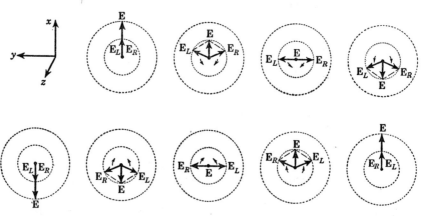

Fig. 12-3. The electric field vector **E** as the resultant of two rotating vectors, $\mathbf{E}_L$ and $\mathbf{E}_R$.

resultant wave would still be plane-polarized, its electric vector and hence its plane of polarization would be rotated through some angle α', as shown in Fig. 12-4. Such a circumstance would arise if the waves associated with $\mathbf{E}_R$ and $\mathbf{E}_L$ were traveling with different speeds, and the effect of an optically active medium is to bring about just such a situation. Since the speed of a light wave in a material medium is conveniently gauged by its index of refraction n, we may say that as far as optical rotation is concerned the essential property of an optically active medium is that it has different indices of refraction n_L and n_R for left and right circularly polarized light, respectively, i.e., that the medium is "circularly birefringent." A quantitative treatment shows that the angle of rotation per unit length α is given by

$$\alpha = \frac{\pi}{\lambda} (n_L - n_R)$$

where λ is the vacuum wavelength of the light beam.

If the cgs system of units be used, α has the dimensions of radians per centimeter. It must be multiplied by $1800/\pi$ to have the more common

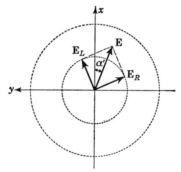

Fig. 12-4. Rotation of $\mathbf{E}$ when $\mathbf{E}_L$ and $\mathbf{E}_R$ make unequal angles with the x axis.

experimental units of degrees per decimeter. For solution work, two other common experimental quantities are the specific rotation $[\alpha]$ and the molecular rotation $[\phi]$, defined below.

$$[\alpha] = \frac{\alpha}{C'} \frac{1800}{\pi}$$

$$[\phi] = [\alpha] \frac{M}{100} = \alpha \frac{18}{\pi} \frac{M}{C'}$$

where C' is the concentration in grams per cubic centimeter of optically active material and M is its molecular weight. The molecular rotation is the most suitable of the experimental quantities just enumerated when one is comparing rotations in different compounds, for comparisons will then be made on a mole for mole basis.

By way of orders of magnitude, we note that for $\alpha = 10$ deg per cm and $\lambda = 550$ mμ, $n_L - n_R \approx 3 \times 10^{-6}$. Ordinary indices of refraction are of the order of unity. Hence the difference between n_L and n_R is only about a millionth of their absolute values. They are really very nearly equal to each other and to the mean index of refraction n of the medium, which is taken to be $(n_L + n_R)/2$.

B. Circular Dichroism. Until now nothing has been said about absorption. But in any real material medium the intensity of a plane-polarized light wave will decay with distance. For the purposes of

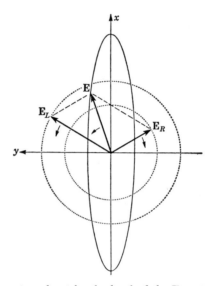

Fig. 12-5. Ellipse traced out by the head of the **E** vector when $\mathbf{E}_L \neq \mathbf{E}_R$.

ordinary absorption spectroscopy, this reduction in intensity can be adequately represented by the equation

$$I = I_0 e^{-kl}$$

Here I_0 is the initial intensity of the wave and I is its intensity after it has traveled l centimeters in the medium whose mean absorption coefficient is k. (The absorption coefficient k is related to the more common molecular extinction coefficient ε by the equation $k \approx 2.303\varepsilon C$, where C is the concentration of absorbing material in moles per liter.)

As might be anticipated, not only do the two circularly polarized components of a plane-polarized wave travel with different speeds in an optically active medium, but they are also absorbed to different extents. Under such circumstances, $\mathbf{E}_L$ is not equal to $\mathbf{E}_R$ as we assumed in Sec. 12-2A, and their resultant **E** no longer oscillates along a single line. Rather the head of the **E** vector now traces out an ellipse, as indicated in Fig. 12-5.   The resulting light wave is said to be *elliptically polarized* and the medium is said to exhibit "circular dichroism."   The *ellipticity* of the wave is defined to be the angle whose tangent is the ratio of the minor to the major axis of the ellipse.

Just as $n_L - n_R$ is small in magnitude compared to the mean index of refraction $n = (n_L + n_R)/2$, so the difference $k_L - k_R$ between the absorption coefficients for left and right circularly polarized light represents only a small fraction (rarely more than a few hundredths) of the magnitude of the mean absorption coefficient $k = (k_L + k_R)/2$.   Hence, in practice, the ellipse is always extremely elongate, and under such circumstances it may be shown that the ellipticity per unit length θ is given by

$$\theta = 1/4(k_L - k_R)$$

Again, for comparison purposes, the most convenient measure is a molar quantity, the molecular ellipticity $[\theta]$, which is given by

$$[\theta] = \theta \frac{18}{\pi} \frac{M}{C'}$$

This may be expressed in terms of the molecular extinction coefficients as

$$[\theta] \approx 2.303 \left(\frac{4500}{\pi} \right) (\varepsilon_L - \varepsilon_R)$$

It should be kept in mind that any medium that exhibits circular birefringence will also show circular dichroism, and both effects occur simultaneously.   Strictly speaking then, one should really refer to the rotation of the major axis of the ellipse rather than of a plane of polarization.   However, as mentioned above, the ellipticities encountered in practice are small, and so, as we shall see, the distinction becomes meaningful only in the immediate vicinity of an absorption band.

12-3.   Microscopic Considerations

A. Partial Quantities.   As noted previously, the origin of the observable macroscopic effects that one encounters in spectroscopy and polarimetry must ultimately be traced back to the interaction of the oscillating fields of the light wave with individual molecules.   It is not too surprising then that these effects, and hence the constants such as n, k, α, and θ which gauge them, will depend upon the frequency of the light wave used in performing the experiment.   For in every molecule there are certain natural frequencies (or groups of such frequencies) which are associated with the spacing of the energy levels of the molecule in accord with the Planck statement $\Delta E = h\nu$, and it is to be expected that the interaction between the wave and the molecule will become more pronounced as the frequency of the wave approaches one of these natural frequencies of the molecule. This is perhaps most apparent in the case of ordinary absorption, where an electron is promoted from a lower to a higher energy level when the frequency ν of the light wave satisfies the Planck condition. But for the other phenomena too, we may anticipate that their associated constants such as n, α, and θ will be frequency-dependent, and that the curves of these constants as a function of frequency (or, equally well, wavelength) will exhibit their most strik-

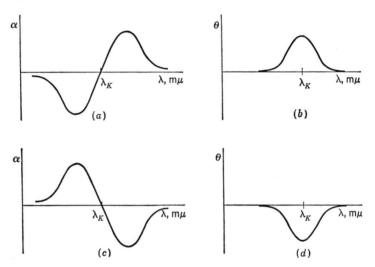

Fig. 12-6. Behavior of α and θ in the immediate vicinity of an isolated absorption band (idealized): (a) and (b) positive Cotton effect, (c) and (d) negative Cotton effect.

ing characteristics in the vicinity of wavelengths corresponding to electronic absorption bands. For the cases of circular birefringence and circular dichroism this is shown in a rather idealized fashion in Fig. 12-6, where we have assumed an isolated absorption band at approximately λ_K.

Of course a contribution of the type depicted in Fig. 12-6 will come from the vicinity of every natural frequency, i.e., from the region of every absorption band in the molecule, and the experimental curves will reflect the cumulative effect of all such individual contributions. One therefore speaks of, say, the observed molecular rotation $[\phi]$ as composed of a sum of "partial molecular rotations" $[\phi_K]$, where $[\phi_K]$ is the contribution of the Kth electronic transition to the molecular rotation, and similarly for the other experimental quantities.   We show this in Fig. 12-7, where the observed $[\phi]$ and $[\theta]$ are superpositions of three partial molecular rotations or three partial molecular ellipticities, respectively.

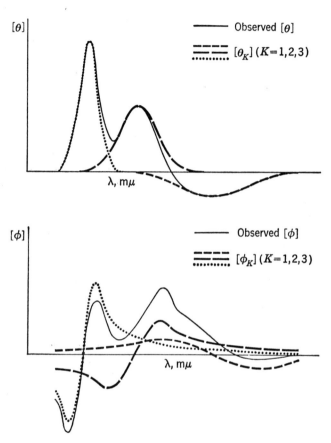

Fig. 12-7.   (*Top.*) $[\theta]$ as the superposition of three partial molecular ellipticities. (*Bottom.*) $[\phi]$ as the superposition of three partial molecular rotations.

B. The Kronig-Kramers Theorem.   The curve shown in Fig. 12-6*a* might also serve to illustrate in a rough way the behavior pattern of the contribution to the index of refraction associated with an isolated electronic absorption band.   The observed index of refraction would be the sum of all such curves plus unity (since the index of refraction is unity in vacuum).   Also because of the form of the "partial refractive indices," ordinary (as opposed to rotatory—we shall always use the word in this sense) dispersion also exhibits "anomalous" behavior in the vicinity of an electronic transition.   Likewise, Fig. 12-6b suggests the form of the contribution of a single electronic transition to the absorption coefficient, and the observed absorption coefficient would be the sum of such bands.   Similarities such as these are representative of the many analogies that can be drawn between the two sets of phenomena of ordinary dispersion and absorption, and rotatory dispersion and circular dichroism.   Since the former are perhaps more familiar to the organic chemist than their rotatory counterparts, we shall use these analogies to extend our discussion further.

Large contributions to ordinary dispersion are always associated with strongly allowed electronic transitions, i.e., with intense absorption bands.   The explanation for this may be sought on the molecular level. The electric field of a light beam traversing a material medium will exert a force on the charged particles that comprise the molecule, and, at optical frequencies, most importantly on the electrons.   From the classical point of view, the presence of these forces will bring about a redistribution of the electronic charge in the molecules, and these new arrangements of charge will correspond to configurations of higher energy.   However, since the fields of a light wave are periodic in time, much of the energy that is taken from the beam in one part of the cycle in order to produce the charge displacements will be returned to the beam in another part of the cycle when the electrons revert to their original and energetically lower distributions.   Speaking quantally, the effect of the light wave is to alter the electronic description of the molecule so that it has some of the characteristics of energetically higher (excited) electronic states that correspond to energetically higher charge distributions.   Again, since the fields of the wave are periodic in time, so is the resultant electron distribution, and a good deal of the energy required to achieve the higher energy states is periodically returned to the light beam.   (This is especially true in transparent regions of the spectrum where an electron will spend so little time in any particular one of the excited states necessary for its description that there is little chance for loss of the excitation energy through dissipative processes of a nonradiative character.)   The effect of this give-and-take process of light energy is to produce a change in the speed of the beam and therefore leads to an index of refraction different from unity.   But this is not the only effect that transpires.   At wavelengths where the Planck condition can be satisfied, a particular one of the excited states will become dominant for the electronic description of the molecule.   Then there is a strong probability that an electron will be raised to the corresponding excited level for a period of time sufficiently long for the promotional energy to find its way into dissipative processes. Hence the over-all intensity of the beam is reduced, and a permanent absorption of light energy takes place which manifests itself by the presence of an absorption band in the spectrum.

As we have already stated, it is reasonable that this type of interaction between radiation and matter should be most marked when the wavelength of the light corresponds to one of the natural frequencies, or, equivalently, energy spacings in the molecule. Moreover, since both the dispersive and absorptive effects take their origin in the same charge displacements and electronic promotions, one might suspect some quantitative connection between them. And such a connection does in fact exist.

Kronig [3] and Kramers [4] have shown that from a knowledge of the absorption as a function of wavelength over the entire spectral range $(\lambda = 0 \rightarrow \lambda = \infty)$ one may predict the corresponding dispersion curve, and, conversely, that the form of the dispersion over the entire region of the spectrum completely determines the shape of the absorption curve. The result is known as the Kronig-Kramers theorem, and the equations that express the result quantitatively are known as the Kronig-Kramers relationships.[5] They are valid not only for the total observed absorption and dispersion but also for the partial absorptions and dispersions associated with any particular electronic transition.

The Kronig-Kramers theorem requires no special model for its derivation, but rests only on the easily acceptable physical assumption that the charge displacements cannot take place before the arrival of the field that produces these displacements, and the supposition that the molecule acts as a linear system, i.e., if cause A induces effect a and cause B induces effect b, the simultaneous application of $A + B$ induces the effect $a + b$. Because of the extreme generality of these assumptions, relations of the Kronig-Kramers type will apply to a wide variety of physical systems and phenomena,[5] and, as we shall see, such a set of reciprocal relationships connects rotatory dispersion with circular dichroism.

The qualitative picture of absorption and dispersion given a few paragraphs ago does not depend upon the particular type of polarization of the light, although the quantitative aspects of the description can vary from one type of polarization to another. In a polarimetry experiment one in effect subjects the molecules simultaneously to left and right circularly polarized waves. If the molecules act as linear systems, the

[3] R. de L. Kronig, *J. Opt. Soc. Am.,* **12,** 547 (1926).

[4] H. A. Kramers, *Atti congr. intern. fisici, Como,* **2,** 545 (1927).

[5] For a review with extensive references see J. R. Macdonald and M. K. Brachman, *Rev. Mod. Phys.,* **28,** 393 (1956).

effects produced by these waves should be simply additive. Further, if the dispersions and absorptions associated with each of the circularly polarized components satisfy a Kronig-Kramers type of relationship, it is not unreasonable to expect that rotatory dispersion and circular dichroism, which arise as cumulative effects of these dispersions and absorptions, will also satisfy a similar set of reciprocal relationships. This is indeed the case, and the relations may be written in the following somewhat simplified form.[6]

$$[\phi_K(\lambda)] = \frac{2}{\pi} \int_0^\infty [\theta_K(\lambda')] \frac{\lambda'}{\lambda^2 - \lambda'^2} d\lambda' \tag{1}$$

$$[\theta_K(\lambda)] = -\frac{2}{\pi\lambda} \int_0^\infty [\phi_K(\lambda')] \frac{\lambda'^2}{\lambda^2 - \lambda'^2} d\lambda' \tag{2}$$

Although the derivation of these equations does not depend upon any detailed suppositions about molecular structure, as written they do presuppose that optical activity follows some sort of Beer's law, i.e., that the molecular quantities involved are independent of concentration. Moreover, in a more rigorous form they require some factor that takes cognizance of the fact that the average electromagnetic field seen by an individual molecule is not quite the same as the field associated with the impinging light wave because of polarizations induced in the solvent medium by the light wave itself. This factor is difficult to evaluate precisely at present. However, the over-all effect of its inclusion on our subsequent considerations would be small, and for our purposes we shall find the reciprocal relations in forms (1) and (2) adequate. Before we can make use of them, however, further discussion is necessary.

12-4. Some Useful Parameters

A good part of the story of the electronic structure of molecules is contained in the variation of the molecular extinction coefficient ε with wavelength in the regions of the visible and the ultraviolet; ε, of course, contains contributions from all the possible electronic promotions, i.e.,

$$\varepsilon = \sum_K \varepsilon_K$$

where ε_K is the partial molecular extinction coefficient for the Kth electronic transition. However, the individual ε_K's are very often sharply peaked functions of the wavelength and fall away to zero fairly rapidly on either side of their maxima. Hence, they may be separated out

[6] W. Moffitt and A. Moscowitz, *J. Chem. Phys.*, **30**, 648 (1959). Equations (1) and (2) are modified forms of Eqs. (57) and (59) of the reference cited.

from one another when their overlapping is not too great, as is shown in Fig. 12-8.   Attention may then be focused on the characteristics of the individual bands.

For some time now chemists and physicists have put to good advantage the information contained in the gross aspects of individual electronic absorption bands.   This fact is well known and needs no particular elaboration here.   Suffice it to recall that parameters, like the maximum value of the extinction coefficient ε_K° and the wavelength λ_K at which it occurs, together with a measure of the half-width Δ_K of the band, characterize an electronic transition sufficiently well to be of value in the solution of structural and analytical problems.   These parameters are indicated in Fig. 12-9, where Δ_K is taken to be the wavelength interval in which ε_K falls to $1/e \approx 0.368$ of its maximum value,

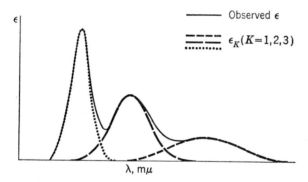

Fig. 12-8.   Resolution of ε into three partial molecular extinction coefficients.

as is often convenient in the case of a band Gaussian in shape (see Sec. 12-5).

The spectroscopist often uses a slightly different but roughly equivalent set of three parameters for his purposes.   In addition to λ_K and Δ_K, he requires some measure of the total area under the band, since this quantity is related to the total intensity of the transition, which can also be calculated from purely theoretical considerations.   Comparisons between theory and experiment may then be used to elucidate much of the electronic structure of complex molecules that is reflected in their absorption bands.   In fact, it was on just such a basis that the orbitals involved in the 290-mμ transition of saturated ketones, which figures so prominently in this book, were characterized.[7,8]

[7] H. L. McMurry and R. S. Mulliken, *Proc. Natl. Acad. Sci. U.S.*, **26**, 312 (1940).

[8] H. L. McMurry, *J. Chem. Phys.*, **9**, 231 (1941).

Mulliken,[9] in particular, has exploited this technique, and he has used for his purposes the *dipole strength* D_K. Experimentally, the dipole strength D_K for the Kth transition may be defined as

$$D_K = \frac{3hc}{8\pi^3 N_1} \int_0^\infty \frac{k_K(\lambda)}{\lambda} \, d\lambda \tag{3}$$

where N_1 is the number of absorbing molecules per cubic centimeter, c is the velocity of light *in vacuo*, and $k_K(\lambda)$ is the partial absorption coefficient for the Kth transition. (The definition of D_K given here differs from Mulliken's by a factor equal to the square of the electronic charge.) In terms of the partial molecular extinction coefficient, D_K may be expressed as

$$D_K \approx 0.92 \times 10^{-38} \int_0^\infty \frac{\varepsilon_K(\lambda)}{\lambda} \, d\lambda \tag{4}$$

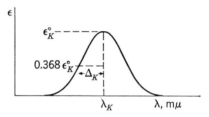

Fig. 12-9. Parameters often useful for cataloguing an absorption band.

For the special case of a Gaussian band, i.e., $\varepsilon_K = \varepsilon_K^\circ e^{-(\lambda - \lambda_K)^2/\Delta_K^2}$, the application of Eq. (4) yields

$$D_K \approx 0.92 \times 10^{-38} \int_0^\infty \frac{\varepsilon_K^\circ e^{-(\lambda - \lambda_K)^2/\Delta_K^2}}{\lambda} \, d\lambda$$

$$\approx \frac{0.92 \times 10^{-38}}{\lambda_K} \sqrt{\pi} \, \varepsilon_K^\circ \Delta_K$$

The reader will note that since $\varepsilon_K^\circ \Delta_K$ is proportional to D_K, the sets of parameters λ_K, Δ_k, and ε_K°, and λ_K, Δ_K, and D_K convey much the same information in the present instance. This statement will also be roughly true for any peaked and fairly symmetrical band that can be approximated by a Gaussian curve or some simple modification thereof. For the purpose of analogy with rotatory phenomena, we shall find the set λ_K, Δ_K, and D_K more convenient.

It might be pointed out here that in the work just described, the vibrational fine structure can often be ignored and the observed absorp-

[9] R. S. Mulliken, *J. Chem. Phys.,* **7,** 14 (1939), and subsequent papers.

tion band replaced by a suitably smoothed-out curve, as shown in Fig. 12-10.   Indeed, the experimental spectrum, especially in solution, more often than not presents itself as a continuum on which are superimposed only a few vibrational profiles.   Some information is, of course, thrown away in the smoothing-out process, but since it is concerned primarily with the force constants of the vibrational sublevels, its loss need not concern us here.

As was pointed out previously, the total observed molecular ellipticity $[\theta]$, like ε, receives contributions that can be associated with each of the possible electronic transitions in the molecule, i.e.,

$$[\theta] = \sum_K [\theta_K]$$

where $[\theta_K]$ is the partial molecular ellipticity for the Kth transition. Subject to the same conditions that were mentioned for ε, $[\theta]$ may also

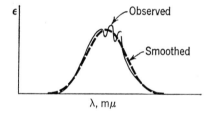

Fig. 12-10.   Approximating an actual absorption band by means of a smoothed-out curve.

be resolved into its partial molecular ellipticities, and each of these in turn characterized by a set of three parameters quite analogous to those used for cataloguing the ε_K.   These parameters will describe a dichroism band to the same degree that λ_K, Δ_K, and D_K do an absorption band.   They are λ_K°, the wavelength corresponding to the maximum ellipticity; Δ_K°, the half-width of the dichroism band; and R_K, the *rotational strength* [10] of the Kth transition, which, analogous to D_K in Eq. (3), is given by [6]

$$R_K = \frac{3hc}{8\pi^3 N_1} \int_0^\infty \frac{\theta_K(\lambda)}{\lambda} \, d\lambda$$

where θ_K is the partial ellipticity for the Kth transition.   However, unlike D_K, which is always positive, R_K may be either positive or negative, and its sign determines the sign of the Cotton effect.   In Fig. 12-11 we indicate in an idealized fashion the resolution of three overlapping di-

[10] See, for example, E. U. Condon, *Rev. Mod. Phys.*, **9**, 432 (1937), especially sec. 3.

chroism bands, one of which has a negative R_K and two of which have positive R_K values. The ordinate there is the molecular ellipticity; in terms of the partial molecular ellipticity, R_K may be expressed as

$$R_K \approx 0.696 \times 10^{-42} \int_0^\infty \frac{[\theta_K(\lambda)]}{\lambda} \, d\lambda \qquad (5)$$

The values of the diagnostic parameters λ_K° and Δ_K° will not, in general, coincide exactly with the values of their analogues for the same transition, λ_K and Δ_K. Still, from the gross point of view, they provide little in the way of readily utilizable information that is not already inherent in the parameters belonging to the corresponding absorption band. However, the "intensity" of the dichroism, as measured by the

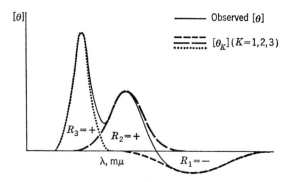

Fig. 12-11.   Resolution of $[\theta]$ into three partial molecular ellipticities.

integration of the partial ellipticity curve according to Eq. (5), does represent new information that can be quite useful when interpreted in terms of the theoretical rotational strength. This viewpoint will be amplified in Sec. 12-6. However, our remarks will be more meaningful if we first examine the part that rotational strength plays in rotatory dispersion.

12-5.   Rotational Strength and Rotatory Dispersion.   Application of the Reciprocal Relations

The importance of the rotational strength for the purely phenomenological aspects of rotatory dispersion is perhaps best illustrated by way of reference to a specific example. Let us suppose that the partial dichroism curve associated with the Kth transition be Gaussian in form, i.e.,

$$[\theta_K] = [\theta_K^\circ]e^{-(\lambda - \lambda_K^\circ)^2/(\Delta_K^\circ)^2}$$

where $[\theta_K^\circ]$ is a constant and equal to the maximum value of $[\theta_K]$. Then by means of the reciprocal relationship given in Eq. (1) we see that

$$[\phi_K(\lambda)] = \frac{2[\theta_K^\circ]}{\pi} \int_0^\infty e^{-(\lambda' - \lambda_K^\circ)^2/(\Delta_K^\circ)^2} \frac{\lambda'}{\lambda^2 - \lambda'^2} \, d\lambda' \qquad (6)$$

When $\lambda_K^\circ \gg \Delta_K^\circ$, as is commonly the case in practice (e.g., in saturated ketones $\lambda_K^\circ \sim 300$ mµ, $\Delta_K^\circ \sim 20$ mµ), the integral in Eq. (2) can be evaluated, and to a very excellent approximation it is found that

$$[\phi_K(\lambda)] = \frac{2[\theta_K^\circ]}{\sqrt{\pi}} \left[e^{-(\lambda - \lambda_K^\circ)^2/(\Delta_K^\circ)^2} \int_0^{(\lambda - \lambda_K^\circ)/\Delta_K^\circ} e^{x^2} \, dx - \frac{\Delta_K^\circ}{2(\lambda + \lambda_K^\circ)} \right] \quad (7)$$

The first term in the brackets in (7) is plotted in Fig. 12-12 with $(\lambda - \lambda_K^\circ)/\Delta_K^\circ$ as the abscissa. It is this function which gives $[\phi_K]$ its

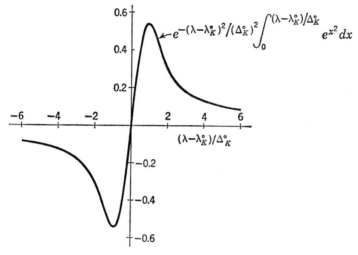

Fig. 12-12. $e^{-(\lambda - \lambda_K^\circ)^2/(\Delta_K^\circ)^2} \int_0^{(\lambda - \lambda_K^\circ)/\Delta_K^\circ} e^{x^2} \, dx$ as a function of $(\lambda - \lambda_K^\circ)/\Delta_K^\circ$.

characteristic shape in the vicinity of the band center at λ_K°, for the second term in the brackets is comparatively small and slowly varying in this region. Actual numbers might be of some aid here, and the functions in brackets are plotted in Fig. 12-13 for the typical saturated-ketone values mentioned above, namely, $\lambda_K^\circ = 300$ mµ, $\Delta_K^\circ = 20$ mµ.

The rotational strength for the Gaussian curve may be calculated from Eq. (5) as

$$R_K \approx 0.696 \times 10^{-42} \int_0^\infty [\theta_K^\circ] \frac{e^{-(\lambda - \lambda_K^\circ)^2/(\Delta_K^\circ)^2}}{\lambda} \, d\lambda$$

$$\approx 0.696 \times 10^{-42} \sqrt{\pi} \, [\theta_K^\circ] \frac{\Delta_K^\circ}{\lambda_K^\circ} \qquad (8)$$

By combining (7) and (8), we may put (7) into the form

$$[\phi_K] \approx \frac{R_K}{0.696 \times 10^{-42}} \frac{\lambda_K^\circ}{\Delta_K^\circ} \frac{2}{\pi}$$
$$\left[e^{-(\lambda - \lambda_K^\circ)^2/(\Delta_K^\circ)^2} \int_0^{(\lambda - \lambda_K^\circ)/\Delta_K^\circ} e^{x^2}\, dx - \frac{\Delta_K^\circ}{2(\lambda + \lambda_K^\circ)} \right] \quad (9)$$

This last result is quite important, for it will be noted now that $[\phi_K]$ is here proportional to the rotational strength. Hence, for a given set of values for λ_K° and Δ_K°, it is R_K that scales in both sign and magnitude the partial molecular rotation.

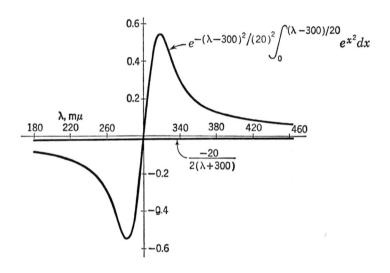

Fig. 12-13. The quantity $e^{-(\lambda - \lambda_K^\circ)^2/(\Delta_K^\circ)^2} \int_0^{(\lambda - \lambda_K^\circ)/\Delta_K^\circ} e^{x^2}\, dx$ and the quantity $-\Delta_K^\circ/[2(\lambda + \lambda_K^\circ)]$ plotted as a function of the wavelength λ for the typical saturated ketone parameters $\lambda_K^\circ = 300$ mμ, $\Delta_K^\circ = 20$ mμ.

As $(\lambda - \lambda_K^\circ)/\Delta_K^\circ$ goes to plus or minus infinity, the function $e^{-(\lambda - \lambda_K^\circ)^2/(\Delta_K^\circ)^2} \int_0^\infty e^{x^2}\, dx$ asymptotically approaches $\dfrac{\Delta_K^\circ}{2(\lambda - \lambda_K^\circ)}$. Therefore, in regions far from the band center, where $|\lambda - \lambda_K^\circ| \gg \Delta_K^\circ$, Eq. (9) can be approximated with little error by

$$[\phi_K] \approx \frac{R_K}{0.696 \times 10^{-42}} \cdot \frac{\lambda_K^\circ}{\Delta_K^\circ} \frac{2}{\pi} \left[\frac{\Delta_K^\circ}{2(\lambda - \lambda_K^\circ)} - \frac{\Delta_K^\circ}{2(\lambda + \lambda_K^\circ)} \right]$$

$$\approx \frac{R_K}{0.696 \times 10^{-42}} \frac{2}{\pi} \frac{(\lambda_K^\circ)^2}{\lambda^2 - (\lambda_K^\circ)^2} \quad (10)$$

Equation (10) is, of course, nothing more than a form of the Drude equation, which was first derived from quantum mechanical considerations by Rosenfeld.[11]

The partial molecular rotation as given by Eq. (10) no longer depends upon the half-width Δ_K°. In effect, then, the shape of the contribution to the rotatory dispersion no longer depends precisely upon the shape of the dichroism curve, i.e., upon how the intensity of the dichroism is distributed among the various sublevels of the electronic transition. Rather it rests merely upon the fact that the transition took place at an average wavelength equal to λ_K°. If one were to apply the reciprocal relations to an infinitely thin band situated at λ_K°, the expression obtained for $[\phi_K]$ would be identical to Eq. (10). The fact that our expression for the partial molecular rotation goes over into Eq. (10) as λ gets farther and farther from λ_K° may be loosely described by saying that any band will appear "sharp" if viewed from a wavelength that is sufficiently far removed from the band center.

The material of the present section was presented in terms of the specific properties of a Gaussian curve. However, aside from Eq. (9), which is peculiar to the Gaussian shape, the general discussion of asymptotic forms and the role of the rotational strength will apply with only meager qualifications to other and more generalized dichroism curves. This perhaps becomes plausible most readily if one allows that many of the band shapes encountered in actual practice can be closely approximated by suitable linear combinations of judiciously chosen Gaussian curves.

12-6. Significance of Rotational Strength

As we have seen, the rotational strength of a transition serves not only to assess the intensity of the dichroism but will, because of the reciprocal relationships, also gauge in sign and magnitude the extent to which a particular transition contributes to the rotatory dispersion. Thus, it is the signed scale factor that determines how strongly a transition participates in phenomena connected with optical activity. And it is in this sense that the rotational strength assumes a particular importance when the transitions involved can be attributed to a chromophore (such as the carbonyl group) which is ordinarily optically inactive but which becomes activated through the influence of unlike vicinal groups. For then the rotational strength serves as a measure of the chromophore's interaction with its asymmetric environment and the concomitant asymmetry induced in the electron distribution within the chromophore. An

[11] L. Rosenfeld, *Z. Physik,* **52**, 161 (1928).

examination of the theoretical expression for the rotational strength might help to make this clearer, but let us first note here that the recent work of Djerassi and his collaborators provides ample empirical demonstration of this property of the rotational strength for the case of ketones.

It will be recalled that both absorption and dichroism take their origin in the charge displacements induced by the perturbing light wave. These movements of charge will lead to the production of induced electric dipoles and induced magnetic dipoles, the latter arising from the fact that a charge circulating about an enclosed area has many of the properties of a simple bar magnet.   A contribution to the charge displacements (and hence to the induced dipoles) will be associated with each transition in the molecule.   For the case of ordinary absorption, the greater the charge displacement so as to correspond to a greater contribution to the induced electric dipole moment, the greater the intensity of the transition.   Since it is D_K that gauges the intensity of the transition, one might logically expect that its theoretical formulation would contain some expression of these charge displacements.   Such is indeed the case.   More specifically, it is calculated according to quantum mechanical prescription as the scalar product of two vector quantities, each of which has the dimensions of an electric dipole moment and which serves as a measure of the contribution of the Kth transition to the induced electric dipole moment.

Similarly, the theoretical expression for R_K[10,11] will depend upon the charge displacements associated with the Kth transition which contribute to the dichroism.   A detailed analysis shows that $(\varepsilon_L - \varepsilon_R)$ [6,12] is related to both the induced electric and magnetic dipole moments. Hence, we may anticipate that the prescription for R_K will in some way be related to both these moments.   It turns out that as in the case of D_K, R_K is also given by the scalar product of two vector quantities, one of which is dimensionally like an electric dipole moment.   However, the other vector quantity now has the dimensions of a magnetic dipole moment, i.e.,

$$R_K = \mu_e^K \cdot \mu_m^K$$

where μ_e^K and μ_m^K have the dimensions of electric and magnetic dipole moments, respectively.

It may be shown [13] that if a molecule possesses either a center of inversion or a reflection plane of symmetry the product $\mu_e^K \cdot \mu_m^K$ must in general vanish for all K because:

[12] E. U. Condon, W. Altar, and H. Eyring, *J. Chem. Phys.*, **5**, 753 (1937).

[13] H. Eyring, J. Walter, and G. E. Kimball, "Quantum Chemistry," p. 346, John Wiley & Sons, Inc., New York, 1944.

(a) $\mu_e^K \neq 0$ but $\mu_m^K = 0$

or

(b) $\mu_m^K \neq 0$ but $\mu_e^K = 0$

or (c) the vectors μ_e^K and μ_m^K are at right angles to each other, so that their scalar product is zero. Since no transition can contribute to either the dichroism or the rotatory dispersion, the molecule will be optically inactive. Such symmetry rules were of course well known to chemists long before the concept of rotational strength was introduced. By way of nomenclature, case (a) above refers to a so-called "electric dipole allowed, magnetic dipole forbidden" transition, and a type (b) transition is designated as "electric dipole forbidden, magnetic dipole allowed."

In many instances, the electrons involved in a particular transition are associated with a particular grouping of atoms in the molecule, i.e., a chromophore, which itself may contain some symmetry element. For example, the 290-mµ transition in saturated ketones concerns primarily the carbonyl group,[7,8] which possesses two orthogonal reflection planes. Because the pertinent electrons are confined mainly to the region of the chromophore, for a first approximation the symmetry rules of the preceding paragraph will apply to the chromophore as if it were the whole molecule. Any optical activity that is associated with the transitions of the chromophore must therefore arise through an unsymmetrical perturbation of the chromophoric electrons induced by an asymmetric environment. That is why the 290-mµ transition will be optically inactive in acetone where the carbonyl group is symmetrically situated between two methyl groups, and optically active in, say, 12-ketocholanic acid where the rest of the molecule is asymmetrically disposed about the carbonyl chromophore. The rotational strength for the 290-mµ transition in acetone would be zero. However, in 12-ketocholanic acid, R_K for the same transition would have a finite nonzero value that would quantitatively measure the interaction of the carbonyl group with its asymmetric molecular environment.

The reader will recognize that the type of optical activity just discussed is the more familiar kind that is associated with the presence of an "asymmetric carbon atom" in the molecule. The asymmetric carbon atom, in effect, serves notice of an asymmetric environment for the symmetric chromophore. It might be well here to distinguish between the origin of this type of optical activity and the kind that arises in say hexahelicene (I), the molecule that was referred to in footnote 12 of Chap. 1.

Hexahelicene (I) consists of six benzenoid rings that are fused into a roughly helical form. There is no symmetry element in the molecule to prohibit optical activity, but, on the other hand, neither is there an asymmetric carbon atom.   Here the entire molecule acts as one big chromophore, and the asymmetry necessary for optical activity is built into the chromophore itself.   There is no need to invoke the perturbation of an asymmetric environment, and, in fact, none is provided.   All the

I

transitions of the chromophore, which in this case is identical with the molecule, are both electric dipole and magnetic dipole allowed, i.e., both $\mathbf{\mu}_e^K$ and $\mathbf{\mu}_m^K$ are in general nonzero to first order.   Hence all the transitions have relatively large R_K, and the rotations exhibited will be enormous.

Before concluding this section, we shall examine the question of convenient units for the rotational strength.   It has been pointed out that R_K has the dimensions of an electric dipole moment times a magnetic dipole moment.   The natural molecular units for these quantities are the Debye, $\mu_D = 10^{-18}$ cgs, and the Bohr magneton, $\mu_B \approx 0.927 \times 10^{-20}$ cgs.   Hence R_K would be expected to take on values of the order of 10^{-38} cgs.   This is in fact the case for many of the R_K values calculated [14] for hexahelicene (I).   However, in the more common type of optical rotation discussed above, the rotational strength usually achieves only a few percent of this value.   This is because either $\mathbf{\mu}_e^K$ or $\mathbf{\mu}_m^K$ for the chromophoric transitions takes on nonzero values only in second order under the influence of the asymmetric molecular environment. Hence it has been suggested [15] that a more suitable unit would be the *reduced rotational strength* $[R_K]$, defined by

$$[R_K] = \frac{100 R_K}{\mu_D \mu_B}$$

$$\approx 1.08 \times 10^{40} R_K$$

Values of rotational strengths expressed in these units would then most frequently be numbers of a convenient magnitude. $[R_K]$ may be obtained from the dichroism curve by means of the following relationship:

$$[R_K] \approx 0.75 \times 10^{-2} \int_0^\infty \frac{[\theta_K(\lambda)]}{\lambda} \, d\lambda \tag{11}$$

[14] A. Moscowitz, Ph.D. thesis, Harvard University, March, 1957.
[15] Private communication from W. Moffitt.

In what follows, we shall always quote rotational strengths in these reduced units.

12-7. Experimental Determination of Rotational Strengths

A. Difficulties Involved.   In principle, the most straightforward way of obtaining empirical values for rotational strengths is by integrating the relevant dichroism curves according to Eq. (11).   Unfortunately, dichroism measurements are not easily performed, and hence the available data are meager.   The desired information is, of course, also contained in the corresponding rotatory dispersion curves, but here another difficulty is encountered.   As we saw in Sec. 12-5, the partial rotation associated with any particular transition falls off comparatively slowly in regions away from the band center according to the Drude-

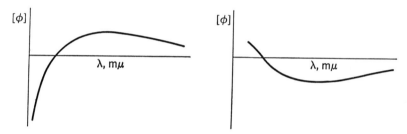

Fig. 12-14.   "Background rotations" that exhibit broad extrema.

Rosenfeld equation, i.e., as $1/[\lambda^2 - (\lambda_K^\circ)^2]$.   This type of decay is much more mild than that exhibited by a typical partial dichroism curve, which often behaves roughly like some sort of decreasing exponential (e.g., a Gaussian).   Hence even in the vicinity of an isolated absorption band, the experimental rotatory dispersion curve will contain significant contributions from many other optically active transitions.   The contribution from the transition under surveillance will have the characteristic shape shown in Fig. 12-6a or 12-6c.   The combined partial rotations from the other transitions will contribute a "background rotation" which will usually be of the plain-curve type mentioned in Chap. 2 and which can be approximated by a multitermed Drude equation.   However, even a multitermed Drude equation can exhibit a broad peak or trough, as shown in Fig. 12-14, and this type of "background rotation" is not unknown.[16]   It should be emphasized here that what we have just called "background rotation" is not to be identified with the *background curve*

---

[16] See, for example, fig. 2 in Ref. 19.

of the parent system mentioned in Chap. 2.   We shall discuss this point further in Sec. 12-8.

In the absence of dichroism data, the problem of obtaining experimental values for the rotational strengths will therefore necessitate separating out the partial rotation of a single transition from the background rotation.   Once this is done, one may ascertain the parameters that govern its shape and from these determine the rotational strength. Several computational and graphical methods have been devised to accomplish this end,[17] and these entail varying amounts of labor and achieve varying degrees of accuracy.   We outline below the one of these methods that at the present time seems to offer the most satisfactory compromise between tractability and accuracy.

B. Rotational Strengths from Rotatory Dispersion Curves.   The method we are about to describe is a computational one that was originally programmed for use on the IBM 704 high-speed digital computer at the Bell Telephone Laboratories in Murray Hill, New Jersey.[18]   The average running time on this machine is approximately 40 seconds per compound.   The procedure is as follows:

1. Assume that the actual partial dichroism curve for the electronic transition under consideration can be adequately represented by a single Gaussian curve.   The contribution of the transition to the observed rotatory dispersion curve will then be of the form of Eq. (9).

2. Assume that in the spectral region of interest, the sum of the partial rotations from all the other transitions can be represented by the abbreviated two-term Drude equation

$$\frac{A}{\lambda^2} + \frac{B}{\lambda^2 - Q^2} \tag{12}$$

where A, B, and Q are constants. Q is chosen with regard to the particular chromophore involved and is always less than λ.

3. By means of a least-squares process for nonlinear functions, fit the sum of Eqs. (9) and (12) to the experimental data.   (In the actual computational procedures used, it was also assumed that the slowly varying term appearing in the brackets in (9) which goes as $1/[2(\lambda + \lambda_K^\circ)]$ could be absorbed by the fairly flexible function $(A/\lambda^2) + [B/(\lambda^2 - Q^2)]$.)   This will determine the parameters λ_K°, Δ_K°, and

[17] W. Moffitt and A. Moscowitz, unpublished work.

[18] The numerical work referred to in this section was carried out while the author was a guest of this laboratory. It is a pleasure to acknowledge the generous hospitality of the Bell Telephone Laboratories made available through the courtesy of S. O. Morgan and W. P. Slichter. The author would also like to express his appreciation to M. E. Terry and Miss Shirley Reed for their competent help and advice in connection with the computational procedures.

$[R_K]$ of the single Gaussian curve that best fits the data in accordance with the above assumptions and subject to the criterion of least squares.

The method just outlined has been applied to date to 28 different ketones whose rotatory dispersion curves were measured by Djerassi and his group. In the large majority of the cases the procedure was found adequate to account for the experimental data. One favorable example of the results of the curve-fitting process is shown in Fig. 12-15, where the agreement is good over a greater range of wavelengths than

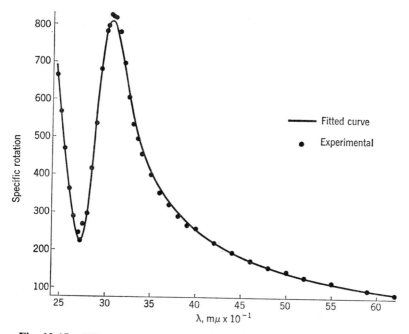

Fig. 12-15. RD curve (methanol) of 12-ketocholanic acid. $[R_1] = +2.5$.

is perhaps justified by the assumptions stated above. The final value obtained for $[R_K]$ is also indicated there; the subscript K has been taken as "one" because the transition being studied is the first to appear on the long-wavelength side in the spectrum.

It must be admitted, however, that in some cases the results were much less satisfactory than would be indicated by Fig. 12-15. This calls into question the major assumptions involved in the procedure. Of these, the second seems quite sound. In the compounds examined, the next higher transition lies some 90 mμ ($\sim$15,000 cm^{-1}) toward the blue. Therefore, so long as no attempt is made to attach any significance to the values for the parameters A, B, and Q, the abbreviated two-term Drude equation will almost certainly suffice over a limited spectral range, for as Heller [19] has noted, ". . . a limited spectral range can be covered satisfactorily with an almost unlimited number of . . . [A, B, and Q] values." Moreover, because of this flexibility in the choice of parameters, the final value achieved for $[R_K]$ will be relatively insensitive to the value chosen for Q. For example, for the case of 12-ketocholanic acid shown in Fig. 12-15, as Q is allowed to vary from 205 to 155, the value obtained for the rotational strength changes over a range of less than 2 per cent.

As to the first assumption, it is readily conceded that such a supposition will not be satisfactory in all cases. However, it might be pointed out that the apparent failure of the single Gaussian assumption need not necessarily mean a poor value for the rotational strength. For example, suppose the actual dichroism band for the single transition were given by

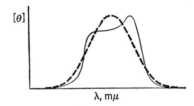

Fig. 12-16. Actual dichroism band and Gaussian dichroism band which have roughly the same R_K values but whose corresponding partial rotations will be different.

the solid curve of Fig. 12-16. Suppose further that the method provides the dotted curve as the best Gaussian. Although the integral transforms of the two functions as given by the reciprocal relation (1) will show marked discrepancies, and although there may be much "low-frequency noise" in the fit, still the areas under the two dichroism curves are such that they correspond to roughly the same rotational strengths.

Certain questions as to the uniqueness of the decomposition of the observed rotatory dispersion also arise. We shall not discuss these here except to point out that the burden of responsibility, so to speak, has been thrown onto the shoulders of the least-squares criterion.

By its very nature, the present method precludes the possibility of using functions more generalized than a simple Gaussian to approximate the dichroism curve. It may be shown, for example, that better approximations to peaked functions can be obtained by an expansion in terms of the so-called Hermite orthogonal functions. The simple

[19] W. Heller, *J. Phys. Chem.*, **62**, 1569 (1958).

Gaussian curve represents the lowest-order function in this group. By using the single Gaussian indicated from the present procedure as the starting point for an expansion in terms of the Hermite orthogonal functions and then utilizing a least-squares approach to find the proper coefficients, one could, in principle, approximate the actual dichroism curve with greater accuracy in certain cases. This would all be subject, of course, to the other assumptions already mentioned, and these do place a limit on the extent to which the present method could thereby be improved.

C. Solvent Effects. In our discussion so far, we have blithely ignored the possibility of interactions between solute and solvent. Nevertheless, the effects of such interactions are recognizable in electronic spectra, e.g., the blue shift of the long-wavelength transition in ketones,[20] and we should expect such effects to manifest themselves in polarimetry. If anything, the rotatory dispersion and circular dichroism should be more sensitive to solute-solvent interactions than the absorption spectrum, since subtle conformational changes (see Sec. 9-3C) will in general be more important for the rotational strength than for the dipole strength. This will certainly be true if the solute-solvent interactions give rise to environmental asymmetries over and above those germane to the solute molecule itself.

We do not mean to sound any warnings here that are unduly ominous but merely wish to point out that such considerations must be kept in mind when trying to correlate rotational strengths with molecular structure. The fond hope is to be cherished in all such work that the immediate molecular environment that the chromophore finds in an isolated solute molecule is far more important to it than one provided or induced by the solvent medium.

12-8. Additional Comments

A. Rotational Strength. Throughout this chapter we have emphasized the effect that the bulk of a molecule has on the optical activity evinced by a particular chromophore. In doing so, we have probably tended to obscure the fact that by its very presence, the chromophore also affects its molecular environment. Hence, when a chromophore is placed in a so-called parent compound, there is no reason to expect that the contributions to the optical rotation associated with the transitions of the parent will remain unchanged. One must therefore exercise caution when comparing the rotation of the parent compound with what we have called the "background rotation."

[20] H. McConnell, *J. Chem. Phys.*, **20,** 700 (1952).

Comparisons of the type just discussed imply the existence of some sort of additivity relationships for optical rotation. Until now, it has been difficult to inquire into the extent of validity of such an assumption. Numerical values of individual rotational strengths do, however, provide the proper criterion for such an investigation, and it is in this broad sense that the concept of the rotational strength may play its most important role. First, it opens up the possibility of a reliable set of empirical rules for the structural chemist, and second, the theoretician will at last have an experimental guide with which to test his hypotheses of the intramolecular interactions that affect optical activity. Important work along these lines was begun some years ago at Princeton University [21] but was hampered by the lack of direct experimental comparisons. With the machinery now at our disposal, we look forward to a more favorable situation in the future.

B. Concluding Remarks. In concluding this chapter, the author would like to make a few personal remarks.

First of all, I should like to state that the bulk of my contact with the phenomenon of optical activity was obtained as a graduate student and postdoctoral fellow in the laboratory of the late William Moffitt at Harvard University. Our investigations there were approached from a quantum point of view with reference to no specific model except, perhaps, a mathematical one. Nevertheless, many of the phenomenological results that we obtained bore a striking resemblance to (although they were not identical with) those achieved by Werner Kuhn of the University of Basel.

Kuhn carried out his own investigations on optical activity in the early 1930's, when the study of the electronic spectra of complex molecules was in its infancy. He preferred to use a classical coupled-oscillator model for his interpretative formalism, and as such we find some of his conclusions and interpretations of limited validity. However, it must be admitted that a good part of our work amounts to a quantum reinvestigation of a problem that Kuhn both posed and solved within the limits of the classical coupled-oscillator model. Moreover, it is clear from Kuhn's work [22] that he recognized the importance of partial quantities and circular dichroism (which he also measured [23]) at

[21] (a) W. J. Kauzmann, J. E. Walter, and H. Eyring, *Chem. Revs.,* **26,** 339 (1940); (b) E. U. Condon, W. Altar, and H. Eyring, *J. Chem. Phys.,* **5,** 753 (1937); (c) E. Gorin, J. Walter, and H. Eyring, *ibid.,* **6,** 824 (1938); (d) E. Gorin, W. J. Kauzmann, and J. Walter, *ibid.,* **7,** 327 (1939).

[22] For leading references, see W. Kuhn, *Ann. Rev. Phys. Chem.,* **9,** 417 (1958).

[23] See W. Kuhn and E. Braun, *Z. physik. Chem.* (*Leipzig*), **(B)8,** 445 (1930).

a time when most other chemists were content to ignore their existence.

I should also like to thank the National Research Council for an American Chemical Society Petroleum Research Fund Postdoctoral Fellowship.   This chapter was written during the tenure of the Fellowship at Washington University in St. Louis.

13 | OCTANT RULE

13-1. Introduction. Orbitals of the Carbonyl Group

The 290-mμ transition of the carbonyl group (in formaldehyde) involves,[1,2] roughly speaking, the promotion of an electron from a non-bonding $2p$ orbital situated on the oxygen atom, to an antibonding π orbital concerned with both the carbon and oxygen atoms of the carbonyl chromophore. The relevant orbitals are indicated in schematic [2b,c] fashion in Fig. 13-1. In the coordinate system chosen, the symmetry planes of the carbonyl chromophore are the xz and yz planes; these constitute nodal planes for the oxygen $2p_y$ orbital and π orbital, respectively. The oxygen $2p_y$ orbital is also symmetric with respect to the yz plane and, similarly, the antibonding π orbital is symmetric with respect to the xz plane.

Using the nomenclature introduced in Chap. 12, the transition under consideration is electric dipole forbidden and magnetic dipole allowed, i.e., to a first approximation $\mu_e^1 = 0$, $\mu_m^1 \neq 0$. In the present instance, the vector quantity μ_m^1 is directed along the z axis. When the carbonyl group is situated in an asymmetric molecule, the asymmetric environment will disturb the orbitals just described and thereby cause μ_e^1 to assume a small, but finite, value along the z direction, so that the product $\mu_e^1 \cdot \mu_m^1$ is no longer zero.

The excited-state orbital is much more diffuse in space than is the oxygen $2p_y$ orbital. Hence it will "see" much more of the asymmetric

[1] H. L. McMurry and R. S. Mulliken, *Proc. Natl. Acad. Sci. U.S.*, **26**, 312 (1940); H. L. McMurry, *J. Chem. Phys.*, **9**, 231 (1941).

[2] (a) J. W. Sidman, *J. Chem. Phys.*, **27**, 429 (1957); (b) J. A. Pople and J. W. Sidman, *ibid.*, **27**, 1270 (1957); (c) J. W. Sidman, *Chem. Revs.*, **58**, 689 (1958).

environment and, in general, undergo much greater distortion through interaction with the rest of the molecule than will the nonbonding orbital. This distortion will manifest itself through a destruction of the symmetry of the excited-state orbital with respect to the symmetry planes of the carbonyl group.   In terms of quantum mechanical formalism, this can be taken care of by "mixing in" with the π orbital still-higher-lying orbitals (e.g., $3d_{yz}$ orbitals of carbon or oxygen) that have opposite symmetry properties with respect to the reflection planes.   The total excited-state orbital for the 290-mμ transition so formed will then be

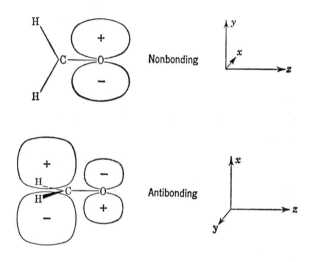

Fig. 13-1. Schematic representation indicating the symmetry properties of the orbitals involved in the 290-mμ transition in formaldehyde.

neither symmetric nor antisymmetric as regards the symmetry planes of the chromophore.

The sign and magnitude of μ_e^1 will depend upon the extent to which the higher-lying orbitals are involved.   This, in turn, will be contingent upon the nature of the perturbation induced by the asymmetrically disposed vicinal groups and also upon their geometry with respect to the carbonyl chromophore.   Preliminary theoretical considerations [3] of these factors indicate that there should exist regularities of the type implicit in the octant rule (discussed below), even though it is presently of qualitative significance only.   For placing the octant rule on a more

[3] W. Moffitt and A. Moscowitz, unpublished observation; see also Paper 68, Division of Physical Chemistry, American Chemical Society Meeting, San Francisco, April, 1958.

quantitative basis, detailed comparisons would have to be performed between theoretical calculations and rotational strengths (Sec. 12-5) of the many cyclic ketones that appear to be within the scope of the octant rule. This has so far not been done, but the qualitative agreement outlined in Secs. 13-3 and 13-4 is of such an order as to place some statistical validity on these simple rules enunciated below.

It should be emphasized that theoretical considerations of the above type have already been taken into account by Kauzmann, Walter, and Eyring,[4] but these were applied only to a single ketone, 3-methylcyclopentanone, with respect to its monochromatic rotation at 589 mµ. The authors [4] themselves were aware of the limitations involved in using $[\alpha]_D$ for making comparisons between theory and experiment.

13-2. Geometry of Cyclohexanones

As was noted in earlier chapters, most of the correlations between structure or stereochemistry and rotatory dispersion have so far been achieved in the area of cyclic carbonyl compounds, especially substituted cyclohexanones. This wealth of experimental material, coupled with the information that most of these substances existed in the chair form, prompted a simplified application of the above theoretical considerations to such cyclohexanones. The resulting set of empirical rules, called the octant rule,[5] allows in many instances a prediction of the sign of the Cotton effect. Its application in stereochemistry will be discussed below.

As shown in Fig. 13-2, using the carbonyl chromophore as the reference point, we can divide a cyclohexanone into eight octants by means of three planes. Plane A is vertical, passing through C-1 and C-4, and the only substituents in that plane are the ones attached to C-4. The horizontal plane B encompasses C-1 and its two adjacent carbon atoms (L2 and R2) [6] and it will be noted that equatorially oriented substituents attached to these two α carbon atoms are practically in plane B. A and B in Fig. 13-2 therefore correspond to the nodal planes xz and yz of the relevant orbitals mentioned in Sec. 13-1 and Fig. 13-1.

Planes A and B afford four octants defined in the planar diagram of Fig. 13-2 and, as will be shown subsequently, these invariably come into

---

[4] W. J. Kauzmann, J. E. Walter, and H. Eyring, *Chem. Revs.*, **26**, 367–372 (1940).

[5] W. Moffitt, A. Moscowitz, R. B. Woodward, W. Klyne, and C. Djerassi, unpublished observation.

[6] L refers to left and R to right; 2 indicates the two α carbons and 3 the two β carbon atoms of a cyclohexanone.

play in practical applications of the octant rule. There is, however, a third plane, *C*, perpendicular to plane *A*, dissecting the oxygen atom and C-1. This produces four additional octants, which need to be considered much less frequently and only in those substances in which substituents lie to the left of plane *C* in Fig. 13-2.

13-3. The Octant Rule. Qualitative Rotatory Contribution of Substituents

For the majority of cyclohexanones for which rotatory dispersion measurements have been performed, only the four octants defined by

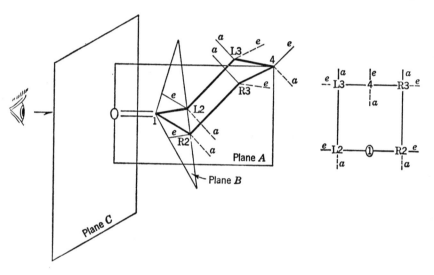

Fig. 13-2. Geometry of cyclohexanone illustrating three planes creating eight octants. Abbreviations: *a*, axial; *e*, equatorial; L, left; R, right.

planes *A* and *B* need to be considered. The octant rule [5] states that substituents lying in these two dividing planes make substantially no contribution and can be ignored.[7] By reference to Fig. 13-2, it will be seen that this includes both substituents attached to C-4 (in plane *A*) as well as the two equatorial substituents [7] connected to carbon atoms L2 and R2 (plane *B*).

Substituents (to the right of plane *C*) that must be taken into con-

[7] This is only true for qualitative predictions, which can be made at the present stage with the octant rule. In actual fact, equatorial substituents do exert a certain quantitatively noticeable effect, as can be seen by comparing the rotatory dispersion curves (Fig. 9-1) of 2α-bromo- and 4α-bromo-androstan-17β-ol-3-one acetate.

sideration are the following: Atoms that are situated in the far-lower-right (axial substituent of R2) and far-upper-left (axial and equatorial substituents of L3) octants make a positive contribution, while those located in the far-lower-left (axial substituents of L2) and far-upper-right (axial and equatorial substituents of R3) octants produce a negative effect.   It will immediately be seen that the "axial haloketone rule" [8] (Sec. 9-2) is only a more specific case of the general octant rule.

As a concrete example, the octant rule will be applied to $(+)$-*trans*-10-methyl-2-decalone (I), which is known [9] to exhibit a positive Cotton effect curve.   In order to fit into the (arbitrary) scheme outlined in Fig. 13-2, the molecule in its conformational all-chair formulation must be

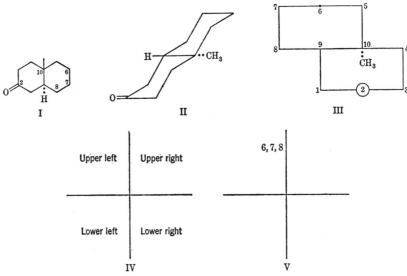

"turned over" as in II.   Applying now the simplified planar representation of a cyclohexanone (Fig. 13-2), we arrive at III, in which the various carbon atoms are numbered as in I.   We can now take a cross-shaped diagram (IV), which contains the four octants produced by planes A and B (Fig. 13-2), and insert in the relevant octant only those carbon atoms that will make a noticeable rotatory contribution.   If this is done with *trans*-10-methyl-2-decalone (I = II = III), it will be noted that the substituents of C-10 (the angular methyl group and C-5) lie in the vertical plane A and thus can be ignored.   There are no axial substituents on carbon atoms 1 and 3, so that no contributors need to be placed into the lower-left or lower-right octants (IV and V).   Simi-

[8] C. Djerassi and W. Klyne, *J. Am. Chem. Soc.,* **79,** 1506 (1957).

[9] C. Djerassi, R. Riniker, and B. Riniker, *J. Am. Chem. Soc.,* **78,** 6362 (1956).

larly, C-4 bears no substituents, thus leaving the far-upper-right octant open, but there are three carbon atoms (notably C-8)—C-8, C-7, and C-6—located in the far-upper-left octant.

Since the octant rule [5] states that substituents in the far-upper-left octant make a positive contribution, (+)-*trans*-10-methyl-2-decalone (I) would be predicted to possess a positive Cotton effect curve; this has, in fact, been observed experimentally.[9]

Obviously, one's chance to predict the sign of a given Cotton effect curve is one out of two, and, therefore, for the octant rule to be statistically convincing to organic chemists, it must predict correctly the observed rotatory dispersion behavior in the vast majority of instances. Many bicyclic (Chap. 5), triterpenoid (Chap. 6), and especially steroid (Chap. 4) ketones have been analyzed [5] by the above procedure and the correspondence between observed and predicted sign has been so impressive as to indicate already at this qualitative stage that the octant rule can be of real utility in stereochemistry.

Before turning to a few concrete applications of the octant rule, it must be pointed out that substituents in only four of the eight octants have been considered so far.   In certain substances, e.g., steroids with a keto group in positions 1 or 11, the situation is more complicated in that some of the substituents lie in one or more of the near octants, i.e., to the left of plane C (Fig. 13-2).   The octant rule [5] states that atoms in these near octants make a rotational contribution that is opposite in sign to that if the same substituent were in the corresponding far octant.   Thus substituents in the near-lower-right or near-upper-left octant make a negative contribution, while a positive one is attributed [5] to substituents in the near-lower-left or near-upper-right octants.

At the present stage it is difficult to assign quantitative values to these contributions, other than to make the fairly safe assumption that the effect will be reduced as the distance is increased from the carbonyl chromophore.   The addition of the various contributions in polysubstituted molecules is at times open to question, especially where it is difficult to assess the quantitative effect of given substituents in more distant rings.   Examples will be given in the detailed paper,[5] but it is pertinent to mention that the presence of several remote substituents in one of the octants may reflect itself in the amplitude of the Cotton effect. For instance, it was shown in Fig. 4-1 that the amplitude of the positive Cotton effect of cholestan-2-one (VI) is considerably greater than that of cholestan-3-one (VIII).   If these two substances are considered in terms of their octant projections (VII and IX), it will immediately be seen that not only does cholestan-2-one (VII) carry an axial substituent (angular methyl group attached to C-10) in the far-upper-left octant (strong positive contribution), but all of rings C and D are also found in that octant. On the other hand, cholestan-3-one (IX) has this angular methyl group in the vertical dividing plane A (Fig. 13-2), the main positively rotating contributions now coming only from carbon atoms 6 and 7. Cholestan-3-one (IX) represents an interesting example in which the contributions of several carbon atoms cancel out (see also Sec. 13-4F), this being true of C-8 versus C-11 and C-14 versus C-12.

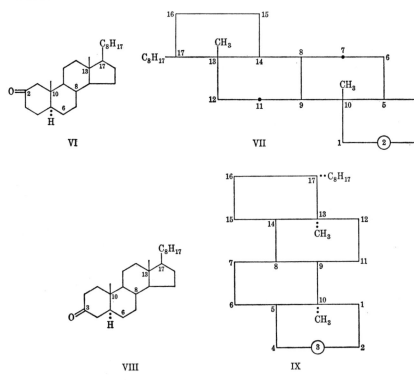

VI   VII

VIII   IX

13-4. Stereochemical Applications of the Octant Rule

A. Introduction. The principal utility of the octant rule, as has already been emphasized in Sec. 9-2 with the related "axial haloketone rule," can be defined in one sentence. If the absolute configuration of the ketone [10] is known, its conformation can be determined by the octant rule, whereas if the conformation of the substance is established, it can be assigned the correct absolute configuration.

[10] On theoretical grounds (see Ref. 2c) it would be expected that the octant rule should also apply to thioketones (see Sec. 14-2).

The simplest example, which has a definite bearing on the subjects discussed in Chap. 7 (monocyclic ketones), is afforded by (+)-3-methylcyclohexanone. This substance can exist in two interconvertible chair conformations represented by X and XI. The octant diagrams accompanying the two conformational formulas show that X would clearly exhibit a positive and XI a negative Cotton effect curve. As the absolute configuration of (+)-3-methylcyclohexanone has been shown by chemical transformations [11] to correspond to stereoformulas X and XI, the observed [12] positive Cotton effect curve is only compatible with that conformer, which possesses an equatorial methyl group (X).

The tenets of conformational analysis [13] would, of course, predict that the chair form with the equatorial methyl group (X) will be energetically preferred over the conformer (XI) with an axial methyl group. Therefore, accepting this premise and assuming that the absolute configuration of the substance were unknown, the octant rule can differentiate easily between the two antipodes X (positive Cotton effect) and XII (negative Cotton effect).

(+)-3-Methylcyclohexanone is only offered for purposes of illustration, since both the conformational and absolute configurational problems have been settled by other means. However, using this approach, it will be shown below that there are several cases for which the octant rule can be of very considerable assistance in doubtful or unsolved stereochemical problems.

B. Preferred Conformation of cis-Decalones. cis-Decalone can exist in two nonequivalent, all-chair conformations, which are exemplified for cis-10-methyl-2-decalone by representations XIII and XIV. This problem has already been discussed in Sec. 5-2B, where it was concluded [14] by the coincidence of the rotatory dispersion curves of coprostan-3-one (required to exist in conformation XIII) and cis-10-methyl-2-decalone

---

[11] For leading references see E. J. Eisenbraun and S. M. McElvain, *J. Am. Chem. Soc.*, **77**, 3383 (1955).

[12] (a) H. S. French and M. Naps, *J. Am. Chem. Soc.*, **58**, 2303 (1936); (b) C. Djerassi and G. W. Krakower, *ibid.*, **81**, 237 (1959).

[13] W. G. Dauben and K. S. Pitzer in M. S. Newman (ed.), "Steric Effects in Organic Chemistry," chap. 1, John Wiley & Sons, Inc., New York, 1956.

[14] C. Djerassi and D. Marshall, *J. Am. Chem. Soc.*, **80**, 3986 (1958).

that the latter should be represented predominantly by XIII.   This conclusion is in contrast to that predicted [15] on certain conformational
grounds, but further support can be adduced by the octant rule.   When
a suitable octant projection is made [5] of the two conformers XIII and
XIV, a strongly positive Cotton effect is predicted for XIV.   On the
other hand, a moderately negative Cotton effect curve would be expected
for XIII, and this is in agreement with the experimental results (Fig.
5-2).[14]

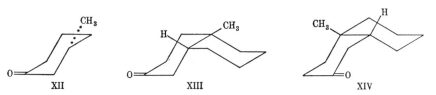

| XII | XIII | XIV |

Even more convincing are the conclusions [5] obtained on application
of the octant rule to the two isomeric *cis*-tetrahydrocyperones XV and
XVI.[16]   Howe and McQuillin suggested that the *cis* isomer with the
α-oriented isopropyl group existed preferentially in the *nonsteroid* conformation XV*a*, because in the alternate *steroid* conformation XV*b*, the
isopropyl group would be axial.   The opposite situation should prevail
with the β-isopropyl isomer (XVI), since there the *nonsteroid* conformation XVI*a* would impose an axial orientation upon the isopropyl group,
not present in the *steroid-like* form XVI*b*.   The octant diagrams [5] predict the following Cotton effect curves: XV*a*, strongly positive; XV*b*,
weakly positive; XVI*a*, strongly positive; XVI*b*, weakly negative.   Experimentally,[17] a substantial positive Cotton effect curve was obtained
for XV and a small negative one, very similar to that of 5β-3-keto
steroids (Fig. 4-5), for XVI.   These rotatory dispersion results are
thus fully consistent with predictions from conformational analysis and

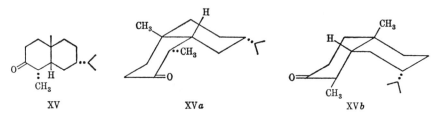

| XV | XV*a* | XV*b* |

[15] W. Klyne, *Experientia,* **12,** 119 (1956).
[16] R. Howe and F. J. McQuillin, *J. Chem. Soc.,* **1958,** 1194. The methyl group
is assumed in each case to be equatorial, since these substances were unaffected
by base treatment.
[17] Unpublished observation by Mrs. T. Nakano in our laboratory.

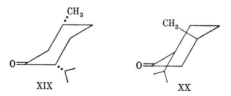

XVI   XVIa   XVIb

also establish the β orientation of the methyl group in XVIb, since its 4α isomer should exhibit a positive Cotton effect.

C. Conformational Mobility in Monocyclic Cyclohexanones. As discussed in detail in Sec. 9-3C, the "axial haloketone rule" affords strong evidence [18] in the case of 2-chloro-5-methylcyclohexanone for a shift in the conformational equilibrium from XVII (positive Cotton effect) toward XVIII (negative Cotton effect) when the polarity of the solvent is reduced. The octant diagrams show that XVII should have a moderately positive and XVIII an extremely strong negative Cotton effect. Recent calculations,[19] using also infrared and dipole-moment measurements, on the position of the conformational equilibrium (XVII ⇌ XVIII) indicate that deductions of a semiquantitative character are justified in this case. Indeed, as soon as quantitative parameters can be assigned to the various substituents, the octant rule will fulfill a very useful function in this area of stereochemistry.

XVII   XVIII

Another important case in which the octant rule is of consequence is represented by the conformational problem of (+)-isomenthone (see Sec. 7-3). The strongly positive Cotton effect (Fig. 7-2) would appear to be only consistent with conformation XIX, exhibiting an axial

XIX   XX

[18] C. Djerassi and L. E. Geller, *Tetrahedron*, **3**, 319 (1958).
[19] N. L. Allinger, J. Allinger, L. E. Geller, and C. Djerassi, *J. Org. Chem.*, in press.

isopropyl group, although evaluation of the rotatory contribution of the equatorial isopropyl group of XX is not too clear.

D. Application to Cycloheptanones.   Under certain circumstances, the octant rule appears to be applicable also to cycloheptanones.   Attention was called in Sec. 7-1 to the puzzling observation [20] that (+)-3-methylcyclohexanone (X) and (−)-3-methylcycloheptanone (XXI), although configurationally related, exhibit Cotton effect curves of opposite sign.   If the cycloheptanone ring can be examined in the same manner as cyclohexanone was (Fig. 13-2), except that plane *A* now passes through the carbonyl carbon and between C-4 and C-5 (XXII), then the main rotatory contributor according to the octant rule should be the methyl group.   Granted this premise, it will be noted that a positive Cotton effect would be predicted for the chair form (XXI*a*) of 3-methylcycloheptanone, but that the boat form (XXI*b*) should exhibit

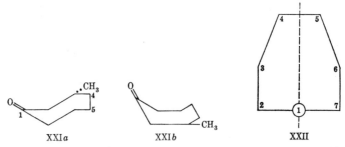

XXI*a*   XXI*b*   XXII

a negative Cotton effect.   The latter is in accord with the experimental observation [20] (see Fig. 7-1) and it is interesting to note that subsequent to these conclusions based on the octant rule, energy calculations were performed [21] which suggest that in cycloheptanone itself the chair form (analogous to XXI*a* without methyl group) is energetically less favored than the boat or a skewed chair conformation.

E. Determination of Absolute Configuration.   It was pointed out in the introductory paragraph of Sec. 13-4 that potentially one of the most significant contributions of the octant rule will be in the field of absolute configurational assignments, particularly where other methods are inapplicable.

A pertinent example is provided by 3-hydroxy-3-nonadecylcyclohexanone (XXIII), which was obtained [22] by hydrogenation of an unsaturated keto-alcohol from Terentang oil.   Its absolute configuration can be attacked by means of the octant rule, because one of the chief

[20] C. Djerassi and G. W. Krakower, *J. Am. Chem. Soc.*, **81**, 237 (1959).

[21] N. L. Allinger, *J. Am. Chem. Soc.*, **81**, 5727 (1959).

[22] J. M. Lamberton, *Australian J. Chem.*, **11**, 73 (1958).

prerequisites, known conformation, is almost certainly met in this compound—with the bulky alkyl substituent assuming an equatorial orientation. Of the two possible antipodal representations, XXIIIa would be expected to show a positive Cotton effect curve (all substituents in the far-upper-left octant) and XXIIIb a negative one. The experimentally observed [17] positive Cotton effect (molecular amplitude in methanol +3000°) is only consistent with the absolute configurational representation XXIIIa.

XXIIIa   XXIIIb

XXIV   XXV

At times the octant rule cannot offer an unambiguous answer with the information available, but it can at least eliminate certain alternatives. A case in point is the keto acid XXIV, derived from the diterpene phyllocladene, for which eight stereochemical possibilities had to be considered and four could be eliminated [23] by application of the octant rule.

F. Ketones with Plain Dispersion Curves. Of the many hundreds of rotatory dispersion curves of diverse carbonyl-containing substances that have been measured in our laboratory, all but a few exhibited Cotton effect curves. The behavior of the occasional cyclic ketone showing a plain dispersion curve can probably be rationalized by assuming a rough counterbalancing of opposite rotational contributions of the various substituents.

For instance, 19-nor-5α,10α-androstan-3-ones (e.g., XXV) exhibit [17,24] plain dispersion curves. Examination of a conformational model of this substance will show that according to the octant rule a negative contribution can be attributed to carbon atoms 6 and 7, while

[23] C. Djerassi, M. Cais, and L. A. Mitscher, *J. Am. Chem. Soc.*, **81**, 2386 (1959); see also L. H. Briggs, B. F. Cain, B. R. Davis, and J. K. Wilmshurst, *Tetrahedron Letters*, no. 8, 13 (1959); P. K. Grant and R. Hodges, *ibid.*, no. 10, 21 (1959).

[24] R. T. Rapala and E. Farkas, *J. Org. Chem.*, **23**, 1404 (1958).

a positive one can be expected from the more distant carbon atoms 11, 12, 13, 16, 17, and 18.   Although more distant substituents will have a smaller influence, the larger number of them in this instance apparently offsets the stronger contribution of the two proximate carbon atoms C-6 and C-7.

13-5.   Conclusion

The weight of the circumstantial evidence [5] strongly supports the basic correctness of the octant rule.   However, the lack of definite quantitative values to be assigned to the various substituents makes it necessary to use the rule with caution, especially in questionable cases. Too little is as yet known about the quantitative effects of distance of a given group from the chromophore to permit a precise adding up of the rotatory contributions of the various substituents in the octants.   At present one is reduced to deciding in an empirical manner upon the relative importance of atoms in more distant rings, and so this is clearly an area where serious error may be introduced.

There is no question that the octant rule, the axial haloketone rule, and similar generalizations will ultimately be put on a fairly accurate quantitative basis and that this will represent a major forward step in the application of rotatory dispersion measurements to more subtle stereochemical problems.   Nevertheless, even at the present empirical and qualitative stage, the judicious use of these rules can settle certain problems unambiguously, while with many others the rules will simply raise questions, especially of a conformational nature (e.g., XIX versus XX), which will warrant further investigation by other means.   Indeed this uncovering or posing of new stereochemical problems per se should already be enough justification for serious consideration of these rules on the part of the organic chemist.

14 | THIONES, NITROALKANES, AND OTHER CHROMOPHORES

14-1. Introduction

The classical rotatory dispersion studies, chiefly by Lowry, Kuhn, and Levene, covered a considerable number of diverse chromophores, although for each case only a few examples were examined. A rather complete list of all these organic compounds (less than 50) for which a Cotton effect was demonstrated experimentally has been compiled in convenient form by Klyne [1] and will not be given here. Rather, emphasis will be placed on those chromophores that may be of particular interest to the organic chemist and that lend themselves readily to rotatory dispersion examination by means of modern photoelectric spectropolarimeters. In particular, attention will be directed toward some of the unpublished results accumulated during the past year in our laboratory.

As indicated in Chap. 1, the most interesting rotatory dispersion curves are anomalous ones, and, for this purpose, chromophores that absorb in a convenient spectral range with low extinction are required. Ample evidence for the utility of this method with carbonyl-containing substances has been presented in the preceding chapters, but there is no question that many other chromophores will lend themselves to the same type of approach. Indeed, in the near future considerable activity and progress is to be anticipated in this area. The purpose of this chapter is to indicate to the reader some of the more promising avenues for research.

[1] W. Klyne in R. A. Raphael (ed.), "Advances in Organic Chemistry: Methods and Results," vol. 1, Interscience Publishers, Inc., New York, 1960, pp. 239–348.

14-2. Thiones

The C=S chromophore, in the form of xanthates and dithiourethanes, was proposed nearly 50 years ago by Tschugaeff,[2] and the wisdom of this choice for anomalous rotatory dispersion work has been demonstrated experimentally by Lowry.[3] The potential importance of the xanthate chromophore in organic chemistry is such that it is considered separately

in Chap. 15. Xanthates, RSC̈OR′, exhibit ultraviolet absorption

maxima [3] near 360 and 280 mμ, the former attributed [3] to the –C̈S– grouping and the latter to the C=S moiety.

In point of fact, no reliable spectral measurements appear to have been made [4,5] of isolated thiones, presumably because of the instability of simple thioketones. Here again, steroids have come to the rescue, and the recent reports [6] in the patent literature on the preparation of rather stable steroidal thioketones have prompted an investigation [7] of their spectral and rotatory dispersion characteristics.

As the simplest model substance androstane-17-thione (I) was prepared,[7] and its rotatory dispersion curve (Fig. 14-1) in dioxane solution was found to be characterized by a nearly symmetrical positive Cotton effect in the visible range of the spectrum. Its absorption spectrum in the same solvent contains maxima at 492 mμ (ε = 12.9) and 239 mμ (ε = 8770) in good agreement with the values reported [6a] for similar steroidal thioketones. As shown in Fig. 14-1, the rotatory dispersion curve intersects the zero rotation line at 505 mμ, thus demonstrating that the 492-mμ absorption band of the thione grouping is strongly optically active. Whether this also applies to the second maximum at 239 mμ cannot be stated at the present time, because the high absorption precluded rotatory dispersion measurements below 300 mμ.

[2] L. Tschugaeff, *Ber.*, **42**, 2244 (1909); L. Tschugaeff and A. Ogorodnikoff, *Z. physik. Chem.* (*Leipzig*), **74**, 503 (1910), and later papers.

[3] T. M. Lowry and H. Hudson, *Phil. Trans. Roy. Soc. London, Ser. A*, **232**, 117 (1933).

[4] A. Gillam and E. S. Stern, "An Introduction to Electronic Absorption Spectroscopy in Organic Chemistry," 2d ed., pp. 62–70, Edward Arnold & Co., London, 1957.

[5] N. Lozac'h, *Record Chem. Progr.*, **20**, 23 (1959); J. W. Sidman, *Chem. Revs.*, **38**, 702 (1958).

[6] (a) R. M. Dodson and P. B. Sollman, U.S. Patent 2,763,669 (Sept. 18, 1956), and private communications; (b) R. M. Dodson and P. B. Sollman, U.S. Patent 2,837,539 (June 3, 1958).

[7] D. Herbst and C. Djerassi, to be published.

An especially attractive example is Δ^4-pregnen-3-one-20-thione (II),[6b] the thioketone analogue of the hormone progesterone, since it contains two chromophores, the thioketone and the α,β-unsaturated ketone, with absorption maxima in widely different spectral regions.   In fact, its

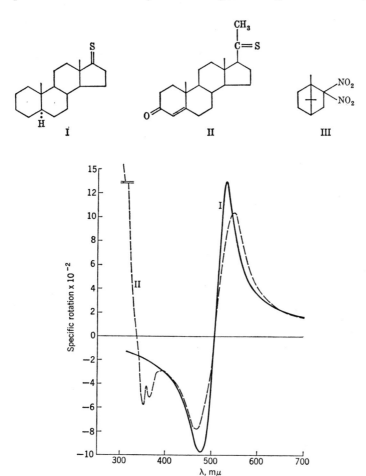

Fig. 14-1.   RD curves (dioxane) of androstane-17-thione (I) and Δ^4-pregnen-3-one-20-thione (II).

rotatory dispersion curve (Fig. 14-1) exhibits the typical positive Cotton effect in the 500-mμ region associated with the thioketone function, as well as the multiple Cotton effect between 380 and 350 mμ characteristic of the Δ^4-3-keto moiety (see Fig. 4-13), thus demonstrating the absence of interaction between the two chromophores.

14-3.   Nitroalkanes and Nitrites

The ultraviolet spectral properties [4] (λ_{max} 270 to 280 mμ with ε below 20) of the isolated nitro group suggest a strong similarity to the carbonyl chromophore. That this analogy also applies to its rotatory dispersion behavior is indicated by the reported [8] large negative Cotton effect of dinitrocamphane (III), and more recent measurements [9] have borne this out. Thus one of the simplest nitroalkanes, (+)-2-nitroöctane

$$CH_3(CH_2)_5CH(NO_2)CH_3$$

IV   V   VI

(IV),[10] exhibited [9] a positive Cotton effect curve in methanol (peak, $[\alpha]_{292.5\ m\mu}$ +90°). Much higher rotations were observed [9] with substances in which the nitro group is attached to a ring, such as 6α-nitro-Δ^4-androstene-3β,17β-diol (V),[11] with its strong negative Cotton effect (Fig. 14-2). Of particular interest was the corresponding double-bond isomer, 6-nitro-Δ^5-androstene-3β,17β-diol (VI),[11] since the only relevant published spectral information [12] of simple conjugated nitroölefins (e.g., 2-nitro-1-propene, λ_{max}^{EtOH} 225 mμ, $\varepsilon = 3300$) indicated the absence of a long-wavelength, low-intensity band. In point of fact, the steroidal nitroölefin VI also exhibited a negative Cotton effect curve (Fig. 14-2), and it is noteworthy that the trough occurred at 350 mμ as contrasted to 317.5 mμ for the allylic nitro analogue V. It is unfortunate that both extrema of these Cotton effects could not be determined, since it was noted that the Δ^5-6-nitro steroid VI had an ultraviolet absorption maximum (dioxane) at 273.5 mμ [13] as contrasted to 286 mμ for the Δ^4-6-nitro isomer V, in spite of the fact that the trough of VI occurred at a longer wavelength. These preliminary results indicate that a more ex-

[8] S. Mitchell and R. R. Gordon, *J. Chem. Soc.*, **1936**, 853.

[9] Unpublished measurements by Mrs. R. Riniker and Mrs. V. Halpern.

[10] N. Kornblum, L. Fishbein, and R. A. Smiley, *J. Am. Chem. Soc.*, **77**, 6261 (1955).

[11] A. Bowers, M. B. Sánchez, and H. J. Ringold, *J. Am. Chem. Soc.*, **81**, 3702 (1959).

[12] E. A. Braude, E. R. H. Jones, and G. G. Rose, *J. Chem. Soc.*, **1947**, 1104.

[13] The position of this maximum is quite solvent-dependent, since in methanol it was shifted to 264 mμ. C. E. Agnostopoulos and L. F. Fieser, *J. Am. Chem. Soc.*, **76**, 532 (1954), report λ_{max}^{EtOH} 258 mμ for several 6-nitro-Δ^5-sterols.

tensive rotatory dispersion investigation with parallel spectral studies of various organic nitro compounds should be of considerable interest.

A series of optically active nitrites (VII) has been studied in a classical investigation by Kuhn,[14] who measured the ultraviolet absorption spectrum, circular dichroism, and rotatory dispersion of these substances. The rotatory dispersion curves were very interesting because

$$\begin{array}{c} CH_3 \\ | \\ H—C—ONO \\ | \\ R \end{array}$$

VII $R = C_6H_5, C_6H_{11}, C_6H_{13}$

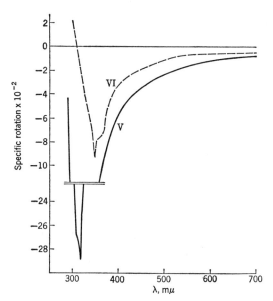

Fig. 14-2. RD curves (dioxane) of 6α-nitro-Δ⁴-androstene-3β,17β-diol (V) and 6-nitro-Δ⁵-androstene-3β,17β-diol (VI).

they were characterized by multiple Cotton effect curves with a series of peaks and troughs between 400 and 350 mμ, corresponding to ultraviolet absorption bands in that region.   Unfortunately, the difficulty in purifying alkyl nitrites [15] and their pronounced instability, especially to light,[15,16] appear to preclude their use as a suitable derivative for alco-

[14] (a) W. Kuhn and H. L. Lehmann, Z. physik. Chem. (Leipzig), (B)18, 32 (1932); (b) W. Kuhn and H. Biller, ibid., (B)29, 1 (1935).

[15] N. Kornblum and E. P. Oliveto, J. Am. Chem. Soc., 69, 465 (1947).

[16] See also K. Freudenberg and H. Biller, Ann., 510, 230 (1934).

hols, whose plain dispersion curve would thus be transformed into an anomalous one.

The reaction of olefins with nitrogen trioxide leads at times to blue nitrosites (nitroso nitrites). Two representatives from the terpene series, caryophyllene nitrosite [17a] and bornylene nitrosite [17b] have been shown to exhibit anomalous dispersion behavior in the visible. A more detailed study of such derivatives of optically active olefins seems warranted from the rotatory dispersion standpoint and is now in progress in our laboratory.

14-4. Aromatic Compounds

Isolated rotatory dispersion studies with some optically active aromatic substances indicate that this may be a fruitful field for further investigation, especially when spectropolarimeters become available for routine measurements of the 260 to 230 mμ region.

Careful studies by Kuhn and Biller [14b] have shown that the benzene absorption band in the 260-mμ region in phenyl methyl carbinol (VIII) and its derivatives is not optically active, while the opposite is true of certain derivatives of mandelic acid (IX) and atrolactic acid. In fact,

$$C_6H_5 CH(OH)CH_3 \qquad C_6H_5 CH(OH)CO_2H \qquad C_6H_5 \overset{\overset{\displaystyle CH_3}{|}}{C}(OCH_3)CO_2H$$

VIII   IX   X

$$C_6H_5\overset{\overset{\displaystyle CH_3}{|}}{C}HCO_2H$$

XI   XII

a positive Cotton effect could be demonstrated experimentally [14b] for the methyl ester and the dimethylamide of atrolactic acid methyl ether (X). It has been possible quite recently, using a Perkin-Elmer or Rudolph recording spectropolarimeter, to observe [18] a positive Cotton effect with (+)-hydratropic acid (XI).

Very few aromatic amino acids appear to exhibit Cotton effect curves,[19] but this is quite definitely the case with certain aromatic

---

[17] (a) S. Mitchell, *J. Chem. Soc.*, **1928**, 3258; (b) S. Mitchell and S. B. Cormack, *ibid.*, **1932**, 415.

[18] Unpublished observation by B. Sjöberg.

[19] J. A. Schellman and C. G. Schellman, *Arch. Biochem. Biophys.*, **65**, 58 (1956).

alkaloids [20] such as morphine, codeine, and dihydrocodeine (XII).   In the latter, the only chromophore is the phenolic ring and it appears, therefore, that the observed negative Cotton effects should be attributed to the 283-mμ absorption band of the aromatic moeity.   Substances where the aromatic ring is attached to an asymmetric center bearing a heteroatom also may exhibit Cotton effects.[20a]

14-5.   α-Halo and α-Azido Acids

Only a single investigation [21] is pertinent to this subject, but one can already predict considerable activity in this field once a spectropolarimeter with extended spectral range becomes commercially available.   The earlier studies showed the presence of strongly positive Cotton effect curves with peaks near 250 mμ for the α-chloro-(XIII) and α-bromo-(XIV) propionic acid esters, whereas the corresponding α-azidopro-

$$\underset{\text{XIII}\quad X=Cl;\ R=CH_3}{\underset{\text{XIV}\quad X=Br;\ R=C_2H_5}{\underset{\text{XV}\quad X=N_3;\ R=CH_3}{CH_3\overset{\overset{\displaystyle X}{|}}{CH}CO_2R}}}$$

pionic acid methyl ester (XV) exhibited a negative Cotton effect (trough near 320 mμ).   Optically active iodides, on the other hand, such as derivatives of α-iodopropionic acid, do not seem to show [22] any noticeable Cotton effect, which agrees with the observation (Sec. 9-1A) that the absorption band due to iodine in certain α-iodo ketones is probably not optically active.

The ease of preparation of α-halo acids would make more extensive investigations quite profitable, especially in compounds with more than one asymmetric center.

14-6.   Disulfides and Diselenides

Whereas sulfides and selenides absorb in a region (e.g., λ_{max}^{EtOH} 210 mμ for tetrahydrothiophene) that is as yet inaccessible from a spectropolarimetric viewpoint, a marked bathochromic shift is encountered [4] in di-

[20] J. M. Bobbitt, U. Weiss, and D. Hanessian, *J. Org. Chem.,* **24,** 1582 (1959).

[20a] G. G. Lyle, *Abstr.,* p. 71-P, American Chemical Society Meeting, Atlantic City, Sept., 1959.

[21] W. Kuhn, K. Freudenberg, and I. Wolf, *Ber.,* **63,** 2367 (1930). For preparation of substances see K. Freudenberg, W. Kuhn, and I. Bumann, *ibid.,* **63,** 2380 (1930).

[22] W. Kuhn and H. Biller, *Z. physik. Chem. (Leipzig),* **(B)29,** 256 (1935).

sulfides. The availability [23] of some optically active representatives permitted a rotatory dispersion study,[18] which shows that their absorption bands are indeed optically active. In Fig. 14-3 are collected the rotatory dispersion curves of (+)-tetrahydrothiophene-2,5-dicarboxylic acid (XVI) and of the related disulfide, (+)-o-dithiane-3,6-dicarboxylic acid (XVII). The former shows only a plain dispersion curve, but the disulfide, by virtue of its ultraviolet absorption [24] shoulder at 280 mμ

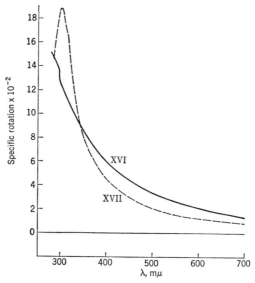

Fig. 14-3. RD curves (methanol) of (+)-tetrahydrothiophene-2,5-dicarboxylic acid (XVI) and (+)-o-dithiane-3,6-dicarboxylic acid (XVII).

($\varepsilon = 150$ in methanol solution), has a strongly positive Cotton effect. Further discussion of disulfides is presented in connection with the rotatory behavior of cystine in Sec. 15-4D.

HO_2C—\[S\]—CO_2H HO_2C—\[S-S\]—CO_2H HO_2C—\[Se\]—CO_2H HO_2C—\[Se-Se\]—CO_2H

XVI   XVII   XVIII   XIX

Even more striking is the situation with the corresponding selenides (Fig. 14-4). (+)-Tetrahydroselenophene-2,5-dicarboxylic acid (XVIII) again possesses a plain curve in contrast to the Cotton effect

[23] A. Fredga, *Arkiv Kemi, Mineral. Geol.*, **11B**, no. 15 (1933); *ibid.*, **12A**, no. 27 (1938).

[24] L. Schotte, *Arkiv Kemi*, **8**, 579 (1955).

curve of $(+)$-o-diselenane-3,6-dicarboxylic acid (XIX) (λ_{max}^{MeOH} 341 and 280 mμ, $\varepsilon = 178$ and 316).[25]

Although polysulfides show an even larger spectral bathochromic shift,[4] the high extinction would appear to preclude rotatory dispersion measurements through the region of absorption unless such substances possess sufficiently high rotations to permit work in very dilute solution, as was possible with the compounds discussed in Sec. 14-7.

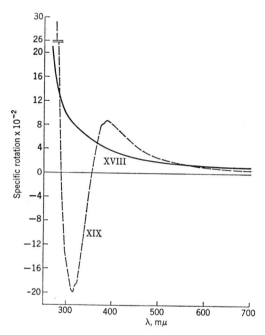

Fig. 14-4. RD curves of $(+)$-tetrahydroselenophene-2,5-dicarboxylic acid (XVIII) (water) and $(+)$-o-diselenane-3,6-dicarboxylic acid (XIX) (methanol).

14-7. Dipyrrylmethenes

A recent rotatory dispersion study [26] of bile pigments has demonstrated that the dipyrrylmethene chromophore (central two rings of XX and XXI) can be strongly optically active.   In spite of the high absorption of these substances around 500 mμ, rotatory dispersion measurements could be performed on the hydrochlorides of stercobilin (XX) and d-urobilin (XXI) which demonstrated the existence of Cotton

[25] G. Bergson, *Arkiv Kemi*, **13**, 11 (1959).
[26] C. H. Gray, P. M. Jones, W. Klyne, and D. C. Nicholson, *Nature*, **184**, 41 (1959).

effects.   That of stercobilin (XX) hydrochloride was negative with a molecular amplitude of 136,000°.   Even more striking is the positive Cotton effect of *d*-urobilin (XXI) hydrochloride, with a molecular

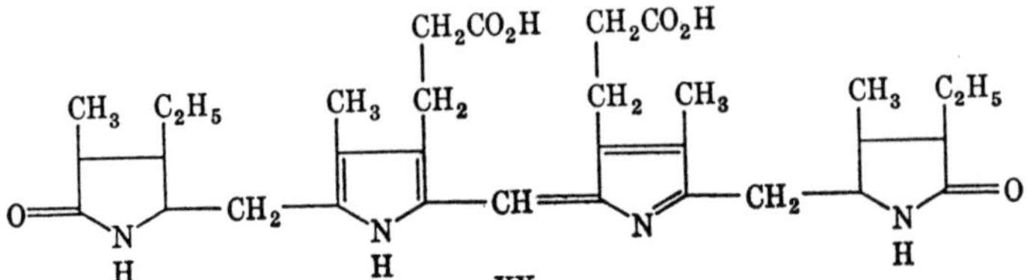

XX

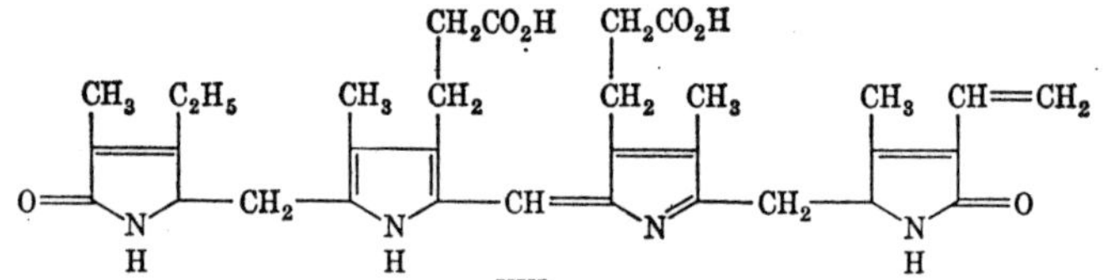

XXI

amplitude of approximately 295,000°; the increase here is probably caused by the fact that the asymmetric centers on either side of the dipyrrylmethene chromophore are also flanked by conjugated systems. Clearly, more extensive investigations of such colored substances are indicated from a rotatory dispersion standpoint.

15 | ALCOHOLS, α-HYDROXY ACIDS, AND α-AMINO ACIDS

15-1. Derivatives of Alcohols. Xanthates

The hydroxyl function absorbs below 200 mμ and it is not surprising, therefore, that organic alcohols exhibit plain dispersion curves (see Chap. 16) with their inherently limited scope for structural and stereochemical conclusions. In many instances, alcohols can be oxidized to the corresponding ketones or aldehydes, whose anomalous rotatory dispersion curves can then be employed in the manner illustrated in Chaps. 4 to 13. Nevertheless, it would be highly desirable to convert a hydroxyl group into a derivative that exhibits a Cotton effect curve. The obvious requirement of such a derivative, aside from ease of preparation, is the presence of an optically active absorption band in a convenient spectral region, and Tschugaeff[1] investigated several colored dixanthates. Subsequent studies, using menthol, borneol, and fenchol as typical alcohols, indicated[2] that xanthates and certain dithiourethanes were suitable for this purpose. Instrumental limitations precluded rotatory dispersion measurements of xanthates through the region of absorption and so were only realized some 20 years later by Lowry and Hudson.[3]

For instance, methyl l-menthyl xanthate (I) exhibits ultraviolet absorption maxima at 353 and 276 mμ and a positive Cotton effect with a peak of $[\alpha]_{385m\mu} + 600°$. Direct determination of the circular dichroism confirmed that the first absorption band was responsible for

[1] L. Tschugaeff, Ber., 42, 2244 (1909).
[2] (a) L. Tschugaeff and A. Ogorodnikoff, Z. physik. Chem. (Leipzig), 74, 503 (1910); (b) ibid., 85, 481 (1913).
[3] T. M. Lowry and H. Hudson, Phil. Trans. Roy. Soc. London, Ser. A, 232, 117 (1933).

this Cotton effect. The corresponding "diphenyldithiourethane," *l*-menthyl N-phenyl-N-thiobenzoylthiourethane (II), showed a maximum in the visible at 515 mμ. This again was shown to be optically active by circular dichroism and rotatory dispersion (negative Cotton effect) measurements.

A recent and more detailed study [4] of such derivatives has shown that the rather high rotatory dispersion amplitudes of the xanthates of borneol [3] and fenchol [3] were somewhat fortuitous, since the appearance

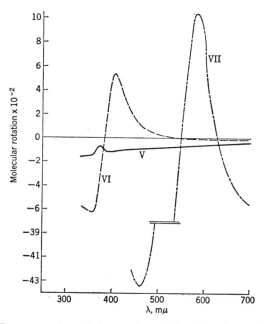

Fig. 15-1. RD curves of methyl *trans*-3-methylcyclohexyl xanthate (V) (isoöctane), trityl *trans*-3-methylcyclohexyl xanthate (VI) (isoöctane), and *trans*-3-methylcyclohexyl N-phenyl-N-thiobenzoylthiourethane (VII) (dioxane).

and amplitude of Cotton effects of xanthates are very dependent upon chemical constitution. The xanthate of a primary alcohol such as methyl 2-methylbutyl xanthate (III) exhibited [4] only a positive plain dispersion curve, while a negative Cotton effect of very small amplitude was encountered with methyl cholestan-3β-yl xanthate (IV). An extensive rotatory dispersion study of xanthates of a variety of alcohols [5] is necessary before more definite conclusions can be reached, and such

---

[4] B. Sjöberg and C. Djerassi, to be published.

[5] In the earlier studies (Refs. 2 and 3) the chromophore was varied and the alcohol was kept constant.

an investigation is now under way in our laboratory. A fairly typical situation is outlined in Fig. 15-1, which shows the rotatory dispersion curves [4] of the methyl xanthate (V), trityl xanthate (VI), and N-phenyl-N-thiobenzoylthiourethane (VII) of *trans*-3-methylcyclohexanol. First of all, the considerably increased amplitude of the Cotton effect of the trityl xanthate (VI) over that of the methyl xanthate (V) confirms the observation of Tschugaeff,[2b] who measured the rotations of the benzyl, diphenyl, and triphenyl (trityl) xanthates of *l*-menthol over the range 657 to 466 mμ. Although he was unable to reach the first extremum and to demonstrate experimentally a Cotton effect, it could already be concluded from his data in the visible region that the rotatory power

I   R=CH₃ S—

II   R=C₆H₅ C—N—

III

IV

V   R=CH₃ S —

VI   R=(C₆H₅)₃ CS —

VII   R=C₆H₅ C—N—

increased with the size of the substituent. Second, the dispersion data of Fig. 15-1, in conjunction with the relevant spectral measurements,[4] show that in each instance the long-wavelength absorption band (V, $\lambda_{max}^{isoöctane}$ 354 mμ; VI, $\lambda_{max}^{isoöctane}$ 370 mμ; VII, $\lambda_{max}^{dioxane}$ 509 mμ) is optically active. From a synthetic standpoint, the xanthates are to be preferred because of their ease of preparation (sodium alcoholate, carbon disulfide, and alkyl halide), but the N-phenyl-N-thiobenzoylthiourethanes (e.g., VII) have the advantage of increased amplitude as well as shift of the Cotton effect curve into the visible spectral range.

15-2.   Derivatives of α-Hydroxy Acids.   Xanthates

A further extension of these rotatory dispersion studies [4] to α-hydroxy acids showed that in this series xanthates are particularly desirable derivatives because Cotton effect curves of appreciable amplitude are obtained in each case and these can be of great utility for establishing configurational relationships.

L-(+)-lactic acid and L-(−)-malic acid are configurationally related,[6] even though their respective rotations at the D line differ in sign. Subsequently, it was demonstrated by Fredga that L-(+)-lactic acid ethyl xanthate (lactic acid ethyl dithiocarbonate) (VIII) [7] still retains a positive rotation, while the corresponding derivative (IX) [8] of L-(−)-malic acid (malic acid ethyl dithiocarbonate) is now positively rotating.

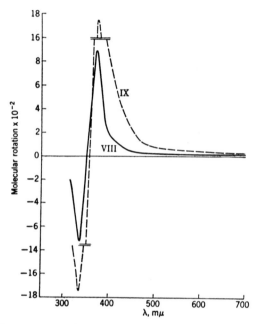

Fig. 15-2. RD curves (methanol) of L-(+)-lactic acid ethyl dithiocarbonate (VIII) and L-malic acid ethyl dithiocarbonate (IX).

In Fig. 15-2 there are reproduced the rotatory dispersion curves of these two xanthates, the positive Cotton effect in each case confirming their configurational identity.

The nature of the hydrocarbon substituent does not appear to play an important role since L-(+)-mandelic acid ethyl xanthate (mandelic

[6] See K. Freudenberg (ed.), "Stereochemie," pp. 662–720, F. Deuticke, Leipzig, 1932; J. A. Mills and W. Klyne in W. Klyne (ed.), "Progress in Stereochemistry," vol. 1, chap. 5, Academic Press, Inc., New York, 1954.

[7] A. Fredga, *Svensk Kem. Tidskr.*, **54**, 26 (1942).

[8] A. Fredga, *Arkiv Kemi, Mineral. Geol.*, **14B**, no. 27 (1941).

acid ethyl dithiocarbonate) (X) also exhibits [4] (Fig. 15-3) a positive Cotton effect. It is interesting to compare this simple measurement with the comparative difficulty encountered [9] in establishing the configuration of the hydroxyl group in mandelic acid by other methods.

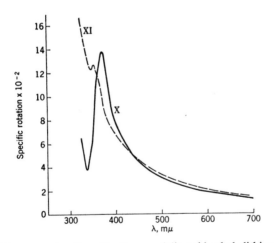

VIII R=H
IX R=CO$_2$H   X   XI

Fredga [7,8] applied the quasi-racemate method to a number of xanthates and their corresponding isomers, where the position of the sulfur and oxygen atoms was reversed. It appeared of interest to examine [4] the effect of this change upon the anomalous rotatory dispersion curve. As demonstrated in Fig. 15-3, L-(+)-mandelic acid ethyl dithiocarbonate (X) [10a] possesses a strongly positive Cotton effect, while this is only

Fig. 15-3. RD curves (methanol) of L-mandelic acid ethyl dithiocarbonate (X) and L-α-mercaptophenylacetic acid ethyl xanthate (XI).

slightly noticeable with the related L-(+)-α-mercaptophenylacetic acid ethyl xanthate (XI),[10b] even though both substances show ultraviolet absorption maxima at identical wavelengths (λ_{max}^{MeOH} 354 and 280 mμ). For secure configurational assignments by means of anomalous rotatory

[9] K. Mislow, *J. Am. Chem. Soc.*, **73**, 3954 (1951), and references cited.
[10] (*a*) A. Fredga, unpublished observation; (*b*) A. Fredga, *Arkiv Kemi, Mineral. Geol.*, **24B**, no. 15 (1947).

dispersion curve comparisons, only the former derivative (oxygen attached directly to asymmetric center) appears useful at this stage.

15-3. Derivatives of α-Amino Acids. Use in Configurational Assignments

A. Dithiocarbamates (N-Dithiocarbalkoxy Amino Acids). The establishment of stereochemical relationships between α-hydroxy and α-amino acids by chemical interrelations [6] is quite complicated, and in several instances the quasi-racemate method [7,11] was found to be effective in comparing an α-hydroxy acid alkyl dithiocarbonate (xanthate) with the corresponding α-amino acid alkyl thiolthionocarbamate (dithiocarbamate or dithiourethane). Since the latter is very readily synthesized by treatment of an alkaline solution of the α-amino acid with carbon disulfide and an alkyl halide and absorbs in an accessible spectral region, a systematic investigation of the rotatory dispersion curves of such derivatives has been undertaken.[12] The results have proved to be very promising and can be summarized briefly as follows:

1. Dithiocarbamates (N-dithiocarbalkoxy derivatives) of α-amino acids show strong Cotton effect curves, whose sign can be related to the configuration of the α-carbon atom.

2. The sign of the Cotton effect of the α-amino acid dithiocarbamate corresponds to the sign of the Cotton effect curve of the configurationally related α-hydroxy acid xanthate, thus affording an extremely convenient means of assigning configurations to such pairs.

3. The amplitudes of the Cotton effect curves of α-amino acid dithiocarbamates are so strong that in the region of the extrema the specific rotation is frequently in excess of 1000°. Therefore even if resort is taken to monochromatic polarimetry rather than to rotatory dispersion curves, the measurements should be conducted in the ultraviolet on the dithiocarbamate, especially if investigations are conducted with partially racemized α-amino acids. For instance, when working with proline, which is 90 per cent racemized, selection of a suitable wavelength in the ultraviolet will still yield specific rotations ranging from 100 to 500°, provided a derivative such as N-dithiocarbomethoxy proline (XIII) is employed.

4. It is very likely that the method can be adapted to a microscale, especially if no effort is made to purify the amino acid derivative. Even when purification is required, it can be conducted in many instances on a small scale. Thus 5.8 mg of L-(−)-proline furnished [12] 2.2 mg of

[11] A. Fredga, Svensk Kem. Tidskr., 53, 221 (1941).

[12] B. Sjöberg, A. Fredga, and C. Djerassi, J. Am. Chem. Soc., 81, 5002 (1959).

the pure, crystalline dithiocarbamate (XIII), which is ample for rotatory dispersion measurements.

The above conclusions are illustrated in Fig. 15-4, where it is shown that the configurationally related dithiocarbamates of L-(+)-alanine [N-dithiocarbethoxy alanine (XII)] and L-(−)-proline [N-dithiocarbo-

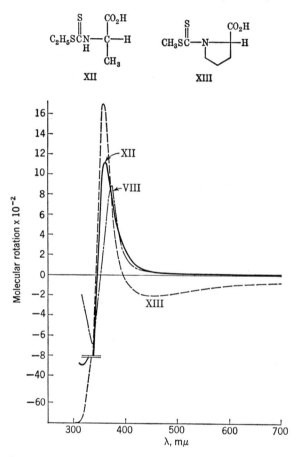

Fig. 15-4. RD curves (methanol) of N-dithiocarbethoxy L-(+)-alanine (XII), N-dithiocarbomethoxy L-(−)-proline (XIII), and L-(+)-lactic acid ethyl dithiocarbonate (VIII).

methoxy proline (XIII)] both show positive Cotton effect curves. Measurements at the sodium D line are particularly confusing in this pair; the amino acids themselves possess opposite-sign specific rotations (while their dithiocarbamates have both negative rotations at the D line), yet are characterized by positive Cotton effect curves. Clearly, the latter is the only reasonable optical rotational criterion for establishing configurations in this series (see also Sec. 15-4D). Included in Fig. 15-4 is the rotatory dispersion curve of the ethyl xanthate (VIII) of L-(+)-lactic acid (lactic acid ethyl dithiocarbonate), which demonstrates the ease with which Cotton effect curves of such derivatives can be employed to assign configurational relationships between α-hydroxy and α-amino acids.

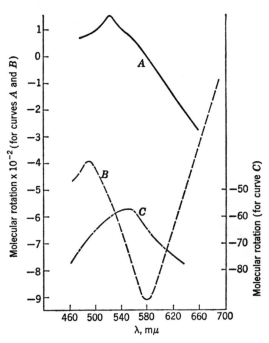

Fig. 15-5. RD curves (water) of copper complexes of L-(+)-alanine (*A*), L-(−)-proline (*B*), and L-(+)-lactic acid (*C*). [*Adapted from experimental data of P. Pfeiffer and W. Christeleit, Z. physiol. Chem., **245**, 197 (1937); ibid., **247**, 262 (1937).*]

It will be noted in Fig. 15-4 that the extrema of the hydroxy acid xanthate curve are somewhat displaced to a longer wavelength as compared with the dithiocarbamates, and this is in complete accord with the actual position of their respective long-wavelength absorption maxima (VIII, λ_{max}^{MeOH} 356 mμ; XII, λ_{max}^{MeOH} 333 mμ; XIII, λ_{max}^{MeOH} 332 mμ).

B. Copper Complexes. The original observation,[13] that the blue copper complex of L-(+)-alanine shows anomalous rotatory dispersion

[13] J. Lifschitz, Z. physik. Chem. (Leipzig), **114**, 491 (1925).

in the visible, prompted a study [14] of these complexes (XIV) in a whole series of α-amino acids. It was observed that amino acids of like configuration at the α-asymmetric center exhibit Cotton effect curves of like sign with an extremum near 530 ± 10 mμ with the exception of the copper complex of L-(−)-proline, for which the entire curve is shifted toward the ultraviolet. This is illustrated in Fig. 15-5, which contains the rotatory dispersion curves of the copper complexes of the same amino acids (alanine and proline), whose dithiocarbamate derivatives (XII and XIII) have already been considered in Fig. 15-4. In α-amino acids possessing only one asymmetric center, rotatory dispersion measurements of copper complexes have proved to be very useful [14a] for configurational assignments and, when suitable precautions are taken,[15] this method can also be employed with amino acids possessing a second asymmetric center.

In one instance [14b] this approach has also been applied when relating the configurations of an α-amino acid with that of an α-hydroxy acid, but this does not seem to be too satisfactory. The example involves the copper complexes of L-(+)-alanine and L-(+)-lactic acid; while both Cotton effect curves (Fig. 15-5) are positive, that of L-(+)-lactic acid has an extremely small amplitude and has to be measured in concentrated solution, because of dissociation of the complex upon dilution. This is an instance in which a comparison of the rotatory dispersion curves (Fig. 15-4) of the corresponding dithiocarbamate (XII) and xanthate (VIII) is much more suitable.

XIV   XV   XVI

One use for which the copper-complex method can be employed to good advantage is in establishing configurational relationships at the α carbon atom of amino acids of the carbohydrate series. Thus the copper complexes of glucosaminic acid (XV) [14b,c] and chondrosaminic

[14] (a) P. Pfeiffer and W. Christeleit, Z. physiol. Chem., 245, 197 (1937); (b) P. Pfeiffer and W. Christeleit, ibid., 247, 262 (1937); (c) P. Karrer and J. Mayer, Helv. Chim. Acta, 20, 407 (1937).

[15] N. Izumiya, M. Winitz, S. M. Birnbaum, and J. P. Greenstein, J. Am. Chem. Soc., 78, 1602 (1956).

acid (XVI) [14c] exhibit Cotton effect curves with a trough near 530 mμ, in contrast to the peak at that wavelength exhibited (Fig. 15-5) by L-amino acid copper complexes, from which it follows that these amino sugar derivatives have the opposite configuration at the α carbon atom. The approach [12] outlined in Sec. 15-3A may be employed only if the amino group is converted selectively into the dithiocarbamate without simultaneous transformation of the hydroxyl functions into xanthates.

15-4. The Rotatory Properties of Natural Amino Acids [16]

A. Historical Introduction. The previous section has shown how the formation of appropriate derivatives and complexes of amino acids introduces groups displaying Cotton effects which are easily studied and which lead to information concerning the configuration of amino acids. In this section, which deals with natural amino acids in which the essential groups remain intact, conclusions must be based mainly, although not exclusively, on plain curves of the type described in Chaps. 2 and 16. This stems from the fact that the absorption bands producing the optical rotation of amino acids are either too intense to permit measurement within them or are located in the as yet unassailable wavelength region below 230 mμ. Thus, although interest and diligence have both been strong, no complete Cotton curve can be recorded.

On the other hand, the status of the rotatory properties of the natural amino acids can by no means be interpreted as unsatisfactory. Much has been learned about the intrinsic rotatory properties of the natural amino acids, and this cannot fail to be of assistance in interpreting the rotatory properties of the more complex molecules of which they form constituent parts. Moreover, with few exceptions, the rotatory properties of amino acids give a clear indication of the configuration at the α carbon atom. The rotatory dispersion approach will be given precedence here, although other techniques will be discussed.

The interrelation between optical rotation and the spatial configuration of amino acids has been quite strong and has played an important role in the history of stereochemistry. Early empirical rules for correlating the optical rotation of amino acids as a function of substitution, pH, wavelength, etc., have proved to be of the highest value. It will be instructive to present the conclusions of earlier work which are appropriate to the problem at hand. Of the wealth of earlier literature, four sets of principles seem most pertinent.

[16] This section was prepared by John A. Schellman, University of Oregon. Many of the results quoted below were obtained in studies supported by the U.S. Public Health Service.

The first of these is the substitution rule, initially utilized by Clough,[17] extended by Freudenberg,[18] and given a broad semitheoretical justification by Kuhn.[19] This rule deals with substances of the types $b-\overset{\displaystyle a}{\underset{\displaystyle d}{C}}-x$

and $b-\overset{\displaystyle a}{\underset{\displaystyle d}{C}}-x'$, where x and x' are similar groups. It states that a given alteration in one of the common groups (a, b, or d) will produce a change in optical rotation of the same sign and magnitude in both substances, provided they are of identical configuration. A shift of opposite sign is an indication of a difference in configuration. This rule is the basis of the commonly accepted fact that the natural amino acids of animal proteins are all of the L configuration.[20] Each new piece of chemical evidence since the original statement of Clough [17] has supported this conclusion and given strength and reliance to the optical rotatory methods of configurational determination.

Second, there is the original correlation of rotatory dispersion and amino acid configuration by Karrer and Kasse.[21] On the basis of studies of just a few amino acids, these workers decided that the natural amino acids in their acidic form "strive toward a positive maximum" at short wavelengths. The investigations of Waser [22] a few years later seemed to discredit this conclusion, and scant attention has been paid to this dispersion technique for the past 35 years. We revive this statement since it will have much in common with our own conclusions.

The third rule stems from the work of Lutz and Jirgensons [23] dealing with the effect of pH on the optical rotation of amino acids, as summarized in Fig. 15-6. These investigators concentrated on the most striking correlation emanating from their studies, namely, the positive shift in rotation which "natural" amino acids undergo when they are transferred from neutral to acid pH. This rule has proved to be most fruitful. It is informative to regard it as a special form of the substitu-

---

[17] G. W. Clough, *J. Chem. Soc.,* **113**, 526 (1918).

[18] K. Freudenberg and M. Meister, *Ann.,* **518**, 86 (1935), and previous papers.

[19] W. Kuhn in K. Freudenberg (ed.), "Stereochemie," p. 412, F. Deuticke, Leipzig, 1932.

[20] A careful review is given by A. Neuberger in M. L. Anson and J. T. Edsall (eds.), "Advances in Protein Chemistry," vol. 4, pp. 297–383, Academic Press, Inc., New York, 1948.

[21] P. Karrer and W. Kasse, *Helv. Chim. Acta,* **2**, 436 (1919).

[22] E. Waser, *Helv. Chim. Acta,* **6**, 54 (1923).

[23] O. Lutz and B. Jirgensons, *Ber.,* **63**, 448 (1930); *ibid.,* **64**, 1221 (1931).

tion rule.   The substitution involved is the conversion of –COO⁻ to
–COOH.   This leads to a positive shift in the rotation for L-amino acids.

The fourth correlation between optical rotation and the configuration
of amino acids which shall be treated is the result of the rotatory dispersion measurements of Patterson and Brode.[24]   On the basis of investigations of 14 amino acids under various conditions of pH over
the spectral range 660 to 440 mμ, they concluded that for L-amino acids
one of the following statements obtains:

"1. the dispersion is normal, positive, and intercepts the zero axis in the
region of the spectrum above 205 mμ squared;

"2. the dispersion is normal, negative, and intercepts the zero axis in the
region below 140 mμ squared;

"3. the dispersion is anomalous and the sign of rotation changes from
negative to positive with decreasing wavelength."

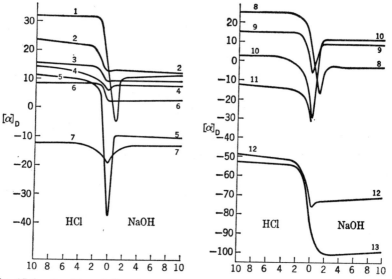

Fig. 15-6. Specific rotation (at sodium D line) of α-amino acids as a function
of pH. The abscissa represents the number of moles of hydrochloric acid or
sodium hydroxide per mole of amino acid in solution (concentration ranging from
0.01 to 0.05 M); temperature, 18 to 20°C. [*Reproduced by permission of the
publisher from D. M. Greenberg in C. L. A. Schmidt (ed.), "The Chemistry of
the Amino Acids and Proteins," 2d ed., p. 578, Charles C Thomas, Publisher,
Springfield, Ill., 1945.*] 1, glutamic acid; 2, arginine; 3, lysine; 4, ornithine; 5,
histidine; 6, alanine; 7, tyrosine; 8, aspartic acid; 9, leucine; 10, tryptophan; 11,
dihydroxyphenylalanine; 12, hydroxyproline; 13, proline.

[24] J. W. Patterson and W. R. Brode, *Arch. Biochem.*, **2**, 247 (1943).

The intercept referred to is the extrapolation of a plot of $1/[\phi]$ versus λ^2, a procedure explained below in Sec. 15-4D. We shall attempt to interpret some of these rules after a consideration of the data.

Most of the dispersion measurements reported in this section are unpublished ones by J. Strem and Y. Krishna Prasad; at the time we were unaware of the extensive study of the rotatory dispersion of 42 amino acids by Otey, Greenstein, Winitz, and Birnbaum.[25] Our own work is given preference only because the details are more readily available to us.

B. Optimum Conditions for Comparison of Rotatory Properties of Amino Acids. This topic has been given a special heading solely to emphasize the fact that most of the following conclusions deal exclusively with the rotatory properties of amino acids under extreme acid conditions. The reasons for this are relatively simple to trace. To get stable sets of measurements one must operate in a pH region in which the rotation is not strongly dependent on pH. As may be seen in Fig. 15-6, an extended plateau exists only under strongly acidic or strongly alkaline conditions. Alkaline conditions are excluded because of the danger of racemization and because of the instability of several of the side chains at high pH. On the other hand, in the neighborhood of pH = 1, all amino acids are stable, soluble, and far from their nearest pK, that of the COOH group. In addition, the rotations display a pattern that is not easily discernible under other conditions. It will be shown that this orderly behavior is attributable to the strong contribution to the rotation of the –COOH group.

C. Structural Features of Alanine. The zwitterion (XVII) of alanine possesses several interesting features as far as its optical rotatory

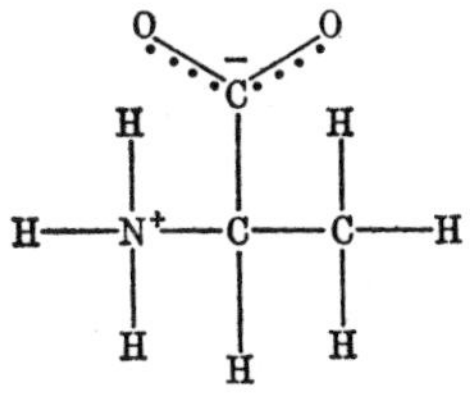

XVII

properties are concerned. Its structure shows that except for the carboxylate ion it has no obvious chromophores. Saturated hydrocarbon moieties generally have no absorption bands above 150 mμ. The NH_3^+ is isoelectronic with –CH_3 and presumably fits into the same category. It is worth noting that in the final analysis the optical rota-

[25] M. C. Otey, J. P. Greenstein, M. Winitz, and S. M. Birnbaum, *J. Am. Chem. Soc.*, **77**, 3112 (1955).

tion must result from the difference in charge of the C and N nuclei, since otherwise the molecule is symmetric.

The symmetry of the four groups in alanine is also interesting. The CH_3^-, NH_3^+, and H- groups are all cylindrically symmetric about the bond connecting them to the asymmetric carbon atom. In addition the $-COO^-$ substituent has a plane of symmetry. For reasons that have been put into quantitative form,[26] high symmetry of groups connected to the asymmetric carbon is very deleterious to the production of optical rotation. The zwitterion of alanine should have a low rotation, and it

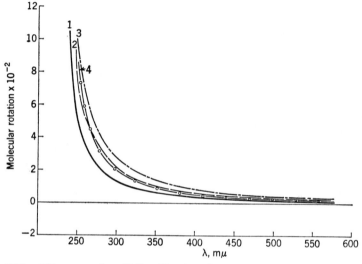

Fig. 15-7. RD curves (aq. HCl, pH = 1) of alkyl-substituted alanines: 1, alanine; 2, α-aminobutyric acid and norleucine; 3, valine and norvaline; 4, leucine.

does: $[\phi]_D^{20} + 1.8°$ This value is of course greatly enhanced at lower wavelengths.

There are a number of ways in which this neat symmetry of alanine can be destroyed. An important one is the addition of acid. This has the effect of introducing the unsymmetrical $-COOH$ group and enhances the rotation. L-Alanine, like L-amino acids in general, shows the positive shift predicted by Lutz and Jirgensons.[23]

The symmetry of alanine can also be destroyed by substituting a group on the β carbon atom. This task has been for the most part done for us by nature and the natural amino acids present us with a family of such compounds. Substituted alanines generally have larger rotations than the present amino acid itself, as may be seen in Figs. 15-7 and 15-9.

[26] W. J. Kauzmann and H. Eyring, *J. Chem. Phys.*, **9**, 41 (1941).

D. Rotatory Dispersion Results. It will be convenient to divide the amino acids that have been investigated into the following categories (see Table 15-1) and to treat them in turn: (1) amino acids with no chromophores [27] beyond the α carbon atom, (2) amino acids with chromophores beyond the β carbon atom, (3) amino acids with β chromophores, (4) amino acids with more than one asymmetric center, (5) cyclic amino acids, and (6) the special case of cystine.

1. *Amino Acids with No Chromophores Beyond the α Carbon Atom.* This heading cannot be taken literally because all groups must absorb somewhere in the spectrum. Yet spectral investigations of alkanes far into the ultraviolet show that in general absorption is negligible above 140 mμ and rather diffuse below this wavelength. Consequently, the saturated hydrocarbon moieties of most molecules, regarded as spectral sources of optical rotation, play a highly suppressed role in the total rotation.[28] Such groups make their presence known largely by means of their interactions on the more active groups of the molecule.

The rotatory dispersion of a number of alkyl-substituted alanines [29] is shown in Fig. 15-7. As discussed above, substitution leads to a slight positive shift of the whole dispersion curve, but the most notable result is the similarity of the plain dispersion curves of this entire group. Evidently the dispersion curves are dominated by the $-CH(NH_3^+)COOH$ part of the molecule and are affected to only a small extent by the nature of the substituent alkyl group.

We should like to draw the conclusion that a major proportion of the rotation of acidic amino acids arises from the carboxyl group. This cannot be done with certainty in the absence of measurements in the region of carboxyl absorption, and such measurements are exceedingly difficult to obtain. Nevertheless, the following evidence points in this direction: (1) the Lutz-Jirgensons rule; [23] the only change that occurs on titration to acidic pH is the formation of the –COOH function; (2) the –COOH group has an absorption band between 215 and 210 mμ; except for amino acids with obvious chromophores, this is the closest band to the visible region of the spectrum and should therefore be prominent; (3) a plot of $1/[\phi]$ versus λ^2 leads to a curve that extrapolates to the vicinity of the –COOH band. As may be seen in Fig. 15-8, this is not the extrapolation of a linear Drude equation (Sec. 1-3) since

[27] We define a chromophore as a group that has a well-characterized absorption band in the Schumann region or above.

[28] In this respect optical rotation differs from the index of refraction, which tends to be dominated by absorption bands of low wavelengths (see W. J. Kauzmann, "Quantum Chemistry," pp. 688ff., Academic Press, Inc., New York, 1957).

[29] A glossary of structural formulas of amino acids will be found at the end of this chapter.

these curves are decidedly not linear.   In fact it should probably be emphasized that within the wavelength range under consideration, no amino acid investigated followed a one-term Drude law.   The rationale behind this extrapolation is as follows.   If one absorption band truly dominates the optical rotation, the plot under consideration will extrapolate linearly to the wavelength of this absorption band.   On the other hand, as dispersion measurements approach an isolated absorption band, its tendency to dominate will become stronger and stronger and the $1/[\phi]$ versus λ^2 plot will turn toward the point on the abscissa that repre-

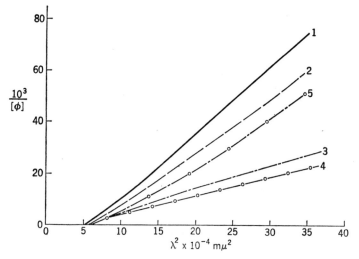

Fig. 15-8. Lowry plots of plain dispersion curves of amino acids: 1, alanine; 2, serine; 3, aspartic acid; 4, asparagine; 5, cysteic acid.

sents the isolated band.   This is a method of locating a powerful rotatory band without making measurements within it, although such extrapolation must be used with caution.   The curves of Fig. 15-8 appear to extrapolate to about $(230 \, m\mu)^2$.

If the premise that the –COOH group dominates the rotation of most acidic amino acids is granted, it will greatly facilitate the interpretation of the results outlined in the sequel.

2. *Amino Acids with Chromophores Beyond the β Carbon Atom.* Most amino acids [29] have substituents that absorb between 160 and 300 $m\mu$.   The guanidinium function of arginine, the –S–CH$_3$ group of methionine, the amide link of glutamine, etc., will serve as examples. Connected directly to the asymmetric carbon atom these groups would presumably contribute to the rotation in a rather powerful way.   It is,

however, a fact that the interactions that lead to optical rotation fall off markedly with distance.[19]   Consequently, chromophoric groups that are distant from the center of asymmetry should contribute less to the optical rotation than those which are close, and this is in accord with the experimental observations.   All amino acids with chromophoric substituents beyond the β carbon atom which have so far been investigated give plain curves similar in form and order of magnitude to the aliphatic derivatives of alanine.   Rotatory dispersion curves for some of the many substances that have been investigated are depicted in Fig.

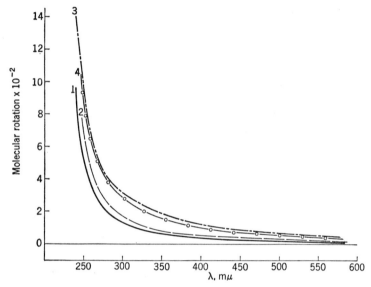

Fig. 15-9.   RD curves (aq. HCl, pH = 1) of: 1, alanine; 2, serine; 3, glutamic acid; 4, lysine and arginine.

15-9.   We shall postpone listing all the amino acids whose dispersion curves fit into the restricted region shown in Figs. 15-7 and 15-9 until the end of the next section, where more additions will be made.

In this chapter, at the present stage of development, similarities in these curves are being stressed.   It is to be hoped that in the future the obvious quantitative differences will lead to additional structural information.

3. *Amino Acids with β Chromophores.*   Substituents on the β carbon atom are evidently sufficiently close to the center of asymmetry to cause large deviations from the general pattern in several cases.   This is demonstrated in Fig. 15-10, where the rotatory dispersion curves of several amino acids, possessing aromatic groups on the β carbon atom,

are compared with the curve for alanine. Absorption with these substances is too intense to permit experimental observations of the Cotton effect, but the absorption bands of the aromatic groups have been implicated by an analytical procedure similar to that described in Sec. 15-4D1. Analysis of the rotatory dispersion of phenylalanine, tyrosine, and tryptophan by means of a two-term dispersion equation leads to Drude terms clearly involving the aromatic absorption band in each case.[30]   Methyl- and ethylcysteine also give curves (e.g., Fig. 15-11) of the same form, and their anomalies are in sharp contrast with the

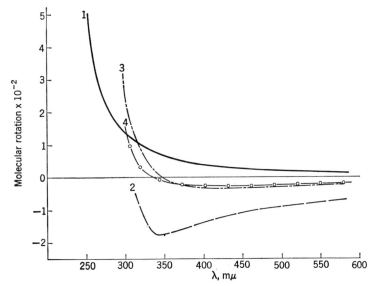

Fig. 15-10.   RD curves (aq. HCl, pH = 1) of amino acids with β chromophores: 1, alanine (reference acid lacking β chromophore); 2, tryptophan; 3, tyrosine; 4, phenylalanine.

"normal" behavior of ethionine and methionine.   This is one of the clearest examples of the suppression of the action of a chromophore in going from the β to the α carbon atom.

Nevertheless, not all β-substituted amino acids behave in this fashion, and the following list contains many amino acids [29] that have plain dispersion curves similar to alanine.   Those marked with asterisks are β-substituted, while the others are members of the first two groups of amino acids: *serine, *cysteine, α-aminobutyric acid, methionine, norvaline, valine, arginine, ornithine, norleucine, leucine, lysine, *aspartic acid, *asparagine, glutamic acid, *histidine, cysteic acid.   Isoleucine

[30] J. A. Schellman and C. G. Schellman, *Arch. Biochem. Biophys.*, **65**, 58 (1956).

will be added to the list in the next section.   It is very likely that several additional amino acids studied by Otey et al.[25] also fall into this category.

In the above list we have not considered the anomalous curves of phenylalanine, tyrosine, tryptophan, S-methyl-, and S-ethylcysteine. Yet it is clear from Figs. 15-10 and 15-11 that at low wavelengths these curves approach the pattern set up by the other amino acids.   Evidently the low-wavelength part of the curves is dominated by the groups attached to the α carbon (presumably the –COOH group).   We see here, even in these cases, a conformance to the rule of Karrer and Kasse: [21]

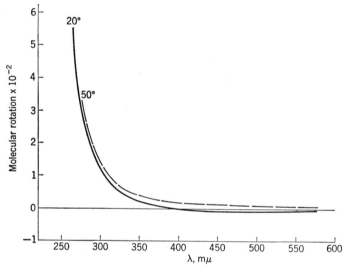

Fig. 15-11.   Effect of temperature on the rotatory dispersion (aq. HCl, pH = 1) of S-ethylcysteine.

The optical rotation of L-amino acids increases positively as the wavelength is decreased.   Rotatory dispersion studies on tyrosine over the range 656 to 527 mμ were used initially to discredit [22] this observation,[21] and this constitutes a telling illustration of the deficiencies of rotatory dispersion measurements conducted only through a narrow spectral region.

α-Substituted amino acids have not been investigated extensively, but studies on phenylglycine show that the rotation is an order of magnitude greater than for the ordinary amino acids.   Presumably the phenyl group dominates in this case (see Sec. 14-4) because of the nearness of its absorption band to the visible region of the spectrum.   Dispersion studies on such systems will be of the greatest interest.

The rotational variations that have so far been encountered in going from one amino acid to another have been described as small, since they amount to only a few degrees at the sodium D line.   It might be argued that these are large changes (30 to 40 per cent) relative to the total rotation of the amino acids, but it is my opinion that the magnitude of rotational shifts and the shape of dispersion curves are usually of much greater significance than the sign and magnitude of individual mono-chromatic rotations.   A demonstration of this is shown in Fig. 15-11. An investigator conducting measurements at 50° would describe S-ethyl-cysteine as dextrorotatory with a normal dispersion curve, while studies at 20° would lead to the conclusion that it is levorotatory with an anomalous dispersion curve.   A comparison of the two curves shows that all that has occurred is a slight shift with temperature which just happens to include the axis of zero rotation.   The total rotation of a molecule is very often the algebraic sum of much larger partial rotations which tend to cancel one another out.   A slight change in one of the partial rotations can change the sign of the rotation but this does not have great physical significance.   We have here additional support for classifying (Sec. 2-2) certain types of curves as "plain" whether or not the rotation changes sign with wavelength.

4. *Amino Acids with More Than One Asymmetric Center.* Hy-droxyproline and cystine belong to this category but will be discussed separately later.   The remaining examples [29] that have been investigated are threonine, isoleucine, phenylserine,[25] and amino tricarballylic acid.[25] Since a new and varying asymmetry is introduced into these molecules, it is not surprising that their rotation bears little relation to the general pattern in most cases.   Curves for the last two amino acids have been described [25] but not presented in detail.   Our own investigations of threonine and isoleucine are shown in Fig. 15-12.   Isoleucine is the only amino acid of this group that gives a plain dispersion curve similar to alanine.   This is presumably because its second asymmetric carbon atom has no strong chromophores attached directly to it.   On the other hand the rotation of isoleucine is the highest at all wavelengths of all the amino acids displaying the typical positive plain dispersion curve.   It is probable that the second asymmetric center supports rather than op-poses the rotation of the α carbon.   Rotatory dispersion studies on *allo*isoleucine would be of interest.

Threonine, on the other hand, has a chromophoric hydroxyl group attached to the second center of asymmetry.   Evidently the rotations from the two asymmetric centers compensate for each other because the dispersion curve is quite flat.   The contribution of the second center is negative and this fact, combined with the substitution rule,[17-19] permits the determination of the configuration of the second center by means of optical rotation. This rule states that a secondary alcohol with the structure XVIII is levorotatory when R2 is smaller than R1. Since the configuration about the α carbon atom is known to be L, the configuration of threonine can now be represented by XIX. This structure was

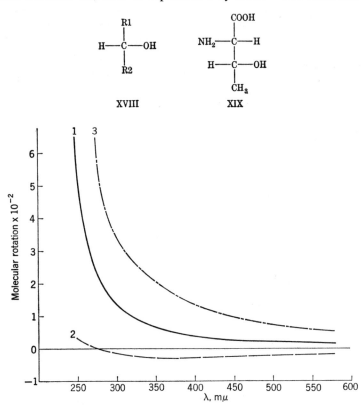

Fig. 15-12. RD curves (aq. HCl, pH = 1) of amino acids with two centers of asymmetry: 1, alanine (reference acid with one asymmetric center); 2, threonine; 3, isoleucine.

clearly demonstrated over 20 years ago [31] and is used here only as a demonstration of the utility of empirical rules of optical rotation.

Greenstein and coworkers have studied extensively [15,25] the rotatory properties of amino acids with more than one asymmetric center. They have, for example, shown [25] that the Lutz-Jirgensons rule [23] applies to the partial rotation of the α carbon atom in some cases even when it apparently is not obeyed by the total rotation. Amino tricarballylic

[31] C. E. Meyer and W. C. Rose, *J. Biol. Chem.*, **115**, 721 (1936).

acid is a particular example because more than one carboxylate group is titrated on addition of acid.

5. *Proline and Hydroxyproline.* These substances fall into a special category because the α carbon atom and the α-amino group are fused into a ring. A rule, proposed by Kauzmann and Eyring[26] on a semi-theoretical basis, states that structural changes which tend to restrict the freedom of rotation about bonds (especially ring formation) produce large increases in the magnitude of the rotation. A comparison of the rotatory properties of the carbonyl group in steroids and other ring compounds (Chaps. 4 to 6) with those of ordinary aliphatic ketones (Chap.

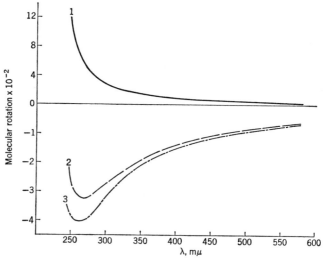

Fig. 15-13. RD curves (aq. HCl, pH = 1) of: 1, norvaline; 2, proline; 3, hydroxyproline.

7) illustrates the generality of this rule. Proline (XX) may be regarded as a ring version of norvaline. Its dispersion curve is negative, shows an extremum, and the magnitude of the rotation is considerably larger at any wavelength than that of norvaline (Fig. 15-13). Since optical rotation is very sensitive to slight structural changes—including free rotation of groups about single bonds—it is not surprising that the drastic limitation of molecular freedom involved in forming the five-

membered ring of proline gives rise to rotatory properties that bear little relation to the remainder of the amino acids. L-Hydroxyproline (XXI) has a hydroxyl group on the α carbon atom which is *trans* to the carboxyl group.[32] Its effect on the rotatory dispersion curve is a simple displacement without change in form. It is interesting that with just these two amino acids the first extremum of a Cotton effect (presumably ascribable to the carboxyl group) appears within the range of measurement. Considerable effort did not permit going to lower wavelengths.

6. *Cystine.* As has often been noted,[26,33,34] optically active disulfides in general are characterized by anomalously large rotations. Cystine (XXII) is no exception; its molar rotation at the sodium D line is −507°, an order of magnitude greater than any other amino acid (Fig. 15-14). The rotation becomes very much greater at neutral pH.[35]

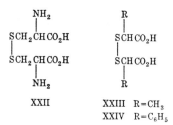

XXII   XXIII R=CH₃
                XXIV   R=C₆H₅

Even if one divides the rotation by two to take into account that cystine is in actuality a double amino acid, the molecular rotation is way out of line with all other amino acids. This anomaly does, however, disappear when the dispersion curve of the corresponding dithiocarbamate is considered.[12]

The rotatory dispersion curve of cystine (XXII) is compared with that of alanine in Fig. 15-14, and two features should be noted: First, the extremum at 268 mμ, which is without doubt associated with a Cotton effect curve centered about the disulfide band of cystine at 255 mμ. The corresponding band of cyclic disulfides (see Sec. 14-6) occurs near 280 mμ; this explains why the cyclic analogues exhibit rotatory dispersion extrema at higher wavelengths.

Second, the sweep and amplitude of the cystine curve is quite distinct from that of alanine, which is rather flat when plotted (Fig. 15-14) on the same scale as the curve of cystine. Similarly, (−)-α-dithio-bis-

[32] A. Neuberger, *J. Chem. Soc.*, **1945**, 429; J. Zussman, *Acta Cryst.*, **4**, 72 (1951).

[33] L. F. Fieser, *Rec. trav. chim.*, **69**, 410 (1950).

[34] A. Fredga, *Acta Chem. Scand.*, **4**, 1307 (1950).

[35] G. Toennies, T. F. Lavine, and M. A. Bennett, *J. Biol. Chem.*, **112**, 493 (1936).

propionic acid (XXIII) [34] and (+)-dithio-bisphenylacetic acid (XXIV) [34] exhibit [36] very steep plain dispersion curves to the limit of the experimental measurements (XXIII, $[\alpha]_{272.5}^{\mathrm{MeOH}} - 5100°$; XXIV, $[\alpha]_{275}^{\mathrm{MeOH}}$ + 8200°), which suggest imminent appearance of the first extremum of a Cotton effect associated with the disulfide band.

A possible explanation for the anomalously high rotations of cystine (XXIII) and certain other disulfides may reside in the fact that the disulfide bridge is an essentially asymmetric group. It is known that this group has a dihedral angle of 90° and that rotation about the bond is strongly hindered.[37] Thus any disulfide compound that is not optically active must consist of a racemic mixture of disulfide groups with

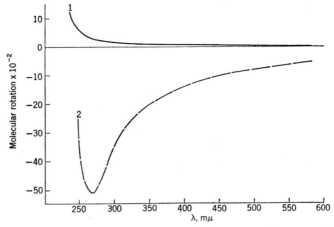

Fig. 15-14.   RD curves (aq. HCl, pH = 1) of: 1, alanine; 2, cystine.

a right- and left-handed screw sense, as is shown in Fig. 15-15.   (The same is true of peroxides but the barrier is much lower.)   In most compounds the two forms have equal energy and equal probability but if, as in cystine, the attached R groups are themselves asymmetric, this equality of probability does not necessarily follow.   In acid solution one has the possibility of hydrogen bonding of the –COOH groups; in neutral solution, the interaction between terminal zwitterions.   With asymmetric terminal groups, one form of the disulfide bridge will be preferred, although which, and to what extent, is difficult to say.   It is worth noting that of all the amino acids, cystine is the only one that has a strong temperature coefficient of molecular rotation, indicating a shift in equilibrium as the temperature rises.

[36] Unpublished observation by B. Sjöberg and C. Djerassi.
[37] M. Calvin, *U.S. Atomic Energy Comm.*, UCRL-2438, p. 3, 1954.

Despite the plausibility of this hypothesis, a glance at the effect of ring formation and pH on the optical rotation of several disulfides reported by Fredga [34] indicates that there are still a number of unexplained phenomena occurring in this group of substances.

E. Determination of Amino Acid Configuration from Optical Rotatory Dispersion Measurements. As shown in Figs. 15-7, 15-9, and 15-10, the determination of the configuration of the α carbon atom of an amino acid is a fairly straightforward matter provided it belongs to one of the first three groups of Table 15-1.

The results can be summed up in a simple rule: L-*amino acids with no or weak chromophores on the β carbon atom give plain positive dispersion curves; amino acids with powerful chromophores on the β carbon atom show anomalies in the near ultraviolet or visible but conform at lower wavelengths.* On the other hand, the amino acids of the last three groups all appear to be rather special cases,[38] and it is difficult

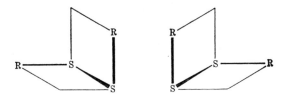

Fig. 15-15.   The asymmetric disulfide group.

to see how rules based on their special rotatory dispersion curves can be applied to amino acids in general except in a fortuitous way.

It is interesting to compare the above method of configurational assignment, made easy in the past few years by the advent of a convenient instrument for ultraviolet polarimetry, with the rules of Lutz and Jirgensons [23] and of Patterson and Brode,[24] which did much good service in the past.   For the first three groups of Table 15-1, we see at once that dispersion measurements near 200 mμ represent a means of giving prominence to the –COOH band and thus have much in common with the acid shift of Lutz and Jirgensons, which also measures the rotation of the –COOH band.   It is accordingly no accident that the results agree with one another.   On the other hand, the dispersion measurements show the very different character of the rotation of the amino acids of the last three categories (Table 15-1) and it seems likely that in some of the cases, e.g., proline (XX), cystine (XXII), etc., the observed positive acid shift for the L form is merely a chance agreement.

[38] Most of these amino acids can, however, be handled readily by considering the rotatory dispersion curves of their N-dithiocarbalkoxy derivatives (Sec. 15-3A).

Table 15-1

Grouping of Amino Acids According to Structural Features * Important to Rotatory Properties

Group 1: aliphatically substituted amino acids	Group 2: amino acids lacking chromophore on β carbon atom	Group 3: amino acids with chromophore on β carbon atom	Group 4: amino acids with two asymmetric centers	Group 5	Group 6
Alanine	Methionine	Serine	Isoleucine	Proline	Cystine and
α-Aminobutyric acid	Arginine	Cysteine	Threonine	Hydroxyproline	derivatives
Norvaline	Ornithine	Aspartic acid	Amino tricarballylic acid		
Valine	Lysine	Asparagine			
Norleucine	Glutamic acid	Tyrosine			
Leucine		Phenylalanine			
		Tryptophan			
		Histidine			
		Cysteic acid			
		S-Ethylcysteine			
		S-Methylcysteine			

* The structural formulas are given in XVIII to XXII and in the glossary at the end of this chapter.

With regard to the rules of Patterson and Brode [24] (given in Sec. 15-4A), it may be shown that it is a characteristic of the plain curves of the first two groups of amino acids (Table 15-1) that at long wavelengths they extrapolate back to λ_0 values above 205 mμ when plotted in the conventional way (see Fig. 15-8). The second rule, *in acid solution*, seems to have special application only to proline derivatives (XX and XXI). The third accounts for the anomalous dispersion curves of Fig. 15-10. It is worth pointing out that the Patterson and Brode rules do not have the pH restriction implicit in the work discussed here. An interpretation of their meaning at other than acid pH will require dispersion measurements over an extended wavelength region.

F. The Optical Rotation of Polypeptides and Proteins.   This minor encroachment on the subject of Chap. 17 is justified because one of the useful results that can come out of a systematic study of the optical rotation of amino acids is more definite information on the manner in which amino acid composition will affect the rotatory properties of a polypeptide or a protein. Under optimal conditions this effect will be minimal, and rotatory dispersion studies on polypeptides are directly connected with the conformation of the polypeptide backbone.

To be sure, there is no direct connection between the optical rotation of a free amino acid and its residue rotation in a polypeptide chain, but some insight can be gained by an application of the Kuhn-Freudenberg substitution rule.[18,19]   Let us consider polypeptides which are long and which contain either the D or L isomer exclusively. The conversion of a free amino acid to an amino acid unit in a peptide chain is equivalent to a double substitution. All those amino acids which are similar enough to have similar dispersion curves should, according to this rule, undergo shifts of the same sign and order of magnitude when converted into a peptide unit. For polypeptides containing these amino acids, the rotatory properties should depend on the polypetide backbone conformation and only little on amino acid composition. This has been confirmed in a number of instances in which a check was possible.[39]   A corollary to this conclusion is that those substituent groups with specific side-chain effects in the form of free amino acids will probably retain them as units in a polypeptide chain. The correlation between backbone configuration and optical rotation is accordingly obscured. Only the first two groups plus a number of members of the third group (Table 15-1) belong to this class of "well-behaved" amino acids. We do not wish to state that regularities between backbone configuration and op-

[39] C. G. Schellman and J. A. Schellman, *Compt. rend. trav. lab. Carlsberg, Sér. chim.*, **30**, no. 27 (1958).

tical rotation do not exist for the special amino acids [40] but only that they differ from those obtained with the more common type of amino acid.

Glossary of Structures of Amino Acids

$$\begin{array}{c} CO_2H \\ | \\ H_2N-C-H \\ | \\ R \end{array}$$

R	Amino Acid
$-CH_3$	Alanine
$-CH_2CH_3$	α-Aminobutyric acid
$-(CH_2)_2CH_3$	Norvaline
$-(CH_2)_3CH_3$	Norleucine
$-CH(CH_3)_2$	Valine
$-CH_2CH(CH_3)_2$	Leucine
$-CH(CH_3)CH_2CH_3$	Isoleucine
$-CH_2OH$	Serine
$-CH_2SH$	Cysteine
$-CH_2CO_2H$	Aspartic acid
$-CH_2CONH_2$	Asparagine
$-CH(OH)CH_3$	Threonine
$-CH_2$ (imidazole ring, N, N)	Histidine
$-CH_2C_6H_5$	Phenylalanine
$-CH_2C_6H_4\text{-}p\text{-}OH$	Tyrosine
$-CH_2$ (indole ring, N, H)	Tryptophan
$-CH_2SO_3H$	Cysteic acid
$-CH_2SCH_3$	S-Methylcysteine
$-CH_2SC_2H_5$	S-Ethylcysteine
$-CH_2CH_2CO_2H$	Glutamic acid
$-CH_2CH_2SCH_3$	Methionine
$-(CH_2)_3NHC(=NH)NH_2$	Arginine
$-(CH_2)_3NH_2$	Ornithine
$-(CH_2)_4NH_2$	Lysine
$-CH(CO_2H)CH_2CO_2H$	Amino tricarballylic acid

[40] See, for example, E. Katchalski, J. Kurtz, G. D. Fasman, and A. Berger, *Bull. Research Council Israel, Sec. A,* **5,** 264 (1956); W. F. Harrington and M. Sela, *Biochim. et Biophys. Acta,* **27,** 24 (1958).

16 | PLAIN DISPERSION CURVES

16-1. Introduction

The vast majority of dispersion measurements [1] prior to 1950 were concerned with plain dispersion curves, as this term is defined in Chap. 2. By their very nature, plain dispersion curves offer much less scope for structural and stereochemical correlations than do Cotton effect curves. Nevertheless, there are several areas in which plain dispersion curves can be of considerable utility and these will be emphasized in this chapter. The special applications of plain dispersion curves to α-amino acids (Sec. 15-4) and helical molecules such as proteins (Chap. 17) are discussed separately by J. A. Schellman and by E. R. Blout.

Improvements in instrumentation resulting in increased spectral range will reduce this aspect of rotatory dispersion, since ultimately every plain dispersion curve becomes anomalous once rotation measurements can be conducted through the region of its optically active absorption band(s). For cases in which this is not feasible experimentally, the Drude equation (Sec. 1-3) can be employed to locate approximately the wavelength corresponding to such an absorption band. The most common organic compounds exhibiting plain curves with the currently available spectropolarimeters are acids and their "nonchromophoric" derivatives (esters, lactones, etc.), alcohols, amines, hydrocarbons, and simple

---

[1] For pertinent reviews see (a) T. M. Lowry, "Optical Rotatory Power," Longmans, Green & Co., Ltd., London, 1935; (b) P. A. Levene and A. Rothen in H. Gilman (ed.), "Organic Chemistry," vol. 2, chap. 21, John Wiley & Sons, Inc., New York, 1938; (c) extensive studies of plain dispersion curves of steroid alcohols and their derivatives as well as of semicarbazones have recently been performed by P. M. Jones and W. Klyne, *J. Chem. Soc.*, **1960**, 871.

olefins.   Ketones and aldehydes may also show plain dispersion curves; this is noted principally with aliphatic substances, in which the chromophore is far removed from the asymmetric center (see Sec. 7-4).   Plain dispersion curves are observed rarely with cyclic ketones, where this phenomenon can be attributed to a counterbalancing of the rotatory contributions of various substituents (see Sec. 13-4F).

Before turning to specific applications, one point must be emphasized. In spite of the inherent limitations of plain dispersion curves, they are still to be preferred to monochromatic polarimetric measurements, especially those conducted at the sodium D line.   Comparisons of rotatory dispersion curves imply comparisons of rotations accumulated at many different wavelengths, and such a procedure is obviously more meaningful than employing only values obtained at one wavelength. A second advantage, illustrated in Sec. 16-2, is that rotations of colorless substances are invariably larger in the ultraviolet than in the visible. This property can be of considerable advantage with compounds exhibiting only a very small rotation in the visible.   Even where monochromatic polarimetric determinations or comparisons are indicated, they will probably be performed eventually at a generally agreed upon wavelength in the ultraviolet (e.g., 300 mμ; see Ref. 1c).

Finally, it should be recalled that the plain dispersion curve of the parent system, lacking a given chromophore, is often required as background for a proper evaluation (see Fig. 2-3) of the shape of the Cotton effect curve due to that chromophore.

16-2.   Examples of Increased Rotation in the Ultraviolet Region

A. Double-bond Isomers.   The wide spread in rotation values which may be observed in the ultraviolet region is exemplified in the plain rotatory dispersion curves of a variety of cholestenes,[2] which differ only in the position of the double bond.   The dispersion curves of three representatives, Δ^4-cholestene (I), Δ^5-cholestene (II), and Δ^6-cholestene

I   II   III

(III) are collected in Fig. 16-1, and it can be seen readily how much larger the specific rotations are at 300 mμ as compared to the sodium

[2] C. Djerassi, W. Closson, and A. E. Lippman, *J. Am. Chem. Soc.*, **78**, 3163 (1956).

D line (589 mμ).   The same behavior has also been encountered [1c] with the corresponding 3α alcohols.

A similar observation has been made in the pentacyclic triterpene series,[3] Δ^{12}-oleanene (IV) exhibiting a positive and $\Delta^{13(18)}$-oleanene (V) a negative plain curve.   At times the effect of the plain dispersion curve may be so strong as to overpower completely the Cotton effect due to a carbonyl group, and this has been noted recently among certain triterpenes [3] with conjugated diene systems.   From a rotatory dispersion standpoint, $\Delta^{11,13(18)}$-oleadien-3β-ol-28-oic acid methyl ester acetate (VI) and $\Delta^{12,18}$-oleadien-3β-ol-28-oic acid (VII) can be considered isomers, since methylation of acid functions or acetylation of hydroxyl groups has been shown [4] to play a negligible role.   As illustrated in Fig. 16-2, the two isomeric dienes possess plain dispersion curves of

IV   V

VI   VII

very steep slope and opposite sign, their specific rotations differing by approximately 9000° at 280 mμ.

B. Carbohydrates.   Sugars have been among the first organic compounds for which extensive rotation data have been accumulated.   Since virtually all the data were obtained at the sodium D line, it is not surprising that this was one of the first areas of organic chemistry in which empirical rules correlating rotatory power at the D line with structure or stereochemistry were enunciated.[5]   In view of the enormous number of D-line rotations recorded in the literature, it is unlikely that this state of affairs will change in the near future.   Nevertheless, it is worthwhile

---

[3] C. Djerassi, J. Osiecki, and W. Closson, *J. Am. Chem. Soc.,* **81,** 4587 (1959).

[4] C. Djerassi and W. Closson, *J. Am. Chem. Soc.,* **78,** 3761 (1956).

[5] For recent refinements and earlier references see A. K. Bose and B. G. Chatterjee, *J. Org. Chem.,* **23,** 1425 (1958).

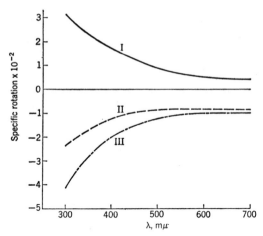

Fig. 16-1. RD curves (dioxane) of Δ^4-cholestene (I), Δ^5-cholestene (II), and Δ^6-cholestene (III).

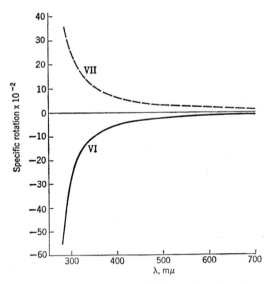

Fig. 16-2. RD curves (dioxane) of $\Delta^{11,13(18)}$-oleadien-3β-ol-28-oic acid methyl ester acetate (VI) and $\Delta^{12,18}$-oleadien-3β-ol-28-oic acid (VII).

to note that a fairly extensive series of investigations with carbohydrates exhibiting plain dispersion curves has been performed [6] and that greatly increased rotations were encountered in the ultraviolet range.

Attention has been called several times [7] to the changes in $[\alpha]_D$ of sugars attending the addition of borate salts. A rotatory dispersion study [8] of this effect may be quite promising, since comparatively small changes in the visible region may be magnified sufficiently in the ultraviolet to become more meaningful.

C. Carboxylic Acids and Derivatives. The steepness of a plain dispersion curve can at times be employed to good advantage, as has been noted [4] in comparing the rotatory dispersion curve of deoxycholic acid (VIII) ($[\alpha]_{250} + 474°$) with that of $3\alpha,12\alpha$-dihydroxyetianic acid (IX)

VIII   IX

($[\alpha]_{250} + 1410°$). Of even greater utility would be a differential study of the plain dispersion curve of a given acid together with those of one or two selected derivatives, similar to the recently reported [1c] rotatory dispersion comparisons of steroidal alcohols and benzoates, in which the latter showed a much greater rotation spread in the ultraviolet than the parent alcohol.

An example is provided in Fig. 16-3 with the rotatory dispersion curves [9a] of (+)-hydratropic acid (X),[9b] its amide (XI), and anilide (XII), the latter exhibiting a plain dispersion curve with greatly in-

[6] T. L. Harris, E. L. Hirst, and C. E. Wood, *J. Chem. Soc.*, **1937**, 848, and preceding seven papers; N. A. Sörensen and B. Trumpy, *Z. physik. Chem. (Leipzig)*, **(B)28**, 135 (1935).

[7] H. S. Isbell, J. F. Brewster, N. B. Holt, and H. L. Frush, *J. Research Natl. Bur. Standards*, **40**, 129 (1948); R. C. Hughes and W. J. Whelan, *Chem. & Ind. (London)*, **1959**, 50.

[8] (a) Preliminary studies along these lines have recently been performed by W. Klyne, Postgraduate Medical School, London (private communication); (b) a rotatory dispersion investigation of the effect of boric acid addition outside the carbohydrate field has already been initiated by K. Nakanishi, Tokyo Kyoiku University (private communication).

[9] (a) Unpublished measurements of B. Sjöberg; (b) several substituted hydratropic acids and derivatives have recently been examined, but unfortunately measurements were not performed below 450 mμ (F. Nerdel and H. Härter, *Ann.*, **621**, 22 (1959); F. Nerdel and H. Würgau, *ibid.*, **621**, 34 (1959).

creased rotation, indicating the effect of the anilide absorption.   Kuhn and Biller [10] found even more striking changes in the dispersion curves of some derivatives of mandelic acid methyl ether, the methyl ester (XIII) exhibiting a negative, and the dimethyl amide (XIV) a strongly positive, dispersion curve.

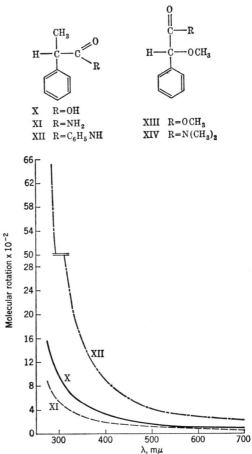

Fig. 16-3.   RD curves (methanol) of (+)-hydratropic acid (X), (+)-hydratropic acid amide (XI), and (+)-hydratropic acid anilide (XII).

Extensive rotatory dispersion studies of a variety of acids and their derivatives will be required before generalizations of stereochemical significance can be made, but one conclusion can probably be reached now—that higher rotations can be anticipated with anilides and substituted anilides as compared to acids and esters.

[10] W. Kuhn and H. Biller, Z. physik. Chem. (Leipzig), (B)29, 1 (1935).

16-3.   Demonstration of Optical Activity

In the field of natural products, it is not uncommon to encounter a substance exhibiting no perceptible rotation at the sodium D line. This is not necessarily a criterion of optical inactivity and, since rotatory power is bound to increase as one proceeds into the ultraviolet, a rigorous decision about optical activity or inactivity can only be reached by an attempted rotatory dispersion study.

For example, the cactus alkaloids [11] pilocereine and piloceredine represent stereoisomeric forms of structure XV and exhibit no per-

XV

ceptible rotation at the sodium D line, although from their origin they would be expected to be optically active. Rotation measurements throughout the experimentally feasible spectral range failed to show any rotation, from which one can conclude that these two alkaloids are in fact racemic modifications.

Even more convincing is the situation found with juniper camphor (XVI), a naturally occurring sesquiterpene [12] of negligible rotation in the visible. This substance was converted into 8,10-dimethyl-8-hydroxy-2-decalone (XVII) as well as 7-isopropyl-10-methyl-1-decalone (XVIII), and, if the parent alcohol (XVI) had been optically active,

XVIII   XVI   XVII

this would have manifested itself in strong Cotton effect curves typical of decalones (Chaps. 5 and 10). The experimental finding that neither ketone showed any rotation over the range 700 to 300 mμ establishes

[11] C. Djerassi, S. K. Figdor, J. M. Bobbitt, and F. X. Markley, *J. Am. Chem. Soc.*, **79**, 2203 (1957); C. Djerassi, T. Nakano, and J. M. Bobbitt, *Tetrahedron,* **2**, 58 (1958).

[12] O. Motl, V. Herout, and F. Sorm, *Collection Czech Chem. Commun.*, **23**, 1293 (1958).

the racemic nature of juniper camphor. Conversely, a degradation product of vitamin B_{12} with no perceptible rotation at 589 mμ was found [13] to exhibit $[\alpha]$ $-68.6°$ at 365 mμ, thus demonstrating its optical activity.

A corollary of the above statements is that the enantiomeric nature of certain naturally occurring substances is best confirmed by rotatory dispersion measurements, rather than just by relying on the coincidence in magnitude and difference in sign of $[\alpha]_D$. $(-)$-Quebrachamine is a well-known alkaloid of undetermined constitution, and recently there was encountered [14] in another plant a new alkaloid, which appeared to be the $(+)$-antipode of quebrachamine. This supposition was confirmed by the observation that the two substances gave plain rotatory dispersion curves, which were of exact mirror-image type throughout the spectral range under examination.

16-4.   Use of Plain Dispersion Curves for Configurational Assignments

Configurational assignments based on rotations obtained at the D line are at times equivocal or even impossible, especially when a plain dispersion curve crosses the zero rotation line somewhere below 589 mμ. This change in sign is, of course, not known to the experimentalist relying only on a measurement of $[\alpha]_D$, and several such examples have been encountered by Sjöberg,[15] who demonstrated the utility of plain dispersion curves for settling certain configurational relationships.

A very instructive example [15] is provided by the three isomeric α-(iodophenoxy)-propionic acids (XIX, XX, and XXI), which have been

synthesized [16] in optically active form for examination of plant-growth-regulating activity. The stereochemical identity as well as absolute configurations of the $(+)$-p-(XIX) and $(+)$-m-(XX) isomers could be settled by the quasi-racemate method,[16] but this failed with the o-isomer

[13] V. M. Clark, A. W. Johnson, I. O. Sutherland, and A. Todd, *J. Chem. Soc.* **1958**, 3283.

[14] F. Walls, O. Collera, and A. Sandoval, *Tetrahedron*, **2**, 173 (1958).

[15] See B. Sjöberg, Abstracts of Papers, *Tionde Nord. Kemistmötet*, Stockholm August, 1959.

[16] Private communication from A. Fredga, University of Uppsala.

(XXI). Nevertheless when the rotatory dispersion curves of these three acids were measured,[15] it was found that all show plain dispersion curves of similar shape (Fig. 16-4), the only difference being that the curve of α-(o-iodophenoxy)-propionic acid (XXI) starts on the negative side in the visible and only crosses the zero rotation axis below 350 mμ. It is clear, therefore, that the p- and m-acids with positive rota-

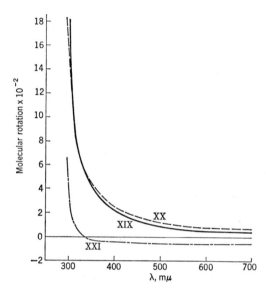

Fig. 16-4. RD curves (methanol) of (+)-α-(p-iodophenoxy)-propionic acid (XIX), (+)-α-(m-iodophenoxy)-propionic acid (XX), and (−)-α-(o-iodophenoxy)-propionic acid (XXI).

tions at the D line and the o-acid with negative sign at the D line are configurationally related. The plant physiological tests,[16] performed subsequent to these dispersion measurements,[15] proved to be consistent with these stereochemical assignments.

A similar "crossing over" has already been recorded [17] with the rotatory dispersion curves of certain diarylpropanols, which represent important reference compounds [18] for absolute configurational assignments of catechins and for which it was pointed out [18] that "no conclusions can be drawn in the diarylpropanol series by comparisons of the signs of rotation of different compounds at the D line."

[17] C. Djerassi, *Record Chem. Progr.*, **20**, 138 (1959), fig. 17.

[18] A. J. Birch, J. W. Clark-Lewis, and A. V. Robertson, *J. Chem. Soc.*, **1957**, 3586.

17 | POLYPEPTIDES AND PROTEINS*

17-1. Introduction

Polypeptides and proteins are polymers composed of α-amino acids joined through secondary amide (peptide) linkages. The amino acids (except glycine) in proteins are all optically active, since the four groups joined to each α carbon atom are different, i.e., each α carbon atom is asymmetric. In addition, certain amino acids (e.g., threonine) have another asymmetric carbon atom in their side chains. As far as is known the *configuration* around the α carbon atom in the naturally occurring amino acids of proteins is the same, and these amino acids belong to the L series. (Some D-amino acids have been shown to be components of naturally occurring low-molecular-weight polypeptides such as the gramicidins and polymixins.) Both synthetic polypeptides and proteins show optical rotatory properties that depend on their amino acid composition and their molecular structure.

Since high-molecular-weight polypeptides and proteins consist of many amino acid residues (typically 100 or more), it is apparent that the atoms in a molecule of the general type shown in Fig. 17-1 can occupy several positions in space, as greater freedom of rotation is possible

around each $-CH-\overset{\overset{O}{\|}}{C}-$ and each $-CH-NH-$ bond of the "backbone"

than around the planar $-\overset{\overset{O}{\|}}{C}-NH-$ bonds. Thus to specify the structure

* The entire chapter is a contribution by Elkan R. Blout.

238

of such molecules it is necessary not only to ascertain the *configuration*[1] of the atoms or molecular groups around the asymmetric (α) carbon atoms, but also to specify the *conformation*[1] or spatial relationships of the various groups comprising the whole molecule. It is in conformational determinations that optical rotatory properties of such molecules are useful.

The synthetic polypeptides that have been described to date are relatively simple (that is, composed of only a few different amino acids) compared with proteins, which generally contain 18 or more different amino acids. Therefore we will first treat the optical rotatory properties of synthetic polypeptides before considering the proteins.

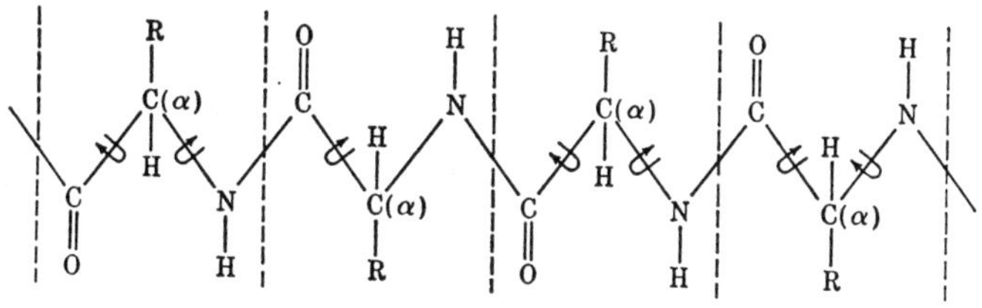

Fig. 17-1. A schematic representation of a portion of a polypeptide or protein molecule.

17-2.   The Optical Rotatory Properties of Synthetic Polypeptides

The intensive investigation of the optical rotatory properties of polypeptides has been undertaken only in the last few years with the availability of methods for the synthesis of polypeptides of high molecular weight[2]—molecular weights over 15,000 and comparable to those of proteins.

A. Random Conformations of Polypeptides. First, we define a polypeptide chain in which the component amino acid residues have no periodic internal structure as being in the random coil or, better, the random conformation. This conformation results when polypeptides

[1] Both "configuration" and "conformation" have been used with the same meaning by workers in this field. We are now convinced that "configuration" should be restricted to its original sense—namely, the spatial relationship around an asymmetric carbon atom—whereas "conformation" refers to the shape of the molecule in its entirety. In this chapter we so use these words.

[2] See, for example, (a) E. R. Blout and R. H. Karlson, *J. Am. Chem. Soc.*, **78**, 941 (1956); (b) M. Idelson and E. R. Blout, *ibid.*, **80**, 4631 (1958); (c) E. R. Blout and M. E. DesRoches, *ibid.*, **81**, 370 (1959); (d) E. Katchalski and M. Sela in "Advances in Protein Chemistry," vol. 13, p. 244, Academic Press, Inc., New York, 1958.

are dissolved in strongly hydrogen bonding solvents, or by appropriately adjusting the pH of aqueous solutions of water-soluble ionic polypeptides.

Rotatory dispersions of polypeptides in the random conformation show what has been described (cf. Chap. 2) as either a positive plain curve or a negative plain curve. Examples of both these types of optical rotatory dispersion data obtained from polypeptides are illus-

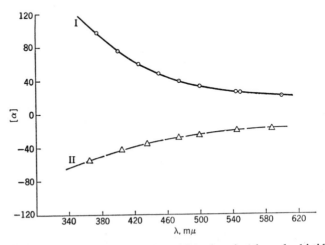

Fig. 17-2. RD curves (dichloroacetic acid) of poly-1-benzyl-L-histidine (I) (Ref. 35) and poly-γ-benzyl-L-glutamate (II) (Ref. 28).

trated in Fig. 17-2. These data may be represented by the simple Drude equation, where the specific rotation $[\alpha]_\lambda$ is a function of λ.

$$[\alpha]_\lambda = \frac{K'}{\lambda^2 - \lambda_c^2} \tag{1}$$

Many proteins exhibit this same type of rotatory dispersion, and these data will be discussed below. In Eq. (1) K' and λ_c are constants; the prime is used to indicate that the refractive-index correction term $\left(\dfrac{n^2 + 2}{3}\right)$ has been incorporated into K'. This equation has the form first proposed by Drude and is called the *simple* Drude equation. It should be noted that λ_c is used here rather than λ_0 since the latter symbol has been reserved for the anomalous dispersion shown by certain polypeptides and proteins [see Eq. (4) below]. It follows from Eq. (1) that $1/[\alpha]$ is a linear function of λ^2; with $1/K'$ the slope and λ_c^2 the intercept on the λ^2 axis. This type of plot was extensively used by Lowry, although the same information may be derived from a plot of $\lambda^2[\alpha]$ versus $[\alpha]$, in which case λ_c is obtained from the square root of the slope and K' from the intercept.[19]   The data in Fig. 17-2 are replotted in Fig. 17-3 in this manner.

The molar rotation is defined as

$$[\phi]_\lambda^T = [\alpha]_\lambda^T \left(\frac{M}{100} \right) \qquad (2)$$

where $[\phi]_\lambda^T$ is the molar rotation at wavelength λ and temperature T and $[\alpha]_\lambda^T$ is the specific rotation. $[\phi]$ is not very useful with large molecules such as polypeptides and proteins because the molar rotation of polypeptides, as well as other high-molecular-weight substances derived from optically active monomers, is a function of molecular weight and con-

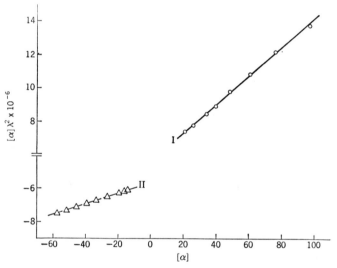

Fig. 17-3. Modified Lowry plot of rotatory dispersion data from Fig. 17-2. Polybenzyl-L-histidine (I) (Ref. 35), $\lambda_c = 290$ mμ, and poly-γ-benzyl-L-glutamate (II) (Ref. 28), $\lambda_c = 180$ mμ, in dichloroacetic acid.

formation.   Therefore, it is apparent that the most informative measure of rotatory properties of such substances would be the rotation per residue or monomer unit.   In practice the mean residue rotation $[R]$, defined by

$$[R]_\lambda^T = \frac{[\phi]_\lambda^T}{n} = [\alpha]_\lambda^T \left(\frac{MRW}{100} \right) \qquad (3)$$

where n is the number of peptide units in the molecule and MRW is the mean residue weight, is useful.   It has been pointed out that this is the most convenient quantity for discussing the rotatory properties of proteins and polypeptides, since all that need be known to evaluate it is the specific rotation [α], and the mean residue weight.   In Table 17-1 there are listed the residue rotations, [R'] ([R] corrected for the refractive index of the solvent) for a variety of polypeptides.

From the data in Table 17-1 it is apparent that the mean residue rotations vary considerably even when the peptides are in random conformation and presumably the only contribution to the rotation is that of the individual amino acid residues.   In those polypeptides in which the attachment to the β carbon atom is a nonoptically active saturated hydrocarbon group, the effect of the side chain is small.   When the β carbon substituent is other than –CH$_2$–, such as in aspartic acid, tyrosine, histidine, or proline, the effect is large.   The implications of these data in the interpretation of optical rotatory dispersions of proteins will be discussed below.

B. Helical Conformation of Polypeptides.   Although it is generally recognized that at present there is no precise theoretical correspondence between optical rotation and conformation, the already determined correlations between rotatory properties and structure make it apparent that optical rotatory dispersion is one of the best qualitative methods for detecting changes in conformation of very large optically active molecules.   Soon after the suggestion by Pauling and Corey [3a] that a totally intramolecularly hydrogen bonded structure, the α helix (see Fig. 17-4), might be the important structural feature in many synthetic polypeptides and in proteins, Cohen pointed out that the changes in optical rotation that accompany the unfolding or denaturation of proteins may be due to changes from helical structures to more random conformations.[4] Since such helices are dysymmetric they might contribute a special "helical" rotation.   Moffitt [5] pursued this suggestion and further proposed that since a polypeptide helix, owing to its internal hydrogen bonding, was a cooperative unit, such helices might behave optically as a single absorbing system, i.e., an exciton system.   Moffitt treated this idea quantum mechanically and concluded from his calculations that the usual spreading of an absorption band characteristic of an exciton system was sufficiently great to cause the optical rotatory dispersion of helices to become anomalous.   He then derived a phenomenological equation:

[3] (a) L. Pauling and R. B. Corey, *J. Am. Chem. Soc.*, **72**, 5349 (1950); (b) R. B. Corey and L. Pauling, *Rend. ist. lombardo sci.*, P1, **89**, 10 (1955).

[4] C. Cohen, *Nature*, **175**, 129 (1955).

[5] (a) W. Moffitt, *J. Chem. Phys.*, **25**, 467 (1956); (b) W. Moffitt and J. T. Yang, *Proc. Natl. Acad. Sci. U.S.*, **42**, 596 (1956); (c) W. Moffitt, *ibid.*, **42**, 736 (1956).

$$[m']_\lambda = [R]_\lambda\left(\frac{3}{n^2+2}\right) = [R']_\lambda = a_0\frac{\lambda_0^2}{\lambda^2 - \lambda_0^2} + b_0\frac{\lambda_0^4}{(\lambda^2 - \lambda_0^2)^2} \quad (4)$$

where $[m']_\lambda$ in Moffitt's terminology is equivalent to $[R']_\lambda$ in our notation (the mean residue rotation at wavelength λ), b_0 and λ_0 are constants

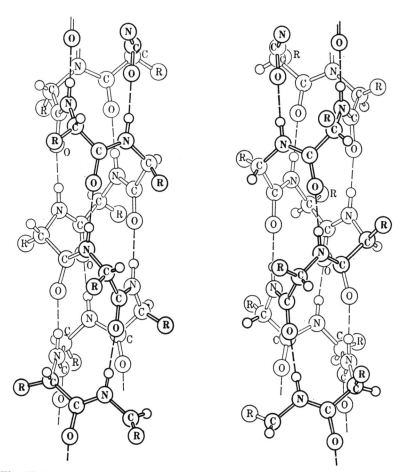

Fig. 17-4. A drawing showing two possible forms of the α helix; the one on the left is a left-handed helix, the one on the right is a right-handed helix. In both, the amino acid residues have the L configuration. [*Reproduced from R. B. Corey and L. Pauling (Ref. 3b).*]

characteristic of the helix, and the a_0 term contains both helix and residue contributions. It should be noted that Moffitt's quantitative calculation has proved to be oversimplified, and since his theory as now

Table 17-1

Residue Rotation $[R']$ (Corrected for Solvent Refractive Index) for Some Synthetic L-Polypeptides in "Helical" and "Random-coil" Solvents

Polypeptides	Wavelength, mμ	"Helical" solvents $[R']_\lambda$	"Helical" solvents Solvent	"Random-coil" solvents $[R']_\lambda$	"Random-coil" solvents Solvent	$\Delta[R']_\lambda^{(e)}$
Group I						
Poly-L-alanine[10]	589	+ 21	CHCl₃:DCA 99:1	−110	TFA	+131
Poly-L-α-amino-n-butyric acid[10]	589	+ 19	CHCl₃:DCA 9:1	−107	TFA	+126
Poly-γ-benzyl-L-glutamate[19]	589	+ 18	EDC	− 28	DCA	+ 46
Poly-γ-benzyl-L-glutamate[19]	546	+ 18	EDC	− 31	DCA	+ 49
Poly-γ-benzyl-L-glutamate[8]	589	+ 16	Dioxane	− 76	TFA	+ 92
Poly-N-carbobenzoxy-L-lysine[a]	589	+ 7	DMF			
Poly-L-glutamic acid[2b]	546	− 9	0.2 M NaCl in H₂O, pH 4.5	−127	0.2 M NaCl in H₂O, pH 8	+118
Poly-L-leucine[10]	589	− 12	Benzene	−111	TFA	+ 99
Poly-L-lysine[a]	589	− 37	0.2 M NaCl in H₂O, pH 11	−132	0.2 M NaCl in H₂O, pH 7	+ 95
Group II						
Poly-L-tyrosine[b]	589	+218	DMF	+ 35	DMF:DCA 1:24	+183
Poly-o-acetyl-L-serine[o]	546	+119	EDC:DCA 3:1	+ 29	DCA	+ 90
Poly-1-benzyl-L-histidine[d]	546	+ 19	Benzyl alcohol	+ 44	DCA	+ 25
Poly-L-serine[c]	546	− 6	10 M LiBr in H₂O	− 18	8 M urea in H₂O	+ 12
Poly-L-histidine · 1/2 H₂O[d]	546	−242	0.2 M NaCl in H₂O, pH 6	− 75	0.2 M NaCl in H₂O, pH 2.5	−167

Poly-β-benzyl-L-aspartate[13]	546	−252	CHCl₃		− 27	DCA	−225
Poly-1-benzyl-L-histidine dichloroacetate salt[a]	546	−345	CHCl₃		+ 44	DCA	−395

Group III

Poly-L-proline[31,32,33]	546	−578	Form II, HOAc		+ 36	Form I, HOAc	−614
Poly-o-acetyl-L-hydroxy-proline[f]	589	−210	Form II, 90% formic acid		+ 30	Form I, 90% formic acid	−240
Poly-L-hydroxyproline[f]	589	−362	H₂O				

Solvent abbreviations: DCA, dichloroacetic acid; EDC, 1,2-dichloroethane; HOAc, acetic acid; TFA, trifluoroacetic acid; DMF, dimethylformamide; CHCl₃, chloroform.

[a] J. Applequist, Ph.D. thesis, Harvard University, 1958.

[b] J. Coombes, unpublished results; E. Katchalski, "Proceedings of the IVth International Congress of Biochemistry, Vienna," Pergamon Press, London, 1959.

[c] G. D. Fasman and E. R. Blout, unpublished results.

[d] G. D. Fasman, K. Norland, E. Katchalski, and E. R. Blout, unpublished results.

[e] $\Delta[R']_\lambda$ as reported here may be considered crudely to consist of two parts. The first, $\Delta[R']_\lambda^H$, represents the change in "helical" or "conformational" optical rotation as distinguished from $\Delta[R']_\lambda^E$, which is the change in the intrinsic residue rotation caused by the environmental changes that accompany the transition from "helix" to "random coil." That is, $\Delta[R']_\lambda = \Delta[R']_\lambda^H + \Delta[R']_\lambda^E$.

[f] J. Kurtz, G. D. Fasman, A. Berger, and E. Katchalski, *J. Am. Chem. Soc.*, **80**, 393 (1958).

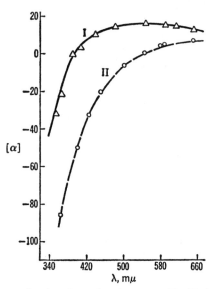

Fig. 17-5. RD curves of poly-γ-benzyl-L-glutamate (I) (Ref. 28) in chloroform and poly-α,L-glutamic acid (II) (Ref. 29) in 2:1 dioxane: H_2O, 0.2 M NaCl, pH 4.7.

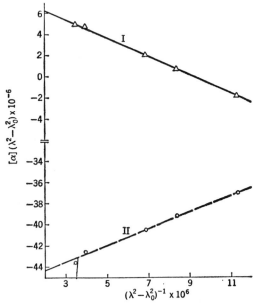

Fig. 17-6. Moffitt plot of the optical rotatory dispersion of poly-γ-benzyl-L-glutamate (I), b_0 −630, and poly-β-benzyl-L-aspartate (II), b_0 +630, in $CHCl_3$ with $\lambda_0 = 212$ mμ.

revised [6] does not take the same form, Eq. (4) should now be regarded as an empirical equation, albeit a useful one, as indicated below.

The optical rotatory dispersions of several polypeptides in weakly hydrogen bond breaking solvents (often called helical solvents) have been measured, and the results for two of them are shown in Fig. 17-5 as plots of $[\alpha]$ versus λ. These data do not fit a simple Drude equation but are "anomalous" (see Chap. 2). Such dispersion results may be plotted in the general form proposed by Moffitt, that is, $[R'](\lambda^2 - \lambda_0^2)$ versus $1/(\lambda^2 - \lambda_0^2)$ (see Fig. 17-6). To determine the value for λ_0 the calculations were plotted for various values of this parameter until a straight line was obtained; this value of λ_0 was found to be 212 ± 5 mμ. The slope of the line determines b_0, and its intercept on the ordinate axis determines a_0. Furthermore, Moffitt and Yang [5b] have found that b_0 and λ_0, at least for polybenzyl-L-glutamate, appear to be substantially independent of the nature of the solvent, provided the helical conformation is maintained. The solvent-dependent term is a_0. These investigations established that b_0, the coefficient of the term that is characteristic of the helical form of polypeptides, had a value of approximately -600 for poly-α,L-glutamic acid and poly-γ-benzyl-L-glutamate in the helical conformation. The values of b_0 for some synthetic polypeptides are shown in Table 17-2. From the derivation of Eq. (4) it follows that the sign of b_0 is negative for right-handed helices and positive for left-handed helices. Soon after Moffitt's work, Cohen and Szent-Gyorgyi [7] pointed out that the coefficient b_0 in his expression could be used as a measure of helix content.

C. Rotatory Dispersion and the Sense of the Helix. A polypeptide helix may have two senses of twist which are nonsuperimposable. Since polypeptides can be made with any proportion of D and L isomers of one amino acid, an investigation of the optical rotation of such polymers in the helical conformation may lead to a determination of the rotation of the helix itself. This information can be obtained by plotting the rotations of a series of synthetic polypeptides comprising varying ratios of the D and L isomers of one amino acid and extrapolating the straight-line portion of the plot to the 1:1 D:L ratio. The plot of data obtained from a series of such polypeptides is shown in Fig. 17-7a, and the extrapolation to 50 per cent D residues is shown by the dashed line. The values for the residue rotations of several polypeptides obtained by this general technique are shown in Table 17-3. The fact that the data in benzene solution are linear over a part of the compositional range im-

---

[6] W. Moffitt, D. D. Fitts, and J. G. Kirkwood, *Proc. Natl. Acad. Sci. U.S.*, **43**, 723 (1957).

[7] C. Cohen and A. Szent-Gyorgyi, *J. Am. Chem. Soc.*, **79**, 248 (1957).

Table 17-2
Dispersion Constants (b_0 and λ_c) of Some Synthetic Polypeptides

Polypeptides	"Helical" Solvents			"Random-coil" solvents		
	$b_0{}^*$	λ_c	Solvent	$b_0{}^*$	λ_c	Solvent
Group I						
Poly-L-alanine	−650[a]		Film	−390[b]		DCA
Poly-γ-benzyl-l-glutamate	−635[b]	NL	EDC	0	210[28]	Hydrazine
Poly-l-glutamic acid[c]	−610	NL	H₂O, pH 4.4	+50	202	H₂O, pH 10.5
Poly-l-leucine[b]	−650		DCA	−177		TFA
Poly-l-lysine[g]	−650		0.2 M NaBr in H₂O, pH 11.5	0	212	H₂O, pH 6.8
Poly-N-carbobenzoxy-l-lysine[g]	−625		DMF			
Group II						
Poly-L-tyrosine[d]	+540	237	0.15 M NaCl in H₂O, pH 10.85†	+450	330	0.15 M NaCl in H₂O, pH 12.3‡
Poly-o-acetyl-l-serine[e]	0	214	DCA:EDC 25:75	0	120	DCA
Poly-1-benzyl-l-histidine[f]	NL	NL	Benzyl alcohol	+350	285	DCA
Poly-l-serine[e]	0	290	10 M LiBr in H₂O 0.2 M NaCl in H₂O	0	250	8 M urea in H₂O 0.2 M NaCl in H₂O
Poly-l-histidine · 1/2 H₂O[f]	0	216	H₂O, pH 6	0	193	H₂O, pH 3.7
Poly-β-benzyl-l-aspartate[13]	+611		CHCl₃			
Poly-1-benzyl-l-histidine dichloroacetate salt[f]	+80	205	CHCl₃	+350	285	DCA
Group III						
Poly-l-proline[32]	0	206	Form II, HOAc	NL	NL	Form I, HOAc

See footnotes on p. 249.

plies that one sense of helix persists in this range of L + D isomers. As the proportion of D residues increases, the negative contributions of the L-asymmetric group is largely canceled out. When the fraction L/(D + L) is less than 0.7, the helices are no longer of one sense.

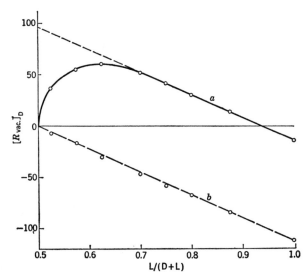

Fig. 17-7. Optical rotation of copolymers of L- and D-leucine: (*a*) in benzene, (*b*) in trifluoroacetic acid. Concentration 0.2 per cent weight per volume. [*Reproduced from A. R. Downie, A. Elliott, W. E. Hanby, and B. R. Malcolm, Proc. Roy. Soc. (London), **A242**, 325 (1957), by permission of the editor.*]

It has been pointed out by several workers that in a strongly hydrogen bond breaking solvent the optical rotation of copolymers of L and D residues is a linear function of composition. An example of such data is shown in Fig. 17-7*b*. As expected, the rotation becomes zero when

Solvent abbreviations: DMF, dimethylformamide; HOAc, acetic acid; DCA, dichloroacetic acid; EDC, 1,2-dichloroethane; TFA, trifluoroacetic acid; NL, non-linear plot.

* b_0 calculated with $\lambda_0 = 212$ mμ.
† Less than 50 per cent ionized.
‡ ~100 per cent ionized.
[a] A. Elliott, W. E. Hanby, and B. R. Malcolm, *Nature, **180**,* 1340 (1957).
[b] K. Imahori, P. Doty, and E. R. Blout, unpublished results.
[c] T. Miyazawa and E. R. Blout, unpublished results.
[d] J. Coombes, unpublished results.
[e] G. Fasman and E. R. Blout, unpublished results.
[f] G. Fasman, K. Norland, E. Katchalski, and E. R. Blout, unpublished results.
[g] J. Applequist, Ph.D. thesis, Harvard University, 1958.

Table 17-3

Helical Rotations of Polypeptides

Polypeptide	$[R']_D^H$	Solvent
Poly-L-leucine[10]	96	Benzene
Poly-γ-benzyl-L-glutamate[8]	90	Dioxane
Poly-L-alanine[10]	82	$CHCl_3$:DCA 99:1
Poly-α-amino-n-butyric acid[10]	81	$CHCl_3$:DCA 9:1
Poly-γ-benzyl-L-glutamate[9]	77	$CHCl_3$
Poly-γ-benzyl-L-glutamate[10]	75	Dioxane, $CHCl_3$, pyridine
Poly-γ-benzyl-L-glutamate[10]	68	Dimethyl formamide, pyridine
Theoretical contribution of a right-handed α helix[11]	96	

the number of L isomers equals the number of D isomers.   Thus the
rotation is proportional to the excess of L over D residues.   There is no
optical rotation due to helical molecules, and the polypeptide chains
must therefore be in random conformation.   In this case, of course, the
assumption is made that the optical rotation of the monomer units is
additive; this assumption has been supported by the straight-line graphs
obtained for a variety of solvents and polypeptides.

Using preformed poly-γ-benzyl-L-glutamate to initiate the polymerization of a series of mixtures of D and L N-carboxy anhydrides and applying appropriate corrections for the excess L residues in the polypeptide,
Doty and Lundberg [8] estimated the rotatory dispersion of $[R']_λ^H$ at λ's between 350 and 750 mμ and found $[R']_D^H = +90°$ where $[R']_λ^H$ is the contribution of a *presumably right-handed helix*.   The dispersion of this
racemic helix showed the form of a positive plain curve; from a Moffitt
plot, $b_0 = -500$ with $λ_0$ set at 212 mμ.   With D,L copolymers of poly-γ-
benzyl glutamate Blout et al.[9] found $[R']_D^H = +77°$ while Downie et al.[10]
obtained $[R']_D^H = +96°$ and $b_0 = -513$ for a racemic polyleucine helix.
In the Fitts and Kirkwood [11] synthesis of the Moffitt model and their
original model of the α helix, the calculated rotatory dispersion of an
infinitely long helical macromolecule is in impressive numerical agree-

[8] P. Doty and R. D. Lundberg, *Proc. Natl. Acad. Sci. U.S.*, **43**, 213 (1957).

[9] E. R. Blout, P. Doty, and J. T. Yang, *J. Am. Chem. Soc.*, **79**, 749 (1957).

[10] A. R. Downie, A. Elliott, W. E. Hanby, and B. R. Malcolm, *Proc. Roy. Soc.*
(*London*), **A242**, 325 (1957).

[11] D. D. Fitts and J. G. Kirkwood, *Proc. Natl. Acad. Sci. U.S.*, **42**, 33 (1956);
J. Am. Chem. Soc., **78**, 2650 (1956); *Proc. Natl. Acad. Sci. U.S.*, **43**, 1046 (1957).

ment with this experimental work. They point out that while the numerical agreement may be fortuitous (calculated $[R']_D = 96°$) the choice of a right-handed helical model, which determines the sign of the rotations, is probably correct. It is of interest that in 1952 Huggins [12] calculated that a right-handed helix of L-amino acids is a more stable conformation than a left-handed helix.

In Tables 17-1 and 17-2 are listed the residue rotations ($[R']$) as well as λ_c and b_0 for several polypeptides in helical conformations. It should be noted that the original observations of the optical rotatory dispersion of polypeptides were made on materials (derivatives of L-glutamic acid and L-leucine) with *negative values of b_0* (around −600). Recently the optical rotatory dispersion of the benzyl ester of poly-L-aspartic acid (the next lower homologue of L-glutamic acid) has been investigated.[13] The solutions in non-hydrogen-bond-breaking solvents such as chloroform showed rotatory dispersions over the range 365 to 600 mµ and fit Eq. (4). In contrast to the data cited above, *the values of b_0 obtained were positive* and of the order of 600 (see Fig. 17-6). Poly-L-tyrosine in pyridine and dimethyl formamide also gave positive b_0 values between 300 and 400.[14] In addition, poly-1-benzyl-L-histidine also showed positive values of b_0.[15]

We are thus confronted with the situation that there are at least two classes of polypeptides whose conformation appears to be helical in weak hydrogen-bond-breaking solvents [13,15] (cf. Tables 17-1 and 17-2). All the optical rotatory dispersion data with one exception can be fitted to the Moffitt equation (with $\lambda_0 = 212$ mµ), but the coefficient for the second term, b_0, may vary in magnitude and sign from −600 to +600. It is now necessary to determine whether this difference in the b_0 parameter is due to different senses of twist in the helices, to other conformational differences, or to side-chain interactions. Experiments are being devised now to ascertain the actual situation. In this context, the recent work of Tinoco [16] on optical rotatory dispersion of oriented polybenzyl-L-glutamate may be of great relevance.

D. Estimation of Per Cent Helix. It has been established that the optical rotatory dispersion of a helical macromolecule is quite different from the optical rotatory dispersion of the same molecule when it is in a random conformation. It is of importance to be able to determine

[12] M. Huggins, *J. Am. Chem. Soc.,* **74,** 3963 (1952).

[13] (a) E. R. Blout and R. H. Karlson, *J. Am. Chem. Soc.,* **80,** 1259 (1958); (b) E. R. Blout, G. D. Fasman, R. H. Karlson, and K. Norland, to be published.

[14] A. R. Downie, A. Elliott, and W. E. Hanby, *Nature,* **183,** 110 (1959).

[15] E. Katchalski, G. D. Fasman, and E. R. Blout, Abstracts of the American Chemical Society Meeting, San Francisco. April, 1958.

[16] I. Tinoco, Jr., *J. Am. Chem. Soc.,* **81,** 1540 (1959).

quantitatively the amount of helix in a macromolecule by measurement of the optical rotatory properties. The possible data that can be used for the determination of per cent helix are $[\alpha]_\lambda$ (the specific rotation), b_0 [a helix constant from Eq. (4)], and λ_c (the dispersion constant from the simple Drude equation [Eq. (1)]). The latter constant, λ_c, has been suggested and used for protein conformational determinations, but approximate per cent helix information can be obtained only in the range up to 40 per cent helix.

$[\alpha]_\lambda$ has long been suggested as a measure of "denaturation," or change in conformation of proteins, and more recently has been applied to synthetic polypeptides. One of the first uses of optical rotation data from polypeptides in this context was that of Robinson and Bott,[17] who measured the optical rotation $[\alpha]$ of a series of copolymers of γ-methyl-L-glutamate with D,L-phenylalanine and found that it varied depending on whether the sample was dissolved in m-cresol or in formic acid; more interestingly, the rotation varied markedly in m-cresol depending on the molecular weight of the sample. From these data it could be concluded that the conformation varied (1) in m-cresol depending on the molecular weight of the polypeptide, and (2) depending on the hydrogen-bonding properties of the solvents.

The use of b_0 for the determination of the helix content of polypeptides seems to have the most theoretical significance. However, owing to the fact that polypeptides show widely differing values of b_0 in helical solvents (Table 17-2), it appears at present that the use of b_0 as a measure of helix content should be restricted to those systems for which the parameters of the component peptides are known, that is, where only helices and random conformations exist and the dispersion data for these forms may be obtained in the same solvent. One such system is that of the copolymers of L-lysine and L-glutamic acid. Examination of the optical rotatory dispersion of a series of these copolymers has recently been reported [18] and it has been found that in aqueous solutions around pH 3, the b_0's became less negative as the amount of L-lysine was increased in the copolymers. Since 100 per cent helical forms of the component polypeptides have $b_0 \cong -600$, one may conclude that the amount of helix decreases with increasing L-lysine content. At pH 8, where the glutamic acid residues are ionized and the amount of helix would be expected to be much lower, the values of b_0 indicate that in all the copolymers examined there is less than 30 per cent helix. The data for this system are summarized in Table 17-4.

Subsequent to the finding that polypeptides can exist in at least two

---

[17] C. Robinson and M. J. Bott, *Nature*, **168**, 325 (1951).
[18] E. R. Blout and M. Idelson, *J. Am. Chem. Soc.*, **80**, 4909 (1958).

Table 17-4

Rotatory Properties of a Series of Copolymers of L-Glutamic Acid and L-Lysine in Water Solutions [18]

Polymer composition L-glu:L-lys	pH 3			pH 8		
	$[\alpha]^{25}_{546}$	$b_0{}^*$	Estimated % helix[a]	$[\alpha]^{25}_{546}$	$b_0{}^*$	Estimated % helix[a]
10:0	− 8°[b]	−625[c]	100	−116°	0	0
7:3	−12	−586	90	− 88	0	0
6:4	−27	−439	70	− 60	−140	25
5:5	−51	−310	50	− 66	−196	30
4:6	−69	−131	25	− 62	[d]	
0:10	−92	0	0	− 63	[e]	0

* Calculated assuming $\lambda_0 = 212$ mμ.

[a] Based on the assumption that $b_0 = 0$ in a completely random conformation and $b_0 = -625$ in the completely helical form of poly-L-glutamic acid and poly-L-lysine.

[b] At pH 4.5.

[c] From Ref. 5b.

[d] These data did not fit either a Drude or a Moffitt plot.

[e] These data fit a Drude (single term, normal dispersion) plot.

different conformations depending on the solvent, investigations were undertaken on the effect of various solvents on the optical rotatory dispersion of poly-γ-benzyl-L-glutamate.[19] The measurements indicate that the optical rotations, $[\alpha]_\lambda$, as well as λ_c are subject to considerable solvent effect.

Experiments have also been reported which show that chain conformation is dependent upon the solute:solvent ratio. For example, it has been shown [10] that even in a strong hydrogen-bond-breaking solvent such as dichloroacetic acid, polybenzyl-L-glutamate exists in a helical conformation at high concentrations, whereas in a low concentration it exists as a random conformation. This raises the important question of whether the conformation of proteins might also be sensitive to small changes in their environment, e.g., varying water content, as has been indicated by other physical chemical measurements with synthetic polypeptides.[20]

E. Effect of Chain Length on Optical Rotatory Dispersion. It has been known for several years, from the work of Brand and his associates,[21] that in a series of lower polypeptides the optical rotation is affected by the chain length in molecules having two to six peptide units. Up to this point we have assumed that the polypeptides we have described contain a large number (100 or more) of peptide units, and furthermore that the effect of end groups or "chain ends" was negligible. However it is apparent that in both polypeptides and proteins different structural units, such as helices and random conformations, can be present in the same molecule. Therefore, it becomes important to ascertain how the rotatory properties of such a molecule vary with the conformation within a single molecular chain. In this connection, it is not only necessary to consider the minimum chain length for the helical conformation but also the possibility that other conformations such as the β (extended) or other nonhelical, nonrandom conformations can exist in proteins.

If the polypeptide chain is all in a random conformation, the length of the chain beyond a certain size, 20 units or so, probably will have little effect on the optical rotatory properties. This was indicated by work previously cited,[17] in which the optical rotation of a polypeptide series of various molecular weights did not change when the solvent was one that induced the random conformation of the polypeptide.

[19] J. T. Yang and P. Doty, *J. Am. Chem. Soc.*, **79**, 761 (1957).

[20] E. R. Blout and H. Lenormant, *Nature*, **179**, 960 (1957); H. Lenormant, A. Baudras, and E. R. Blout, *J. Am. Chem. Soc.*, **80**, 6191 (1958).

[21] B. Erlanger and E. Brand, *J. Am. Chem. Soc.*, **73**, 3508, 4025, 4027 (1951); E. Brand, B. Erlanger, and H. Sachs, *ibid.*, **74**, 1849, 1851 (1952); H. Sachs and E. Brand, *ibid.*, **75**, 4608 (1953); *ibid.*, **76**, 1811 (1954).

Now, consider the effect of helix length on the optical rotatory properties. Schellman [22] argues that it is only for quite long helices (more than 30 residues) that one would expect the end effects to become unimportant. In any helix there are six peptide links, three at either end, which do not have the three neighbors on either side that are required to give each residue an identical environment. Since the infrared evidence indicates that helices may be formed in organic solvents when the chain length is only slightly above six residues,[23] the question of chain length becomes quite important in interpretations of optical rotation data on small peptides and in globular proteins, in which short helices almost certainly exist because of factors such as –S–S– cross-linking and ionization. Furthermore, helix stability may be lower in aqueous media [22,24] than in organic solvents, since the heat of formation of a hydrogen bond in water is less than in organic solvents. To determine the effect of helix length on a quantitative basis it will be necessary to synthesize both organic-soluble and water-soluble polypeptides of known chain length in the range 6 to 30 residues and to examine their optical rotatory properties. This work has been started by Goodman and his associates,[25] whose results so far indicate that there is a change of optical rotatory properties of γ-methyl-L-glutamate polypeptides in dioxane when the chain length is five; when the chain length reaches eight the specific rotation approaches that observed for a polymethylglutamate preparation whose chain length was approximately 100. However, it will be desirable to investigate the *dispersive* properties of this series of polypeptides, and this work is now in progress.

F. Effect of Other Structures on Optical Rotatory Properties. In order to interpret the optical rotatory dispersion of proteins, polypeptide structures other than helical and random should be considered. The "β" conformation of a polypeptide is one such structure. In this conformation extended polypeptide chains are *intermolecularly* hydrogen bonded to other such chains through amide hydrogen bonds. A β structure is a two-fold screw and, as such, unlike a helix, has no screw sense. It is not clear how such a structure can give rise to rotational effects. One suggestion, made by Cohen, is that the source of the dysymmetry may be an additive effect from the peptide groups which is not due to conformational dysymmetry.

[22] C. G. Schellman and J. A. Schellman, *Compt. rend. trav. lab. Carlsberg, Sér. chim.,* **30**, no. 27 (1958).

[23] M. Idelson and E. R. Blout, *J. Am. Chem. Soc.,* **79**, 3948 (1957).

[24] J. A. Schellman, *Compt. rend. trav. lab. Carlsberg, Sér. chim.,* **29**, nos. 14 and 15 (1955).

[25] M. Goodman and E. Schmitt, *J. Am. Chem. Soc.,* in press.

Whatever the cause, it has been shown that β-polypeptides exhibit quite different optical properties from helical conformations. This difference was first demonstrated by infrared spectroscopy.[26,27] Following this work an examination was made of the optical rotatory properties of a low-molecular-weight (β_L) polypeptide of polybenzyl-L-glutamate.[19] The dispersion measurements showed that at high concentrations in chloroform solution, positive rotations were found, and these increased with diminishing wavelength, unlike high-molecular-weight samples in either the helical or random conformations. At low concentrations of the β-polypeptide in chloroform, the rotations became more negative with decreasing wavelength and were similar to those observed in dichloroacetic acid. The optical rotatory dispersion data of β-polypeptides show the same dependence on concentration as that observed in the infrared studies. This behavior is a consequence of *inter*molecular hydrogen bonding and suggests that this is the primary cause of the dysymmetry that gives rise to the optical rotatory properties. These investigations serve to emphasize the fact that the conformation of a polypeptide may depend not only on the solvent in which it is dissolved and its concentration but also on its molecular weight. In addition it emphasizes the importance of considering the contributions of conformations other than α-helical and random when interpreting rotatory dispersion data.

G. Effect of Optical Isomers on the Conformational Stability of Polypeptides. It has been pointed out above that polypeptides may change conformation depending on the solvents.[28] As the solvent is varied between a "helical solvent" and one favoring random conformations, a sharp transition or change in optical rotation is observed when the polymer is composed only of residues having one configuration. This type of experiment has also been carried out with several D,L-copolymers of γ-benzyl-L-glutamate in chloroform–dichloroacetic acid mixtures,[9] and the results are shown in Fig. 17-8. It may be seen that with increasing D-residue content the transition occurs at lower dichloroacetic acid concentrations and the range of the transition is broadened. Since the molecular weights of these polymers were of the same order of magnitude (approximately 100,000), it is clear that the introduction of optical isomers brings about a proportional weakening of the helix, which is conveniently detected by means of optical rotatory studies.

H. Temperature Dependence of Optical Rotation. If the stability of a polypeptide's conformation is marginal in a particular solvent, tem-

---

[26] E. G. Ambrose and A. Elliott, *Proc. Roy. Soc.* (*London*), **A205**, 47 (1951).

[27] E. R. Blout and A. Asadourian, *J. Am. Chem. Soc.*, **78**, 955 (1956).

[28] P. Doty and J. T. Yang, *J. Am. Chem. Soc.*, **78**, 498 (1956).

perature variations should affect the conformation, and the consequent changes in conformation should be observed as changes in optical rotatory properties. Two such optical rotation studies may be cited, the first, polybenzyl-α,L-glutamate in a dichloroacetic acid–ethylene dichloride mixture,[28] and the second, poly-α,L-glutamic acid in a dioxane-water mixture.[29]   With polybenzylglutamate in the organic solvent system, a

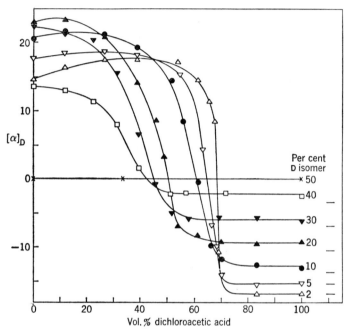

Fig. 17-8. Specific rotation (sodium D line) of poly-γ-benzyl glutamate as a function of the amount of dichloroacetic acid added to chloroform solutions. The lines on the right indicate the rotation expected if rotations of D and L residues are additive.   The data for the pure L-polypeptide ($[\alpha]_D$ 13.8° in $CHCl_3$) have been omitted because they fall so close to the polymer containing 2 per cent D residues.   [*Reproduced from E. R. Blout, P. Doty, and J. T. Yang, J. Am. Chem. Soc.*, **79**, 749 (1957), *by permission of the editor.*]

rather sharp change in specific rotation from −14° to +14° is observed around 30°C.   Since the more positive value of optical rotation is associated with the helical conformation of this polypeptide, this form is the more stable at higher temperatures.   Although this situation is the opposite of protein denaturation, it is argued that the negative-heat-content change, and hence the negative-entropy change for the helix→

[29] P. Doty, A. Wada, J. T. Yang, and E. R. Blout, *J. Polymer Sci.*, **23**, 851 (1957).

random-coil conversion, arises from the dominating entropy loss suffered by the dichloroacetic acid molecule upon being immobilized through solvation in the random conformation. Schellman [30] states that inverted transitions of the type mentioned above [28] can occur only in solvent mixtures, and then only when the entropy of unfolding changes sign.

In replacing dichloroacetic acid as the solvating agent with water, one might expect, since the entropy of melting is somewhat less, that the entropy loss due to solvation could be reduced below the conformational entropy gain of the polypeptide. The result would be that the entropy and heat content of a helix→random-coil conversion in an aqueous solvent would be positive, as in the typical protein denaturation. This is the case with the poly-L-glutamic acid system, where it has been observed that increasing the temperature from $20°$ to $70°$ results in more negative rotation values characteristic of the random conformation.

I. Proline and Hydroxyproline Containing Polypeptides. Proline and hydroxyproline, although components of proteins, are not truly amino acids but *imino* acids. When linked in peptides or in proteins, these imides can only form hydrogen-bonded structures through their C=O groups, since the nitrogen of the proline residue carries no hydrogen. Furthermore, as a result of the cyclic imino group, there is no free rotation between the imino group and the α carbon atom. This in turn limits the conformational possibilities of proline-containing polypeptides, and prevents poly-L-proline from existing in an α-helical conformation.

As a result of these chemical differences and conformational restraints it is not surprising that the optical rotatory properties of proline, hydroxyproline, and proline-containing polypeptides are quite different from those of other polypeptides. Poly-L-proline was first prepared by Berger, Kurtz, and Katchalski,[31] who then showed that the material as originally obtained from the polymerization reaction of L-proline-N-carboxyanhydride had a small positive rotation, but upon solution in acetic acid this rotation changed over a period of some 100 hours, becoming negative and finally reaching a value of about -540.[32] The original material was designated polyproline I, the final product of acetic acid treatment, polyproline II, and it was suggested that the conversion poly-L-proline I→II might involve a *cis→trans* change around the peptide links. A reconversion of polyproline II to polyproline I occurred when a solution of the former in formic acid was diluted tenfold with

[30] J. A. Schellman, *J. Phys. Chem.*, **62**, 1485 (1958).

[31] A. Berger, J. Kurtz, and E. Katchalski, *J. Am. Chem. Soc.*, **76**, 5552 (1954).

[32] J. Kurtz, A. Berger, and E. Katchalski, *Nature*, **178**, 1066 (1956); I. Z. Steinberg, A. Berger, and E. Katchalski, *Biochim. et Biophys. Acta*, **28**, 647 (1958).

n-propanol.   Blout and Fasman [33] have prepared high-molecular-weight samples of polyproline I and II and have studied their optical rotatory dispersion as well as their infrared spectral properties.   The optical rotatory dispersion of polyproline I and II are shown in Fig. 17-9; the differences are obvious.   The dispersion data for form II in several solvents at wavelengths from 365 to 586 mμ can be fitted with the single-term Drude equation.   For poly-L-proline I in acetic acid, Drude plots deviate from the straight line typical of normal dispersive behavior and also do not fit a Moffitt plot.   These data indicate that poly-L-proline I has a conformation that is neither random nor α-helical.

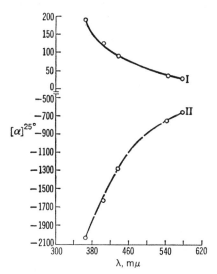

Fig. 17-9.   Rotatory dispersion of the two forms of poly-L-proline in glacial acetic acid.   (*Reproduced from E. R. Blout and G. D. Fasman in "Recent Advances in Gelatin and Glue Research," Pergamon Press, London, 1958, by permission of the publisher.*)

From the above data it could be argued that significant amounts of sequential prolyl units either in the form of polyproline I or polyproline II would, as a consequence of their conformation, markedly affect the optical rotatory properties of proteins.   In form II, since its residue rotation is so highly negative (approximately -600), even a small amount of (prolyl)$_n$ residues will affect the optical rotation of a protein. The λ_c of polyproline II is 206 mμ, very close to that of collagen (*vide infra*).

[33] E. R. Blout and G. D. Fasman in "Recent Advances in Gelatin and Glue Research," p. 122, Pergamon Press, London, 1958.

J. Optical Rotatory Dispersion Measurements of Polypeptides at Short Wavelengths.

In all the data recorded so far optical rotation measurements have generally been obtained in the readily accessible ultraviolet region and in the visible, that is, from approximately 350 to 700 mμ. The short wavelength limit has been imposed largely because of instrumental problems. Recently, however, through the use of high-pressure, high-intensity ultraviolet light sources it has been possible to extend optical rotation measurements to 240 mμ. The importance of measurements at shorter wavelengths is apparent, since many synthetic polypeptides that have been investigated contain chromophoric groups in their side chains, e.g., benzyl, which absorb in the region 240 to 300 mμ. In addition, proteins that contain phenylalanine, tyrosine, and tryptophan will show absorption in this region, and as measurements are obtained through an absorption band it would not be surprising to see Cotton effects (see Chap. 2) such as those found with simpler, lower-molecular-weight organic molecules. Optical rotation measurements on poly-γ-benzyl-L-glutamate in ethylene dichloride have been reported to wavelengths as low as 265 mμ.[34] These data show a slight departure from the straight line at short wavelengths but fit Eq. (4) in the visual-wavelength range. However, it is reported that the effect is small and may not be outside experimental error.

In our laboratory we have recently investigated the optical rotatory dispersions of poly-β-benzyl-L-aspartate, poly-β-benzyl-D-aspartate,[13] and poly-1-benzyl-L-histidine trifluoroacetate salt[35] from about 240 to 350 mμ. The results for the benzyl aspartate polymers are qualitatively similar to those for the polybenzyl-L-histidine salt shown in Fig. 17-10, and may be a consequence of passing through or approaching an optically active absorption band of the system. It should be noted that both of the above polypeptides belong to the class (group II) previously described as being substituted by a group other than –CH_2– on the β carbon atom. For helical poly-L-glutamic acid (pH 4.4) no anomaly is observed in this range of wavelengths,[36] demonstrating that it is not characteristic of the helical conformation as such. The optical rotatory dispersion of the random conformation of polyglutamic acid (pH 10) has the form of a negative plain curve with $\lambda_c = 202$ mμ from 240 to 600 mμ. Experiments are in progress to determine if the anomalies observed with the afore-mentioned polypeptides are characteristic of the residues or are a consequence of conformation or both.

[34] P. Doty, "Proceedings of the IVth International Congress of Biochemistry, Vienna," vol. 8, Pergamon Press, London, 1959.

[35] K. Norland, G. D. Fasman, E. Katchalski, and E. R. Blout, unpublished results.

[36] T. Miyazawa and E. R. Blout, unpublished results.

One final point should be mentioned in connection with the measurements through an absorption band, namely, that if a nonoptically active dye is bound to a helical polypeptide, one would expect it to be bound in an asymmetric manner. Thus, on passing through an absorption band of the dye, it is possible that the Cotton effect might be observed in the vicinity of the absorption band. Experiments by L. Stryer [37] have indicated that this is the case when acriflavin is bound to the helical form of poly-L-glutamic acid. In fact, the enhancement of the optical rotation in the neighborhood of the absorption band of the dye is so large that this might indeed provide a method for the determination of helical structures in other polypeptides and in proteins.

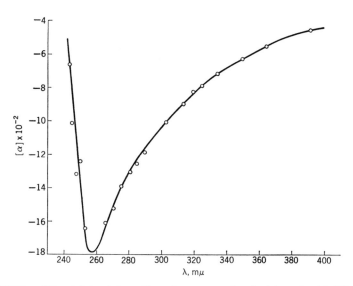

Fig. 17-10. Ultraviolet rotatory dispersion curve of poly-1-benzyl-L-histidine trifluoroacetate salt in chloroform (Ref. 35).

K. Conclusions from Optical Rotatory Results on Synthetic Polypeptides. Recent investigations have indicated that when synthetic polypeptides are in a random conformation their rotatory properties are simple and may be described by a one-term Drude equation. When such polypeptides are in an α-helical conformation, the rotatory dispersion of group I (Table 17-1) may be described by the Moffitt equation. Furthermore, aside from configurational factors relating to amino acid composition, the important influences on the optical rotatory properties of polypeptides are (1) the conformation of the polypeptide

[37] E. R. Blout and L. Stryer, *Proc. Natl. Acad. Sci. U.S.,* **45,** 1591 (1959).

chain, (2) the nature of the side chains attached to the β carbon of the component amino acids, and (3) the length of the polypeptide chain.

With respect to (1), it is evident that by the use of Moffitt's equation it is possible to estimate the helix contents of some polypeptides. In systems comprising only group I polypeptides, assuming only helical and random conformations, the per cent helix may be estimated from the coefficient b_0; with 100 per cent helix, $b_0 \cong 630$, and with 0 per cent helix, $b_0 = 0$. At present group II and group III polypeptides (Table 17-1) do not appear subject to this type of analysis, although Harrington and Sela [38] have been examining the problem relative to proline-containing polypeptides.

With respect to (2), it has been demonstrated that the group II polypeptides show different optical rotatory properties from those of group I. It is significant that all the group II polypeptides have constituents other than methylene attached to the β carbon atom of the component amino acids. However, recent work in our laboratory [13b] has indicated that in copolymers of group I and group II polypeptides, the dominating factor is the group I component, and therefore it appears that with proteins there is a sound basis to apply optical rotatory analysis to determine the general conformation.

With respect to (3), it has been pointed out previously that the molecular weight of the polypeptide markedly affects its optical rotation.[13a,39] Considering only the possibility of the existence of helical and random conformations, this is not surprising. It is clear from Schellman's calculations that the stability of helical conformations will be affected by the nature of the solvent, as well as by other factors, many of which will depend on the polypeptide chain length. As a minimum number of residues are necessary to form helical structures, it follows that the chain length of a polypeptide may also affect its optical rotatory properties.

Finally, it should be emphasized again that the influence of macromolecular structures other than helical and random are likely to affect the rotatory properties of polypeptides. As yet, however, too little data are available to assess the effects of all such structures. Before protein conformations can be determined with certainty from rotatory measurements, it will be necessary to evaluate the effects of many other possible polypeptide conformations, the effects of chain length, and the effects of cross-linkages on optical rotatory properties.

[38] W. F. Harrington and M. Sela, *Biochim. et Biophys. Acta,* **27,** 24 (1958).

[39] E. R. Blout, "Proceedings of the IVth International Congress of Biochemistry, Vienna," vol. 8, Pergamon Press, London, 1959.

17-3. The Optical Rotatory Properties of Proteins

Because optical rotatory measurements on simple synthetic polypeptides known to be in helical and random-coil conformations indicated that there were definite changes in the optical rotatory properties on helix→random transitions, much work has been stimulated recently on the determination of the detailed conformation of proteins. In this section we shall first review the available optical rotatory data on proteins and then examine the status of conformational determinations of proteins by means of optical rotatory measurements.

A. Factors Affecting Optical Rotatory Changes. It may be said, a priori, that the following factors must be evaluated in assessing the observed optical rotatory changes of proteins: (1) composition, that is, the number and kinds of amino acids making up a protein; (2) sequence, the order of the amino acid residues in the protein (are the rotatory properties independent of the order of the component amino acids?); (3) molecular weight (does the molecular weight of the protein affect the rotatory properties?); (4) and most important, does the *conformation,* that is, the shape, of the protein molecule affect the rotatory properties? Although detailed and rigorous proof of the effects of these various factors is not at hand, it is possible at this time to estimate some of their effects in order to evaluate the total situation.

1. To ascertain the effects of composition consider the residue rotations of various amino acids in helical and random conformations, as shown in Table 17-1. Inspection of these data makes it clear that composition will affect the optical rotatory properties of proteins, but any compositional effect will probably be secondary to conformational effects except in the case of polypeptide chains containing large amounts of proline, hydroxyproline, histidine, and possibly serine. Insufficient data are available to determine the effects of cysteine, cystine, and methionine residues.

2. At this time there is no specific indication of the effect of amino acid sequences upon protein conformation. Until detailed amino acid sequential analysis of proteins is carried out on a number of proteins and various classes and various compositions, it will be impossible to assess the importance of this factor.

3. Except as molecular weight affects the stability of a particular conformation, e.g., helical, its effect on the optical rotatory properties of proteins is probably small, provided the material being examined contains at least 100 amino acid residues.

4. It has been demonstrated with polypeptides that the α-helical conformation produces anomalous rotatory dispersion. That proteins con-

sist of helices having only one sense of twist is not at all certain.   Recent evidence indicates that certain synthetic polypeptides and proteins may exist with senses of helix opposite to those normally encountered.[13] Furthermore, the effect on the optical rotatory properties of coiled coils or superhelices [40] of polypeptides must be evaluated.

From the optical rotatory data on polypeptides it is quite evident that the major factor affecting the optical rotatory properties of proteins will be the conformation of the polypeptide chains.   The conformation of these chains will be affected not only by the above-mentioned factors but also by the solvent in which the protein is dissolved.   Factors such as pH, ionization, and salt concentration might well affect the conformation and in turn the optical rotatory properties of proteins.   Second, the presence of cross-linking between parts of the chain, by either disulfide bridges or phosphate ester cross-links, could affect the possible conformations in which a single polypeptide chain may exist, and therefore will change the optical rotatory properties.   At this point we have no knowledge of the effect of the sulfhydryl groups in cysteine on the optical properties of polypeptides, nor do we know the effect of disulfide bridges, but this problem is being investigated in model polypeptide systems.[41] Since, as far as is now known, proteins contain only L-amino acids, the effects of configuration of the amino acid need not be considered.

One simplifying factor in the study of the conformation of proteins lies in the fact that since proteins are copolymers of many amino acids, some complicating additive-group-interaction effects observed in polypeptides made from one amino acid will be canceled out.   Thus it has been possible to interpret the general conformation of certain proteins by means of optical rotatory measurements.

B. Criteria for Estimating Conformational Changes.   Since it is evident that conformational changes will modify the optical rotatory properties of proteins, it is now appropriate to determine what criteria should be used for estimating the extent and kind of conformational changes. The problem is more complex than that of the *simple* polypeptides (composed of one amino acid), for which the changes in rotatory properties ($[\alpha]$, b_0) could be correlated in large part with helix→random transitions.

It has long been known, as a result of empirical observations on several proteins, that there is a change in specific rotation $[\alpha]_D$ from the range -10 to $-60°$ for the native state, to about -60 to $-120°$ for the denatured state.   It was evident several years ago that advance in

[40] F. C. Crick, *Acta Cryst.*, **6**, 689 (1953); L. Pauling and R. B. Corey, *Nature*, **171**, 59 (1953).

[41] D. B. Wetlaufer and E. R. Blout, unpublished work.

understanding of protein structure might come about by the measurement of optical rotatory properties. The first correlation between optical rotatory dispersion and structure was the observation that the rotatory dispersion of many proteins followed the one-term Drude equation, and that the dispersion constants λ_c varied systematically with extent of folding, i.e., hydrogen-bonded structures as determined by other means.[42] The early measurements indicated that a value of λ_c of about 220 mμ denoted little or no folding of the molecule and that a higher value indicated more folding, although it was difficult to establish the degree of folding.

Besides the specific rotation and the dispersion constant λ_c, the third criterion for the determination of conformation of proteins followed directly from Moffitt's theoretical work on the optical rotatory dispersive properties of helical macromolecules [Eq. (4)]. As mentioned above, if it is assumed that the λ_0 for the helical and nonhelical conformations of proteins lie close together *and* no other factors contribute to the complex nature of the optical rotatory properties, then one can use b_0 as a measure of helical content.[7]

Imahori and Doty (see Ref. 34) have proposed a fourth measure of helical content of proteins based on an empirical equation that is a modification of the Moffitt equation. They propose that the Moffitt coefficient of the first term, a_0, is composed of two parts, one depending on the intrinsic residue rotation a_0^R and the second due to the helical conformation a_0^H. It is hoped that sufficient data will soon be available to evaluate this suggestion.

Thus at this time there are at least three possible numerical criteria for estimating the extent of conformational changes in proteins, namely, $[\alpha]$ or $[R']$, λ_c, and b_0. Since there is no strict theoretical correlation between $[R']$ and the conformation of a protein molecule, any deductions from $[R']$ data must be purely empirical. Experiments with synthetic polypeptides (Tables 17-1 and 17-2) although admittedly few in number are sufficient to indicate that such empirical correlations are very difficult to make with any degree of certainty at this time.

C. Relation between λ_c and Per Cent Helix. Following the initial correlation of λ_c and structure of certain proteins,[42] additional observations have been made on a variety of proteins.[19] These data and others are summarized in Table 17-5.

After poly-α,L-glutamic acid was shown to be helical at low pH in aqueous solution and to have a random conformation at high pH,[29] an attempt was made by Yang and Doty [19] to determine at what per cent

[42] K. U. Linderstrom-Lang and J. A. Schellman, *Biochim. et Biophys. Acta,* **15,** 156 (1954).

Table 17-5

$[\alpha]_D$, λ_c, and b_0 of Proteins *

Protein	"Native"				"Denatured"		
	$[\alpha]_D$	λ_c	b_0	Solvent	$[\alpha]_D$	λ_c	Solvent
Paramyosin[7]	− 11	NL	−600	H_2O, 0.6 M KCl	− 63		H_2O, 9.5 M urea
Pinna nobilis tropomyosin[46]	− 12	NL	−650	pH 7, μ = 0.6, phosphate–KCl buffer	−109	210	pH 7–7.5, H_2O, 8 M urea
Light meromyosin fraction I[7]	− 13	NL	−660	H_2O, 0.6 M KCl	−118	212	H_2O, 9.5 M urea
Tropomyosin[7]	− 16	NL	−620	H_2O, 0.6 M KCl	−118	213	H_2O, 9.5 M urea
Light meromyosin[7]	− 20	NL	−490	H_2O, 0.6 M KCl	−107	215	H_2O, 9.5 M urea
Ovalbumin[48]	− 28	266		H_2O, pH 7.1	− 98	226	H_2O, 8.6 M urea, pH 7.1
β-Lactoglobulin[48]	− 28	245		H_2O, 0.1 M NaCl, pH 5.5	−117	225	H_2O, 8.5 M urea, pH 5.5
Myosin[7]	− 29	NL	−370	H_2O, 0.6 M KCl	−108	218	H_2O, 9.5 M urea
Insulin[48]	− 29	266		H_2O, pH 1.8	− 88	226	H_2O, 9 M urea, pH 5.5
Heavy meromyosin[7]	− 35	NL	−300	H_2O, 0.6 M KCl	−103	215	H_2O, 9.5 M urea

Lysozyme[48]	— 50	257	H₂O	— 64†	218	H₂O, pH 5.4, 8 M urea, acetate buffer
Pepsin[44]	— 63†	216	H₂O, pH 4.6, acetate buffer	—110	213	H₂O, 9.5 M urea
Fibrinogen[7]	— 58	—210	H₂O, 0.6 M KCl	—109	221	H₂O, pH 5.5, 8 M urea
Bovine serum albumin[48]	— 59	265	H₂O, pH 5.5	—112	220	H₂O, pH 3, 8 M urea
α-Chymotrypsinogen[48]	— 66	241	H₂O, pH 3, 0.1 M NaCl	—109	220	H₂O, pH 5.6, 8 M urea
Ribonuclease[48]	— 74	233	H₂O, pH 5.4, 0.1 M KCl	—117	224	H₂O, pH 6.5, 8 M urea
Chymotrypsinogen[48]	— 78	239	H₂O, pH 6.7	— 68	228	H₂O, pH 7, 6 M urea
Insulin (oxidized A chain)[48]				— 91	228	H₂O, pH 4
Oxidized ribonuclease[48]				—112	201	H₂O, pH 6
Clupein[48]	—350	205				
Collagen[47]			H₂O, pH 3.7, 11°C, 0.15 M citrate buffer	—110	205	H₂O, pH 3.7, 40°C, 0.15 M citrate buffer

NL, nonlinear plot.

* Because they could not be readily adapted to this table, the data from B. Jirgensons [43,50] are not included. The reader is urged to consult these references for the data.

† Measurement made at 600 mμ.

helix the optical rotatory dispersion became complex. It was calculated that the rotatory dispersive properties of mixtures of helices and random chains become complex only when the helical content exceeds 40 per cent. Below 40 per cent helical structure, λ_c is defined by the one-term Drude equation. λ_c varies from the value of 212 mμ at no helix content to a value of 255 mμ at 30 per cent helix. From this work it was concluded that λ_c is the preferred method for estimating the helix content of proteins in aqueous solution, but obviously a more general method is needed for use with proteins of higher helix contents and those in which structures other than helical and random are present in significant amounts.

Jirgensons also has recently investigated the optical rotatory properties of a number of proteins.[43]   As a result of his measurements he proposes to classify proteins in three groups: (1) those proteins that show a decrease in λ_c upon ionization and denaturation (most proteins fall in this group, which includes the serum albumins, β-globulin, and taka-amylase); (2) those proteins whose dispersion constants vary little upon denaturation (ovalbumin, chymotrypsinogen, ribonuclease, and lysozyme); (3) proteins whose λ_c rises upon denaturation (pepsin, rennin, γ-globulin, Bence-Jones protein).

Perlmann [44] has investigated in detail the changes in λ_c of aqueous solutions of pepsin in various conditions and finds that λ_c slightly increases under the influence of denaturing agents. It is interesting to note that several proteins that are enzymatically active—pepsin, pancreatic amylase, and soybean trypsin inhibitor—show low values of λ_c. An interpretation of these data in terms of conformation is that low values of λ_c mean low helix content and decreases in λ_c mean decreases in helix content. However, the fact that proteins show varied rotatory behavior upon "denaturation" indicates the complexity of the problem and the need for additional information in order to make structural determinations.

D. Relation between b_0 and Per Cent Helix. Over the limited wavelength range so far investigated, most globular proteins do not show complex rotatory dispersion; in other words, the rotatory dispersion data from globular proteins can be fitted by the simple one-term Drude equation [Eq. (1)]. However, Cohen and Szent-Gyorgyi [7,45] have investigated a series of fibrous proteins that show in the condensed state α-type

[43] B. Jirgensons and L. Straumanis, *Arch. Biochem. Biophys.*, **68**, 319 (1957); B. Jirgensons, *ibid.*, **71**, 148 (1957); *ibid.*, **74**, 57 (1958); see also Ref. 50.

[44] G. E. Perlmann, *Proc. Natl. Acad. Sci. U.S.*, **45**, 915 (1959).

[45] C. Cohen and A. Szent-Gyorgyi, "Proceedings of the IVth International Congress on Biochemistry, Vienna," Pergamon Press, London, 1959.

wide-angle X-ray diffraction diagrams. These fibrous proteins, with the exception of fibrinogen, show complex rotatory behavior in aqueous solution. The data obtained can be fitted to Moffitt's equation for helical systems and are also summarized in Table 17-5. It has been suggested by these investigators that since these fibrous α proteins may consist of cables of α helices in a supercoil conformation,[40] such a conformation, which involves a superimposed backbone dysymmetry, does not markedly affect rotatory behavior. On the basis of the available data, this is a likely assumption, but it remains to be tested and proved definitively in simpler systems, such as synthetic polypeptides.

It should be noted that the original measurements on fibrous proteins [7] as well as those reported recently on Pinna tropomyosin [46] indicate that in the denatured state b_0 is approximately zero, and Eq. (4) therefore reduces to the one-term Drude equation, with λ_c in the range 214 ± 4 mμ. This is similar to the λ_c observed for the denatured state of many globular proteins [42] and in certain (but not all) synthetic polypeptides in the random conformation.

E. Optical Rotatory Dispersion of Collagen and Gelatin. In addition to the globular and fibrous proteins mentioned above, another class of proteins whose optical rotatory properties have been examined are those of the collagen-gelatin system. Native collagen shows a specific rotation of about $-350°$ at $11°C$. This highly negative specific rotation has been attributed to a specific collagen fold or structure. On heating above $30°C$, collagen is converted to gelatin with a change in rotation to approximately $-110°$. Upon cooling of the gelatin solution, the rotation returns to more negative values of $[\alpha]_D$ around $-300°$. Measurements of the optical rotatory dispersion between 436 and 589 mμ indicate that the data for both collagen and gelatin may be fitted with a single-term Drude equation.[47] Furthermore λ_c for both collagen and gelatin is the same, 205 ± 15 mμ. Other physical methods (X-ray diffraction and infrared absorption) indicate that collagen possesses a helical conformation (*not* an α helix) in its native state which is then converted to a random conformation when the transition to gelatin is induced by raising the temperature. In these high-proline-content proteins, although the specific rotation changes markedly upon "denaturation," the λ_c changes very little if at all, similar to the situation with polyproline I and II. A theoretical interpretation of the optical rotatory data of the collagen system remains to be worked out.

F. Effect of Temperature Changes on Optical Rotatory Properties. It is well known that heating a protein may change its properties (the

[46] C. M. Kay and K. Bailey, *Biochim. et Biophys. Acta,* **31,** 20 (1959).

[47] C. Cohen, *J. Biophys. Biochem. Cytol.,* **1,** 203 (1955).

classical example being the boiling of egg white) and it has been deduced that such changes are a result of changes in the structure of the protein. A question naturally arises: Can these conformational or structural changes be analyzed in a quantitative manner by means of optical rotatory measurements? A review of the available data indicates that almost all proteins show a change in specific rotation upon being heated to a sufficiently high temperature. However, whether this change is toward more positive or more negative values depends in large part upon the pH of the solution and the other solutes, such as salts, which may be present.[48–50] It would be of small use to list all the changes that have been observed in protein rotation upon heating, since insufficient data

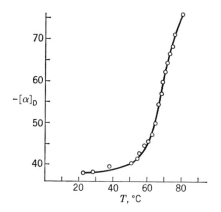

Fig. 17-11. The specific optical rotation as a function of temperature for insulin at pH 3.60. [*Reproduced from J. A. Schellman, Compt. rend. trav. lab. Carlsberg, Sér. chim., 30, 423 (1958), by permission of the publisher.*]

are on hand to interpret the effects of temperature changes. Probably the largest change is that previously mentioned, the change in the collagen-gelatin system, which has been interpreted with the help of other physical chemical techniques as a change from a helical conformation to a random conformation.

Some data on the thermally induced transition of insulin at pH 3.6 are shown in Fig. 17-11. Schellman [48] reports that the temperature curve is completely reversible except for a very slow reaction at the highest temperature. The data are in accord with other results which

[48] J. A. Schellman, *Compt. rend. trav. lab. Carlsberg, Sér. chim.,* **30,** nos. 21–26 (1958).

[49] R. B. Simpson and W. Kauzmann, *J. Am. Chem. Soc.,* **75,** 5139 (1953).

[50] B. Jirgensons, *Arch. Biochem. Biophys.,* **74,** 70 (1958); *ibid.,* **78,** 227 (1958); *ibid.,* **78,** 235 (1958).

indicate that this transition is indeed a thermal unfolding of the native folded form to a denatured unfolded form. The temperature dependence of protein conformation is so complex that it is impossible at this time adequately to account for all the observed changes in terms of conformational parameters.

G. Effect of Solvents on the Optical Rotatory Properties of Proteins. It has been pointed out above that by changing the solvents one can effect a helix→random transition in polypeptides. It has of course been known for some time that urea and guanidine hydrochloride are effective denaturing agents for proteins, presumably by virtue of their hydrogen-bond-forming properties; in this way they compete for the potential internal-hydrogen-bond-forming sites in proteins. Optical rotatory changes of proteins in the presence of urea or guanidine have been observed for ovalbumin, serum albumin, β-lactoglobulin, and insulin.[48] Schellman has pointed out that in these cases treatment with concentrated urea solutions invariably results in more negative values of $[R]$ and a lowering of λ_c to around 210 to 220 mμ. These results are consistent with those cited above for the effect of urea solutions on the fibrous proteins and are generally consistent with the fact that urea treatment involves an unfolding of a protein molecule, a loss of specific structure, and hence a change in the optical rotatory properties (decrease in λ_c) toward those of a random polypeptide chain. This is not a general conclusion because it has recently been shown that urea and guanidine hydrochloride have little effect on the optical rotatory properties of pepsin; [44] whether in this particular case it indicates that the pepsin molecule is largely in a random conformation or is fixed in another conformation remains to be determined.

In addition to solvents such as aqueous solutions of urea or guanidine, which generally make the optical rotation of proteins more negative and decrease λ_c, there have recently been discovered two types of solvents that often increase λ_c in proteins and change the specific rotation toward less-negative values. Harrington and Schellman [51] have investigated the effect of lowering the activity of solvent water by dissolving in it lithium bromide and similar substances possessing high-activity coefficients. If proteins and polypeptides are dissolved in aqueous solutions of these salts, the formation of a maximum number of intramolecular hydrogen bonds should occur. On the other hand, Doty [34] has chosen to change the hydrogen bonding in proteins by dissolving them in an organic solvent that is miscible with water but has less hydrogen-bonding capacity. It has been found that 2-chloroethanol increased the helical content

[51] W. F. Harrington and J. A. Schellman, *Compt. rend. trav. lab. Carlsberg, Sér. chim.*, **30**, 167 (1956).

of proteins, as measured by rotatory dispersion, in nearly every case. Table 17-6 lists the right-handed helical contents of various proteins

Table 17-6
Estimated Excess Right-handed Helical Contents of Proteins [34]

Protein	Water solution		2-Chloroethanol solution*
	$-b_0/630$	$a_0^H/650$	
Tropomyosin	0.88	0.87	1.10
Insulin	0.38	0.57	0.45
Bovine serum albumin	0.46	0.58	0.75
Ovalbumin	0.31	0.50	0.85
Lysozyme	0.29	0.39	0.63
Pepsin	0.31	0.26	0.44
Histone	0.20	0.30	0.72
Ribonuclease	0.16	0.17	0.67
Globin H	0.15	0.09	0.74

* Determined by average of $-b_0/630$ and $a_0^H/650$.

in water as determined by optical rotatory dispersion and compares them with their solutions in 2-chloroethanol. A word of caution on the use of 2-chloroethanol as a solvent is necessary. 2-Chloroethanol, unless carefully purified, contains hydrogen chloride. Thus, when polypeptides and proteins containing free carboxyl groups are dissolved in 2-chloroethanol, the possibility of esterification by the alcohol exists and, in fact, has been found to proceed rapidly with certain synthetic polypeptides.[52]

H. Use of Optical Rotatory Dispersion in Determining the Conformation of Proteins. As can be seen from the foregoing, the precise interpretation of the optical rotation data of proteins is difficult. The reasons for this are several: (1) there are undoubtedly interactions between side chains in proteins which affect the optical rotatory properties; (2) many proteins are intramolecularly cross-linked, with concomitant changes in conformation from a simple helix or random coil; (3) conformations other than helical or random coil (such as extended or β) may be present in a single molecule and affect the optical rotatory properties; (4) it is possible that proteins consist of sections of right-handed and left-handed helices.

[52] F. Wallace, G. D. Fasman, E. Katchalski, and E. R. Blout, unpublished results.

Since we have no knowledge of the effect of (2) and (3) on optical rotatory properties and little knowledge of (1) and (4), it is not surprising that it is difficult to interpret some observed changes in optical rotation in proteins in terms of specific conformational changes. In spite of this some progress has been made.

First, it has been shown that many of the fibrous proteins show properties similar to simple polypeptides, that is, in the native state their optical rotatory dispersion is complex and the per cent helix can be estimated from the b_0 value, the coefficient of the second term in the Moffitt equation. Second, in certain globular proteins, unfolding leads to a decrease in the rotatory dispersion constant λ_c of a simple Drude equation. Estimates have been made of the helical content of such proteins using this change in λ_c. Third, solvents have been found which increase the per cent intramolecularly hydrogen bonded (perhaps helical) form of certain globular proteins. In addition, studies of optical rotatory dispersion have led to thermodynamic studies of conformational stability of polypeptide chains.[22,24,30,42] From these studies it is evident that the helical conformation has a marginal stability in aqueous solutions which can be varied either upward or downward, depending on the solvent, salt concentration, pH, and perhaps on the nature of the side groups attached to the backbone polypeptide chain. Summarizing, at this time it appears that it is possible to determine the *general conformation* of a few proteins by use of rotatory dispersion measurements. However, the determination of the *detailed conformation* of many types of proteins is a formidable problem and one that is not yet fully solved.

I wish to acknowledge the invaluable aid of Kenneth Norland in compiling the tables and in participating in many critical discussions.

BIBLIOGRAPHY *

Reviews of Earlier Literature

Optical Rotatory Power, a general discussion in *Trans. Faraday Soc.,* **26,** 265–461 (1930).

W. Kuhn and K. Freudenberg, Drehung der Polarisationsebene des Lichtes, "Handbuch und Jahrbuch der chemischen Physik," vol. 8, part 3, Akademische Verlagsgesellschaft, Leipzig, 1932.

T. M. Lowry, "Optical Rotatory Power," Longmans, Green & Co., Ltd., London, 1935.

E. U. Condon, Theories of Optical Rotatory Power, *Rev. Mod. Phys.,* **9,** 432 (1937).

P. A. Levene and A. Rothen, Rotatory Dispersion, in H. Gilman (ed.), "Organic Chemistry," vol. 2, chap. 21, John Wiley & Sons, Inc., New York, 1938.

W. J. Kauzmann, J. E. Walter, and H. Eyring, Theories of Optical Rotatory Power, *Chem. Revs.,* **26,** 339 (1940).

W. Heller, Polarimetry, in A. Weissberger (ed.), "Physical Methods of Organic Chemistry," 2d ed., vol. 1, part 2, chap. 23, Interscience Publishers, Inc., New York, 1949.

W. Kuhn, Optical Rotatory Power, *Ann. Rev. Phys. Chem.,* **9,** 417 (1958).

Reviews of Recent Investigations

C. Djerassi, Structure et dispersion rotatoire, *Bull. soc. chim. France,* **1957,** 741.

J. A. Schellman, The Optical Rotatory Properties of Proteins and Polypeptides, *Compt. rend. trav. lab. Carlsberg, Sér. chim.,* **30,** 363–500 (1958).

K. Nakanishi, Rotatory Dispersion and Organic Chemistry, *Kagaku no Ryôiki,* **13,** 2 (1959).

C. Djerassi and M. Suzuki, Rotatory Dispersion, *Kagaku no Ryôiki,* **13,** 75, 169 (1959).

* This list of leading review articles is by no means complete, but it covers all important facets of rotatory dispersion.

K. Imahori, The Uses of Rotatory Dispersion for Physical Chemistry, *Kagaku no Ryôiki*, **13**, 92 (1959).

C. Djerassi, Some Recent Applications of Optical Rotatory Dispersion Studies to Organic Chemical Problems, *Record Chem. Progr.*, **20**, 101 (1959).

W. Klyne, Optical Rotatory Dispersion and the Study of Organic Structures, in R. A. Raphael (ed.), "Advances in Organic Chemistry: Methods and Results," vol. 1, Interscience Publishers, Inc., New York, 1960, pp. 239–348.

W. Klyne and A. C. Parker, Optical Rotary Dispersion, in A. Weissberger (ed.), "Physical Methods in Organic Chemistry," 3d ed., chap. 34, Interscience Publishers, Inc., New York, 1960.

List of Publications on Rotatory Dispersion from the Author's Laboratory

Optical Rotatory Dispersion Studies. I. The Androstane Series, by C. Djerassi, E. W. Foltz, and A. E. Lippman, *J. Am. Chem. Soc.*, **77**, 4354 (1955).

Optical Rotatory Dispersion Studies. II. Steroid Hormones, by E. W. Foltz, A. E. Lippman, and C. Djerassi, *J. Am. Chem. Soc.*, **77**, 4359 (1955).

Optical Rotatory Dispersion Studies. III. The Cholestane Series, by A. E. Lippman, E. W. Foltz, and C. Djerassi, *J. Am. Chem. Soc.*, **77**, 4364 (1955).

Optical Rotatory Dispersion Studies. IV. Steroidal Sapogenins, by C. Djerassi and R. Ehrlich, *J. Am. Chem. Soc.*, **78**, 440 (1956).

Optical Rotatory Dispersion Studies. V. The Effect of Isolated Carbonyl Groups and Double Bonds in the Cholestane Series, by C. Djerassi, W. Closson, and A. E. Lippman, *J. Am. Chem. Soc.*, **78**, 3163 (1956).

Optical Rotatory Dispersion Studies. VI. The Bile Acid Series. Polycarbonyl Compounds and Stereochemical Differentiations, by C. Djerassi and W. Closson, *J. Am. Chem. Soc.*, **78**, 3761 (1956).

Optical Rotatory Dispersion Studies. VII. Applications to Problems of Absolute Configurations, by C. Djerassi, R. Riniker, and B. Riniker, *J. Am. Chem. Soc.*, **78**, 6362 (1956).

Optical Rotatory Dispersion Studies. VIII. α,β-Unsaturated Ketones and Solvent Effects, by C. Djerassi, R. Riniker, and B. Riniker, *J. Am. Chem. Soc.*, **78**, 6377 (1956).

Optical Rotatory Dispersion Studies. IX. Intermediates in the Total Synthesis of Steroids. Allotment of Absolute Configuration by Rotatory Dispersion Measurements, by C. Djerassi and W. Klyne, *Chem. & Ind.* (*London*), **1956**, 988.

Optical Rotatory Dispersion Studies. X. Determination of Absolute Configuration of α-Halocyclohexanones, by C. Djerassi and W. Klyne, *J. Am. Chem. Soc.*, **79**, 1506 (1957).

Optical Rotatory Dispersion Studies. XI. Structure et dispersion rotatoire, by C. Djerassi, *Bull. soc. chim. France*, **1957**, 741.

Optical Rotatory Dispersion Studies. XII. Absolute Configuration of Eperuic and Labdanolic Acids, by C. Djerassi and D. Marshall, *Tetrahedron*, **1**, 238 (1957).

Optical Rotatory Dispersion Studies. XIII. Assignment of Absolute Configuration to Certain Members of the Guaianolide Series of Sesquiterpenes, by C. Djerassi, J. Osiecki, and W. Herz, *J. Org. Chem.*, **22**, 1361 (1957).

Optical Rotatory Dispersion Studies. XIV. α-Haloketones (Part 2), by C. Djerassi, J. Osiecki, R. Riniker, and B. Riniker, *J. Am. Chem. Soc.*, **80**, 1216 (1958).

Optical Rotatory Dispersion Studies. XV. Application to Steroidal Ketols and Cardiac Aglycones, by C. Djerassi, O. Halpern, V. Halpern, O. Schindler, and C. Tamm, *Helv. Chim. Acta*, **41**, 250 (1958).

Optical Rotatory Dispersion Studies. XVI. Synthesis and Conformation of Optically Active Octalones and Decalones, by C. Djerassi and D. Marshall, *J. Am. Chem. Soc.*, **80**, 3986 (1958).

Optical Rotatory Dispersion Studies. XVII. Detection of Conformational Alterations. Effects of Alkyl Groups and Double Bonds in Polycyclic Systems, by C. Djerassi, O. Halpern, V. Halpern, and B. Riniker, *J. Am. Chem. Soc.*, **80**, 4001 (1958).

Optical Rotatory Dispersion Studies. XVIII. Demonstration of Conformational Mobility in 2-Chloro-5-methylcyclohexanone, by C. Djerassi and L. E. Geller, *Tetrahedron*, **3**, 319 (1958).

Optical Rotatory Dispersion Studies. XIX. 8-Methylhydrindanones, by C. Djerassi, D. Marshall, and T. Nakano, *J. Am. Chem. Soc.*, **80**, 4853 (1958).

Optical Rotatory Dispersion Studies. XX. Transannular Nitrogen-Carbonyl Interaction in Cyclic Aminoketones and Optical Rotatory Dispersion, by N. J. Leonard, J. A. Adamcik, C. Djerassi, and O. Halpern, *J. Am. Chem. Soc.*, **80**, 4858 (1958).

Optical Rotatory Dispersion Studies. XXI. Effect of Ring Size, by C. Djerassi and G. W. Krakower, *J. Am. Chem. Soc.*, **81**, 237 (1959).

Optical Rotatory Dispersion Studies. XXII. Detection and Stereochemical Implication of Hemiketal Formation, by C. Djerassi, L. A. Mitscher, and B. J. Mitscher, *J. Am. Chem. Soc.*, **81**, 947 (1959).

Optical Rotatory Dispersion Studies. XXIII. α-Haloketones (Part 3), by C. Djerassi, I. Fornaguera, and O. Mancera, *J. Am. Chem. Soc.*, **81**, 2383 (1959).

Optical Rotatory Dispersion Studies. XXIV. Effect of Distance of a Single Asymmetric Center from an Aliphatic Carbonyl Function, by C. Djerassi and L. E. Geller, *J. Am. Chem. Soc.*, **81**, 2789 (1959).

Optical Rotatory Dispersion Studies. XXV. Effect of Carbonyl Groups in Pentacyclic Triterpenes, by C. Djerassi, J. Osiecki, and W. Closson, *J. Am. Chem. Soc.*, **81**, 4587 (1959).

Optical Rotatory Dispersion Studies. XXVI. α-Haloketones (Part 4), by C. Djerassi, L. E. Geller, and E. J. Eisenbraun, *J. Org. Chem.*, **25**, 1 (1960).

Optical Rotatory Dispersion Studies. XXVII. Quantitative Studies of an α-Haloketone by the Rotatory Dispersion Method, by N. L. Allinger, J. Allinger, L. E. Geller, and C. Djerassi, *J. Org. Chem.*, **25**, 6 (1960).

Optical Rotatory Dispersion Studies. XXVIII. The Absolute Configuration of the Sesquiterpenoid Petasin, by A. Aebi and C. Djerassi, *Helv. Chim. Acta*, **42**, 1785 (1959).

Optical Rotatory Dispersion Studies. XXIX. Absolute Configuration of Phytol, by P. Crabbé, C. Djerassi, E. J. Eisenbraun, and S. Liu, *Proc. Chem. Soc.*, **1959**, 264.

Optical Rotatory Dispersion Studies. XXX. Demonstration of Boat Form in a 3-Keto Steroid, by C. Djerassi, N. Finch, and R. Mauli, *J. Am. Chem. Soc.*, **81**, 4997 (1959).

Optical Rotatory Dispersion Studies. XXXI. Anomalous Dispersion Curves of Dithiocarbamates of α-Amino Acids and Peptides. Stereochemical Correlations Between α-Hydroxy and α-Amino Acids, by B. Sjöberg, A. Fredga, and C. Djerassi, *J. Am. Chem. Soc.*, **81**, 5002 (1959).

NOMENCLATURE AND
STEREOCHEMICAL CONVENTIONS

Although the nomenclature throughout the book largely follows accepted organic chemical practice, many names are presented in such a way that the stem name appears first, thus facilitating the search for compounds in the Index.

B-1. Steroids

Details for steroid nomenclature and other aspects of steroid chemistry will be found elsewhere.[1] The numbering system employed is outlined in structural formula I (cholestane). Solid lines denote a bond above the plane of the paper (referred to as β), dotted lines imply a bond below the plane of the paper (referred to as α), and wavy lines denote unknown configuration. Bonds without attached atoms (e.g., 18, 19, 21, etc., in I) represent methyl groups. The four rings are

conveniently referred to as A, B, C, and D. This system is also used for monocyclic (Chap. 7) and bicyclic (Chap. 5) substances and the α and β convention is known to be correct in terms of absolute configuration.

[1] L. F. Fieser and M. Fieser, "Steroids," Reinhold Publishing Corporation, New York, 1959.

B-2. Triterpenoids [2]

Although no changes in numbering are required for the tetracyclic triterpenes discussed in Chap. 6, since they are based on a steroid skeleton, the pentacyclic triterpenes are numbered as illustrated below for

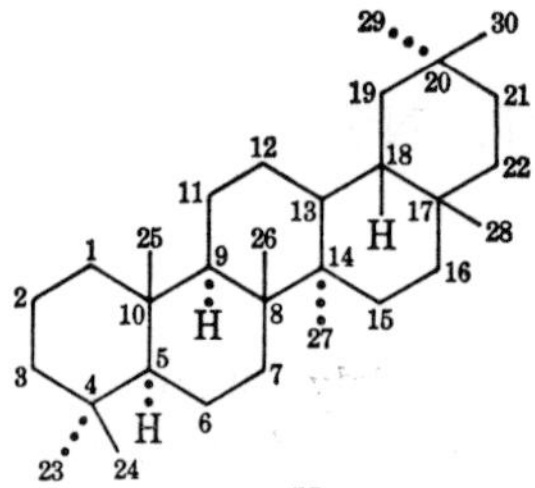

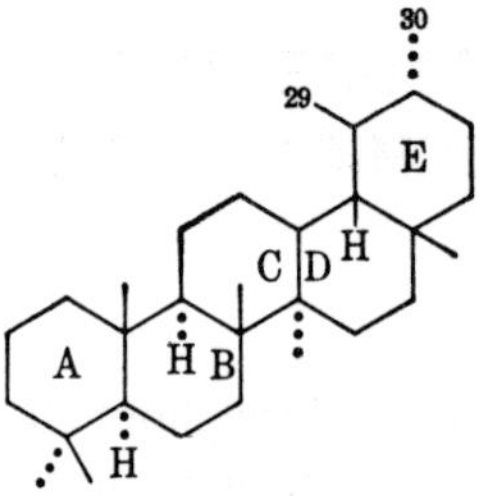

the three main classes, oleanane (II), ursane (III), and lupane (IV). The steroid convention with respect to solid (β) and dotted (α) bonds is retained here with the same absolute configurational implications.

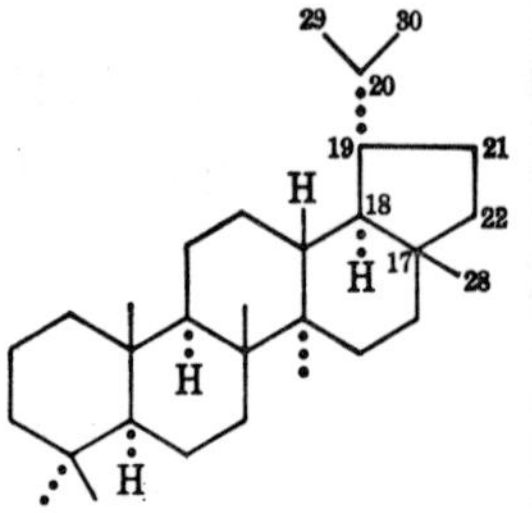

[2] See also J. P. Mathieu and G. Ourisson, "Pouvoir rotatoire naturel. Triterpenes," pp. 4–15, Pergamon Press, London, 1958.

NAME INDEX

281

INDEX OF COMPOUNDS

A general subject index is omitted in view of the detailed Contents, which largely serves the same purpose. The nomenclature employed in the Index of Compounds is based on ease of detection and is, therefore, sometimes at variance with official rules. In questionable cases, a substance is indexed under several names.